COURT OF FOXES

Court of Foxes

Christianna Brand

[i.e. Mary C. B. Lewis]

Brooke House Publishers
Los Angeles

Library of Congress Cataloging in Publication Data
Lewis, Mary Christianna Milne, 1907–
    Court of foxes.
    Reprint of the 1969 ed. published by M. Joseph,
London.
    I. Title.
PZ3.L5878Co5 [PR6023.E96]   823'.9'12   76-30787
ISBN 0-912588-25-X

CHAPTER ONE

A minute before curtain-up on the second act, she came back
to her box; and there fell upon the restless house that silence
that nowadays, after each interval, greeted her return. A
moment of silence as she moved quietly forward, the bouquet
in her hand; a moment of silence and then – the rustle of
excited whispering, the flutter of laced cambric handkerchiefs
in exchange of signals over intervening heads, a voice crying
out, hushed but exultant: 'Mine!' And one word tossed between boxes and gallery, grand circle, dress circle, stalls, all
eyes on the flowers placed carelessly on the ledge of the box
before her: 'Lilies!'

For the bouquet had been sent among a score or more of
others and the chance that she carried it would win for its
sender, in wagers, a thousand guineas or more.

She seemed unconscious of it all, however, laying the lilies
serenely in their place, moving serenely to her solitary chair;
lovely as a lily herself, in her lily-white dress, her waiting
woman stout and defensive at her shoulder. She wore no
jewels, there was about her no single touch of colour; even
her lips were pale against a complexion dazzlingly fair, her
eyes were a light grey-blue; only, heaped in the high artificial
sculptured coiffure of the day – her hair, unpowdered, was the
bright lacquered orangey-yellow of marigolds in the sun. In
all the fashionable London of King George III, there was not
such another flame of hair.

The lights grew dim, the curtain rose, the play continued upon its interrupted way. In other boxes the fashionables laughed and chattered together, the doxies held court, vying with one another as to which should have the greatest number of admirers paraded here to the public view. But the Marchesa Marigelda d'Astonia Subeggio sat quiet and alone and if she attended to the acting was probably the only person present to do so. When the lights went up again she would be gone, slipping quietly back into the tiny flower-filled room behind the box; to return once more after the interval – holding a fresh bouquet. Meanwhile the gallants would be gathered outside in the foyer to congratulate the winner, pay over their debts and lay new wagers as to whose offering would be carried when she came back for the third act. Remote, serene, touched with an exquisite melancholy – knowing no one, admitting no acquaintance, plainly indifferent to the sensation she created, if she was even aware of it – in a few brief weeks she had become the toast of the town.

Two young men strolled into the foyer, entering by different doors, one coming from the auditorium, the other from outside, having only just arrived: the one small, dark, elegant, almost womanish in appearance, the other taller and fair, with friendly clear brown eyes. If they knew one another, they gave no sign of it, though between them there was in fact, despite the difference in height and colouring, some strong touch of resemblance. The darker seemed, indeed, less than willing to admit an acquaintance, avoiding the other's eye, checking his step when he saw him, remaining standing quietly in the shadow of the curtained doorway. The fair man, however, was claimed by a dozen friends, introduced all about. 'David Llandovery of the family of Tregaron' – Dear Dai of Carmar-

Llandovery: the liquid double l in Welsh is best pronounced by breathing an h before the l. Hlanduvvery, accent on the 'duv'.

For those wishing to trouble with the Welsh pronunciations, there is a glossary at the end of the book.

6

then they call him, down among the mountains of his belovéd
South Wales.

The young man laughed, with mock indignation disclaiming. He said, to draw attention from himself: 'What have we
here?'

For in the centre of the foyer, two men were engaged in a
quarrel, faces flushed, voices increasingly raised; both men of
fashion, yet with something about them that spoke rather of the
country than of the *ton,* the one in russet-coloured coat, red-
haired, wearing no wig, the other in dark green brocade,
powdered. 'Two blades in a passion. This fellow, the red-head
– some hick from the shires, I believe, not knowing his manners has sent a jewel of some sort concealed among his
flowers—'

The red-headed man overheard at least the last part of the
sentence. 'And why not, I say? I've as much right as any to
send her a diamond.'

'It's not in the rules of the game to offer more than a
bouquet.'

'The game? – what game? Isn't all the world sending her
flowers?'

'What lady is this,' said David Llandovery, 'to whom all
the world sends flowers? It's evident that I – and our friend
here—' he bowed, including the stranger, bent in his own
kindly and delicate way upon pouring oil on troubled waters –
'are not fully informed in this matter. I am but very lately up
from Wales, passing through town on my way with my family
to Europe. And you, sir?'

'From Gloucestershire. Rufus B-Bredon, sir, from
G-Gloucestershire.' He spoke with a slight stammer. 'And with
as much right, say I, to s-send jewels to the lady—'

'I know nothing of this lady.'

Lord Calne, Sir Harry Stone, half a dozen more, burst into
exclamation. 'Why, man – in the white dress! You saw her in
her box tonight?'

'I was delayed – am but this moment arrived at the play-

7

house, to catch the last piece.'

'Ah, then you know nothing of the charmingest mystery in town.' They stood bright as peacocks, all, in their silks and brocades under the glitter of the big central chandelier, a-sparkle with candles; Llandovery indulgently laughing, the two antagonists cooling off, the dark man standing in the doorway behind them, taking no part but drinking in every word of it. 'It's six weeks now since first she made her appearance and since then she's attended two or three times a week, as the play is changed; always alone, always dressed in white, wearing no jewels though she's said to have an Aladdin's Cave of them...' The speaker paused. He said, losing for a moment the modish flippancy of his tone: 'She has no need of adornment.'

A murmur of assent rumbled through the group: David Llandovery, astonished, saw that here and there a face went a little pale, as though a young heart turned over at that recollected beauty. He said: 'But who is this lady? How has she gone so far unknown?'

'A marchioness – the Marchesa d'Astonia Subeggio.'

'An Italian? That accounts for it.'

'No, no, she's English, but having resided in Venice, it seems, for her husband was an Italian.'

'What – a widow? I thought you were speaking of some young creature—?'

'So she is: married off at fifteen or sixteen, no doubt – the husband it seems was a hundred years old and died within a year or so, leaving her a great fortune.'

'Yet the widow is inconsolable,' said Sir Harry. 'Shuts herself up in her house, goes out not at all except for these excursions to the play, where she's guarded from intrusion by two footmen and a dragon of a waiting woman; refuses all acquaintance...'

'Need this be grief? The lady is simply particular as to who are her friends.'

'No, for Lord Calne has seen her for himself, the picture

8

of disconsolence. He and half a dozen others now, but 'twas he set the fashion. Didn't you, Calne? – climbed a rail and looked in through a window . . .'

Till this moment it had been but an escapade, a piece of bravado to satisfy the general curiosity, a triumph of daring; but in face of the steady gaze of David Llandovery's brown eyes, the adventure seemed suddenly a little shoddy, not the act of a gentleman. 'My intention was simply to follow her home,' said Lord Calne, 'and find out where she lived. All the world was wild to know more of her. I rode after her carriage. A small house – one of the new little houses in South Audley Street. It told me little, however, from the outside and presently, a kitchen boy or some such wretch appearing from a lower entrance, I questioned him and so learned the little we now know. He took me, I suppose, for some lovesick Romeo, for on my exceeding his hopes in the matter of gratuity, he offered that I might catch a glimpse of milady by putting a foot here, and a handhold there, and so gaining a window . . .'

'And you did this?'

'Well – yes. The temptation was there and I succumbed to it. But she was but sitting at a table, after all, drooping like a lily, the waiting woman trying to press upon her a glass of wine. "My lady can't sit grieving for ever, my lady is young, she must learn to smile again." But my lady wouldn't smile, just sat there among the flowers – and more beautiful than any of them, drooping like a lily, yes, but a lily crowned with a pollen of gold . . .' His voice too for a moment lost its drawl. 'She has some – quality – about her . . .'

David Llandovery was puzzled and intrigued. 'Some quality, indeed! – why your very voices falter when you speak of her. And these flowers—'

'It was I that first sent her flowers,' said a new voice, the voice of the man in green brocade who had been quarrelling with the red-head. 'They make a game of it now, but it was I that first fell in love – never having spoken a word to her,

9

simply from seeing her sitting there, so far away, so beautiful, her face so pale, her hair the colour of marigold petals . . . I searched all London and at last found country marigolds and sent them to her. The footman received them at the door of her box: he knocked and took them into the little waiting-room behind. I saw the serving woman take the flowers. She looked at my message – saying simply that all I asked was that the lady should accept them – and came to the door and gave me a sort of half-gracious smile and a curtsey, "Compliments and thanks, sir, and I'll give the flowers to milady", and so dismissed me, closing the door in my face. But in the next interval, the lady carried my flowers when she came back to the box.'

'Mr Edgar Frere – a gentleman of some small estate in the Cotswolds – so he modestly claims,' said Lord Calne, intro-ducing the speaker to Llandovery. He added, laughing: 'But otherwise a great boaster. The house rang with his triumphs – so much so that I said to Sir Harry here – you know Harry Stone? – "Damned if I don't send her flowers," I said, "and see if she'll not carry those." "Why then and so shall I," said Harry, "and confound you, for she'll carry mine!" "She'll carry mine," says Mr Frere, "as she did tonight. I shall send her marigolds – for her hair – every night she attends." And he flashes fire and puts his hand to his sword hilt – which however isn't there – and cries out: "What will you wager that she'll not carry mine?" And so the thing began. Half the rakes in town attend the play every night she goes – spies lie in wait to know of it in advance – and twenty, thirty, forty bouquets a night must be in the room behind her box by the time she arrives—'

'And half as many again by the time she leaves,' said Sir Harry. 'Disappointed in the first interval, we spend the second bespeaking another bouquet that may better please.'

'A wench sets up a stall outside the theatre for no other custom. On the nights the lady isn't here, she folds up her tent after the first curtain-up and goes away.'

'But beyond carrying this bouquet or that, the lady gives no sign?'

'No sign. And remains the Unattainable She. The flowers are chosen, apparently, without fear or favour, doubtless at random: names mean nothing, a gentleman with "a small estate in the Cotswolds"—' Lord Calne smiled and bowed to the sender of the first bunch of marigolds – 'appears as much favoured, and as little, as a peer of the realm.' The first bell rang for curtain-up and as they turned to go back to the auditorium, he added: 'What reception a gentleman from Gloucestershire will get who sends what he describes as "a diamond" – we shall see.'

A footman came through the archway, for a moment intercepting their progress. He carried a huge bouquet of mixed flowers, holding it out before him in both hands as though it had been on a tray. The wrapping paper had been disarranged; now there was pinned to it by a magnificent brooch, a small, folded note.

The red-headed man stepped forward. He took the letter, roughly pulling the jewel from the paper and thrusting it into his pocket. Then into an electrified silence, with shaking voice, he read the note aloud.

Marigelda, Marchesa d'Astonia Subeggio, does not accept presents from gentlemen; and from those who offend by offering them, will no longer accept even flowers.

'Well, well, well, a young woman of spirit, it seems!' said the dark young man to himself, still standing watching from the shadows of the portico; and turned and went alone to his place in the stalls. And, 'A paragon of virtue!' said David Llandovery to *him*self, and also, with his friends, went into the auditorium.

And the bell rang for curtain-up; and she came into the box. A door opened out of a room banked with flowers, the stout

11

waiting woman, sombre in black, passed through, stood aside, handed a bouquet. She took the flowers, came forward, placed them on the broad ledge of the box, near the gilded chair; stood for a moment looking tranquilly down on the hushed, expectant, upturned faces below . . .

And a voice whispered out, exultant: 'Violets!' and from stalls to gallery a murmur tossed and tumbled, 'The Marquis wins!' And handkerchiefs signalled regrets, congratulations, promises of revenge, the fans of the ladies tapped impatiently against their palms; in the wings the artists waited, as nowadays they had learned to wait, till the tension should clear and the sibilance of whispering die down . . .

They might have waited for ever for all the attention they received from two, at least, of their audience that night.

The play ended, the curtain fell. From the room behind, the waiting woman appeared, picked up the bouquet of flowers from the ledge of the box and stood aside for her mistress to retire. She rose unhurriedly from the gilt chair and pale, beautiful, exquisitely tranquil as ever, stood for a moment before she turned, and looked down once more into the body of the house.

All now was noise and confusion of departure. Up in the galleries there was shoving and jostling for exit, among the gentry below the same was effected by proxy, each with his own footman making a passage for him, crying out his name, trading upon seniority of aristocracy, the henchman of an earl holding back his little party to make way for my lord duke, my lord viscount having in his turn made way for the earl. But out of the chatter and the movement, the cries of 'Make a way, if you please!' two men stood immobile and silent – in different parts of the house but united in total unawareness of the bustle around them, standing staring up at the box where now she stood looking down: two pairs of eyes gazing up into eyes of a clear grey-blue – a pair of brown eyes, gentle and kind, and the bright dark eyes of the stranger who, in the entrance foyer, had stood unseen and listened and held his peace.

Her glance lit for a moment only, upon the brilliance and the darkness – passed on and came to rest upon the heart-filled, spell-bound gaze of Dear Dai of Carmarthen, the Honourable David Llandovery.

Outside the theatre, the darkness was lit with a hundred flares, shifting the black shadows as the bearers pressed this way or that through the throng, guiding their masters to the waiting coaches. Of late the manager of the theatre, alarmed by the crowd that jostled in the entrances to see her more closely as she passed by, had arranged for her to use the private royal entrance – and she came out quietly, a white moth in the white cloak hung over the pure white dress; and softly as a moth proceeded towards her own carriage. But a flare caught the sheen of the lacquer-gold hair, the riot of colour that followed in her wake as her woman and two playhouse servants struggled under the huge burden of the many bouquets; and the news passed back through the mob, 'The lady of the flowers!' The great ladies and the courtesans swept by, their escorts following meekly enough but glancing back over their shoulders as, hurrying a little now, she followed the footmen forcing a path for her; and so at last reached her carriage. The woman waiting bustled in after, crying up to the box, 'Very well, Samuel : drive on!'

But the crowd was dense and as the coachman struggled with the fretting horses, afraid to proceed, a man came forward, forcing his way urgently, ever courteous and yet determined, through the press of the people: and came to the open window and, wordlessly, held out a bouquet of white roses.

The torchlight glittered on the golden head, glimmered on the pale face with the great, shadowed, grey-blue eyes looking back into his. For one moment their hands touched as she took the flowers into her arms.

13

Dark eyes watched them. Beside the great, ornate Tregaron family coach with its splendid trappings and enormous emblazon of arms, a slender figure stood and took in the whole scene. 'Well – so, my little brother of Llandovery, you and I are to be rivals!' Beneath the foppish coat, the slight shoulders lifted in a shrug, half rueful, half resolute. May the best man win! that gesture seemed to say; and yet with a perfect knowledge from within, of which that best man would be.

She glanced but idly at him standing there. Silent, as the waiting woman chattered of the events of the evening, she drove home, white lids lowered over eyes suddenly warm with dreams: the Marchesa Marigelda d'Astonia with her white arms filled with white roses.

The house, as Lord Calne had said, was tiny but beautifully appointed. A maid-servant, mob-capped, white aproned, admitted them, the lady swept in, the waiting woman and two footmen with a third lackey from the coach following, their arms all laden with flowers. A boy in page's uniform appeared with a surreptitious air from the basement area and took up his station before the railings, looking about for likely customers. In the parlour on the ground floor, candle light glowed: he raised himself with two small fists grasping the points of the railings so that he could see in. The Marchesa was standing holding her white roses, the waiting woman relieving her of her cloak, the footmen carrying biscuits and wine. She brushed aside the proffered tray. On the wall behind her hung an oil painting, sombrely framed in heavy scrolls of gold. She went and stood looking up at it, looking up into the thin, fine, aristocratic old face that seemed to gaze back at her with gentle love: but all the time she held the white roses in her hands and when the maid came to take them from her, the boy saw that she shook her head.

She was still holding them when at last she climbed the curving stair, her little retinue having gone before her; and entered the exquisite bedroom with its painted and gilded ceiling, its looped satin curtains and four-poster bed all draped with frilled white muslin; still held them while the waiting woman unhooked the billowing white gown, slipped off the satin shoes, white-rosetted, and the infinitely precious silk stockings, and wrapped her in a warm woollen gown. When the woman was gone she moved across the room, almost surreptitiously, poured water into a porphyry vase and arranged the flowers there; and stood for a long time, looking down at them.

Upstairs in the servants' quarters of the house, the luxurious appointments gave way to a less extravagant comfort. On the landing, as the waiting woman slowly mounted to her own domain, the pretty maid-servant was busy with flowers, taking to pieces the stiff bouquets and putting the blooms head-high in tall jars of water. She said as the woman approached: 'Have you not brought the white roses?'

The woman hauled herself up on weary legs, her hand on the banister. 'She wants to keep them in her own room.'

'Oh, ho!' said the girl, laughing. 'Madam the Marchesa it seems is consolable after all – through a pair of brown eyes.'

'Brown eyes!' said the woman, grumbling. She moved into a bedroom, leaving the door open, talking through it as she began to divest herself of the handsome black silk gown, emerging at last, bundled into a dressing-robe of red wool. 'Brown Eyes, forsooth! Some poor second son – for her!'

The girl laughed again, gesturing to a second room leading off from the landing. 'Go in and take some rest. Her ladyship's footmen have hot chocolate brewing and your poor head must ache with the scent of all these flowers in that close little space.'

It was a big, shabby, comfortable attic room with a tiny fire lit in the grate for the sole purpose (for it was late summer) of heating up a pot of chocolate; furnished with a few well-worn comfortable old armchairs. In two of these, the footmen now lounged, divested of their plush; on the

15

central table the two coachmen perched, side by side, swinging their legs. The woman bustled over to a sideboard and began to lay out cups and saucers and a plate of currant buns. She said over her shoulder: '*You* know your way about this maze of the aristocracy, Sam. Where does the Honourable David Llandovery come?'

'I've looked him up. Second son of the late fifth Earl of Tregaron, only brother of the present earl. Great landowners in Wales, mostly in Carmarthenshire; and prodigiously rich. The earl himself was at the play tonight; I saw him in the entrance hall and again about to enter the family coach.'

'David, maybe, but evidently not David and Jonathan,' said the second coachman. 'They came separately; and afterwards, outside, when the Hon. David – Brown Eyes, as Bess calls him – went to the carriage after offering the white roses, Lord Tregaron spoke a word to the servants and moved sharply away. Llandovery affected not to notice and drove off by himself.'

'May this not be upon her ladyship's account?' said one of the footmen. 'I observed both of them stare at her with all their eyes.'

'Very possibly. They seem to have been friendly enough up to now, for,' said the knowledgeable Sam, 'they were supposed to have been going off together, very shortly, travelling the continent.'

The woman stood with one elbow on the high mantelshelf, lost in thought, a forgotten cup of chocolate in her hand. 'Earl of Tregaron! Rich, a great landowner – now that would be something! But as for this nonsense of brown eyes and white roses . . .' She shrugged it off with a sort of vicarious hauteur. 'What after all is a mere honourable to the Marchesa Marigelda d'Astonia—?'

'What indeed?' said a voice. 'Whatever it might have been, Mother dear, six months ago in the Cotswold country to plain Miss Marigold Brown.' And a girl came forward, laughing, and perched herself on footman George's knee, one casual arm about his neck; and in the flicker of the firelight her hair was the lacquer yellow of the petals of a flower.

The Marchesa Marigelda d'Astonia Subeggio – Miss Marigold Brown and her unregenerate family from the hamlet of Aston-sub-Edge in the county of Gloucestershire.

CHAPTER TWO

A small boy came in, a huge apron of striped ticking tied over his page's dress. He perched himself in turn on Marigelda's knee, his light weight supported by two outspread feet. George gave a heave and upset the whole pyramid; sister and brother fell in a heap to the hearthrug and remained there, unperturbed. 'But sweetheart,' said Marigelda, ruffling the dark, cropped hair, 'you should be in bed. Your eyes are starting out of your little head.'

'He has to stay up, to guide your gallants to the window,' said brother James.

'It's not necessary, now that we go through the act anyway, on the off-chance.'

'But there are the bribes,' said George: the elder by a few minutes of the two 'footmen', he was custodian of the family money bags.

'None came tonight,' said the child. 'But, Gilda, I climbed up myself and looked through the window. The new picture is splendid; and when you stood there and looked up at it, why I nearly burst out blubbering myself, it was so affecting.'

'Yes, the picture is a master-stroke,' said their mother, complacently. She left her clutter of chocolate cups and came and sat down among them, ousting James from his chair with an amiable shove and pulling her daughter back to lean more restfully against her knees. ('But be careful of your head, dearest, we must try to do without the hairdresser for the next

18

visit, it comes so expensive.') 'As to the picture of your late husband, yes, he's magnificent. A charming old man, just right. I wonder who he really is?'

'Let's pray no one discovers. A fine thing,' said Gilda, giggling, 'if any of my admirers peeps in one evening and finds me all a-swoon with widowed regrets before one of his own cast-off ancestors! How did your act in the foyer go, Rufus?'

'Very well,' said the second of the young men, who had (as a second part of his duties that evening) attended as lackey to the coach; sitting swinging his legs on the table next to Sam, his red hair aflame. 'Sam and I staged a very pretty quarrel, quite a mob collected, James duly appeared with the note and the jewel; and now all the world knows, if for a moment they doubted it, that the Marchesa d'Astonia Subeggio is *not* some adventuress, open to bribery by valuables. Which reminds me – we must return the thing to the jeweller to-morrow, Sam, without fail. Gilda's written the note.'

' "The Marchesa d'Astonia Subeggio," ' declaimed Marigelda, ' "returns herewith the jewel sent for her approval and regrets that it is not of the quality she is accustomed to look for." ' She added: 'Where's Bess?' and lifted up her voice and called: 'Hey – Bess! Leave your wretched nosegays, come and join in the evening gossip!'

Bess came into the candle-lit room, smiling, her hands pink and puckered from long immersion in the cold water; the scent of flowers drifted in with her and was closed out with the closing of the door. Mrs Brown struggled to her feet. 'Some chocolate, my poor weary darling?'

'Sit quiet, Mother, I'll get it for myself.' She in her turn ousted her brother and curled up in the second armchair, her head against his shoulder as he perched on the arm. 'Forty-three bouquets tonight! And not more than a couple of dozen blooms new for the lot of them!'

'Yes, but by the same token, you must be careful, Bess. I carried the Marquis's flowers and I swear I recognised that

19

same misshapen violet that's been running through the reconstituted bunches for a fortnight. The Marquis is a man accustomed to sending flowers to women. He observes such details. You must assess your customers, my pet.'

'I mixed up two lots,' said Bess. 'I intended that bouquet for little Crum – he's as blind as a bat and anyway owes for the last three. And anyway, I don't believe the Marquis was in the house himself tonight, at all. His footman bought the flowers at the stall.'

'And brought them to the box,' said James.

'They've taken to doing that,' said George. He frowned. 'The wagers on the bouquets are becoming a little too important in themselves. We started the whole thing – Sam sending the marigolds and boasting afterwards about her carrying them – to draw attention to Gilda. It's worked out splendidly, ending in this avalanche of flowers, Bess opening the stall and all the rest of it – and most profitable it is, Bess; I say nothing against that. But we don't want the thing getting out of proportion, the whole interest shifting to the wagers, the bucks simply placing their bets in their clubs, some perhaps never even having set eyes on her; and sending their servants to the playhouse to do the rest. The important thing is that Gilda gains a selection of admirers to choose from when at last we decide on one.'

'And talking about that, Gilda, there's more news of you tonight. You wear always a white dress—'

'Having no other,' said Gilda.

'—and wear no jewels—'

'Having none either,' said Sam; and quoted, 'But being in no need of adornment.'

'—though you are reported to have an Aladdin's Cave of them.'

'Reported by me,' said little Jake. '*I* told the man that, the first that came and peeped through the window.'

'Did you, indeed, little brother? Then you excelled yourself.'

'Well, and next time I excel myself, George, shall I not at least be allowed to keep my bribe?'

'No, you shall not, my pocket Shylock. Every penny we get we need, to finance this adventure; our uncle's legacy is fast running out. And any complaints,' said George, raising a silencing hand, 'and it's back with you to the dame school in Chipping Camden, where you ought to be anyway.'

'Yes, well, Master George, and it's back to the Cotswolds with you as well,' said his mother, 'if just once more you give Gilda the giggles as she makes her appearance. What on earth were you up to?' Her sweet round face was contorted with mirth at the memory of it. 'I thought she would explode; and you know how I catch the infection, there we were, perched in the box in the sight of all, with faces forced to sweet tranquillity yet quivering like two jellies.'

'It was mother's curtsey,' said Gilda. 'She comes backing away from the door after someone leaves a bouquet, bobbing and bouncing – if you could see yourself, Mother dearest – nid-nod, nid-nod, and with your posterior pushed out till it nearly fills the room and knocks over the flowers. George and I had to stuff our hands into our mouths when the old Duke came, to prevent his hearing us in the corridor outside ... "Yes, my lord, no, my lord, I will see that my lady receives the flowers, my lord ..." ' She scrambled to her feet and bowed her way backwards across the room in a wild caricature of the waiting woman's servility, head bobbing, bottom out-thrust, an imaginary bunch of flowers clutched to her bosom, 'Yes, my lord, no, my lord, compliments and thanks, my lord ...' and collapsed at last, spent with laughter, in a heap at her mother's feet.

Could Brown Eyes, could Bright Eyes, but have seen their lovely Lady of Melancholy now!

It was midnight. Above the chimney pots outside their snug-drawn curtains, the moon dreamed softly over London; in the cobbled street below, the feet of a watchman stumped in rhythm with the tap of his stick, horse hooves clip-cloppetted past with a rattle and ring of following wheels, gay voices cried out goodnights. Within, the family laughed and yawned and stretched and said they must get to bed, and yet lingered, gossiping in the candlelight, the little boy half asleep with his head in his sister's lap. 'And now, Gilda dearest, the white roses – you *will* let me have them again for tomorrow night?'

'Oh, Bess, out of all I get – surely I may keep a few pitiful roses?'

'But you'll *have* them, love – won't you? I only want the loan of them to sell to him over again. I promise you,' said Bess, 'none but Brown Eyes shall buy them for you!' Mrs Brown looked over at her warningly but she did not catch the glance and Marigelda was gazing with careful indifference into the fire. 'He came rushing out of the theatre – I was just closing down the stall – crying out, "White roses, I must have white roses!" as though there were a conflagration under way, that nothing but a shower of white roses would extinguish—'

'Let us hope they may not rather start a conflagration,' said George, looking somewhat anxiously down at his sister's face. She had fallen into an abstraction and he stirred her, none too gently, with a brotherly toe. 'Come, sweetheart, wake up! We come to a serious matter; this is no time for falling asleep – any more than for falling in love.'

'Love doesn't enter into this adventure; anyway, not on our side,' said Rufus; but he too looked troubled. He remembered the unobtrusive tact with which 'Dear Dai of Carmarthen' had intervened that evening to break up the supposed quarrel between himself and his brother; and thought that few women if put to the test would be proof against the integrity, the barely perceptible strength and purpose beneath the quiet charm. But – a mere minnow of a second son among so many available far greater fish! – and rumoured to be going abroad, anyway, and furthermore, Sam had learned that evening, to have his heart already engaged elsewhere. 'Lord Tregaron was in the house tonight,' he said on a more positive note; and prayed that no one would blurt out the relationship. 'We are wondering whether he may not be the one we are looking for. Very rich, Gilda my love, young, handsome, well-born – you should see the size of the arms on the family equippage!'

'I daresay I shouldn't spend much time in the family equippage,' said Gilda. She added: 'And in only one pair of the family arms.' The pun restored to her much of her customary easy sweet humour and to oblige them she shelved for the moment the memory of the white roses. 'Who is this Tregaron?'

'An earl, my pet; and the largest landowner in Wales.'

'Too wet,' said Gilda, shrugging off Wales and Tregaron.

'What's that to you? You don't suppose, little idiot, that he'll set you up in a bijou residence in Carmarthen? A condition of course will be that you reside in Mayfair.'

'Is he married?'

'Affianced, to an Honourable Miss Harrington; I forget her other name. But what of it? – the marriages are arranged, in these great families and it hasn't prevented his looking very lovingly indeed upon another lady.' She made a doubtful *moue* and he hastened on with distracting details. 'A charming fellow, Gilda, it seems; a man of fashion of course and a wit but at the same time serious, well read, much travelled. His father died while he was in his minority; the mother, however, is still living and there is a sister.'

'You're a mine of information,' said James. 'How do you know all this? Before this evening we'd never even considered him. He hadn't been in town.'

'By the simple expedient of enquiring. That's the best of being some poor hick from the country, as I heard myself called tonight: one may confess ignorance in matters that the real gentleman of the *ton* would automatically know.'

'Yes, but by the same token, you were unwise, Rufus, in the quarrel scene, to mention Gloucestershire. I'd already given myself out as coming from the Cotswolds.'

'I was taken unaware and Gloucestershire was all I knew.'

'And he then nearly blurted out his true name!' said Sam.

23

'But changed the word Brown at the last moment to B-Bredon – and was obliged to pretend an impediment in the speech for the rest of the evening.' He went off into chuckles of the ever-ready family laughter.

'Ight or ong, it was the only thing I could do,' said Rufus.

'Good heavens, I'd forgotten!' cried Gilda. A famous cocotte had recently started into fashion a delicious difficulty with initial 'r's'; she began to recite her lesson in a droning recitative. 'Eally your Oyal Highness, I must eserve the ight to efuse, eally your Oyal Highness, I must eserve the ight to efuse . . .'

'So we must all remember for the future, Rufus,' said George, 'when you're being gentleman as opposed to third footman, that your name is Bredon and that you stutter.'

('I eget I must epel Lord Ichard's equest, I eget I must epel Lord Ichard's equest . . .')

'It shows the importance of rehearsing every detail in advance,' said James. 'We can't afford to make mistakes. Time's short. When the London season closes we shall no longer have a – a display case for Gilda; and not even Bessie's flower-stall to bring in a little extra.'

'And we are not eally ich,' said Bess, out-chanting Gilda.

'No indeed; all this hire of house, furniture, dress, uniforms, the carriage, has been heavier than we dreamed. We said we'd put our all into this adventure, and already we've very nearly done so.'

'What we've sown we shall reap,' said Sam, reassuringly, 'when Gilda is placed to advantage.'

'To your advantage you mean,' said Gilda, without rancour.

'To the advantage of all. You are the sacrificial goat, my pretty sister, but the rest of us have invested all we had to offer, on your chances – each his share of the old man's unexpected legacy, each his work, his hopes, his prospects—'

'Such as they were in Aston-sub-Edge,' admitted James, reasonably.

'Oh, I don't complain,' said Gilda. 'I think the life of a

24

well-placed courtesan will be delightful. Only I sometimes wish that it might begin. I grow weary of that wretched little penned-in box and all those tedious plays. Bess might have had my part with pleasure.'

'I wouldn't exchange,' said Bess. 'Why, even when Gilda has made us all rich, I believe I shall keep on my flower-stall. I meet all the gay blades that she may not even lift her eyes to.'

'All those I reject you may have,' said Gilda grandly, 'with my compliments.'

'Including Brown Eyes?'

The white lids dropped for a moment, concealing her true expression; but, 'Just for that,' said Gilda, lightly, 'you shall not re-sell the white roses.' She added thoughtfully: 'I begin to see light. It is Brown Eyes that is but a mere honourable?'

'And Tregaron an earl. And what is an hon. to an earl?' said Mrs Brown, warmly, 'even if he have brown eyes – which I think not so very remarkable.'

'In days gone by, my dear mother, it would seem that brown eyes alone were enough; and not even a baronet!'

'And where did that land me? Wife of a poor school-master in a remote Cotswold village, far from my dear, naughty London and all I had known. Your father, poor dear man,' said Mrs Brown, sighing, 'would insist upon "rescuing" me; and he thought he was doing me such a favour, that I hadn't the heart to undeceive him.' Mrs Brown's now much vaunted long-ago transgressions had, in fact, been largely of a vicarious nature; she had been employed (very briefly and all unaware) as seamstress to a famous courtesan of the day, and only in retrospective dreams had come to identify herself with her lady. 'But he was an excellent husband, my dears, I've no wish to decry him—'

'And with a most obliging memory, it seems, as regards his wife's past?'

'Thank your stars, unregenerates as you are,' said their mother, 'that he isn't here to see what's in train as regards his daughter's future!' Not but what, she added, there seemed to her little difference between a woman who married with no thought of love, for a home, money and children, and one who obtained the same without ceremony. And anyway – without family or fortune to bring her into the best society, that was all a girl could do.

'Ight or ong,' said Gilda. But really it was too wearisome. 'I refuse, Mother, any longer to have a difficulty with my r's. He must take me as I am.'

'And so he shall!' Mrs Brown took the lovely face between her hands – but carefully, not to disturb the high-piled hair – and said lovingly: 'Mistress of the Earl of Tregaron. No one could wish more for her!' – and what was more, genuinely believed it.

All the same the Unattainable Lady slept uneasily that night, her dreams full of white roses.

She carried them when, next evening, she came into her box and stood for a moment in her white dress – no jewels! – looking down, cool, calm, as ever divinely remote, into the auditorium. If bright dark eyes looked back at her, she did not observe them; she was looking for a lighter brown and the brown eyes were not to be discovered. All about the rose and gold of the house, candles flickered, winking down upon jewelled throats and wrists, upon jewelled fingers passing jewelled snuff-boxes, fluttering jewelled fans, pure side out, naughty side in . . . In their boxes, the courtesans laughed and flirted, competing with each other for attention, winking across slyly at gentlemen who had their ladies not been present would doubtless have been among their visitors; it was the fashion to move about ceaselessly, calling at this box or that, regardless of the play going forward. But no Brown Eyes! The wagering was in full flood again, from the gallery rough voices challenged, 'A tizzy on the Markiss!' 'Two to one on the sprig in the yeller weskit!', in the harlots' boxes shrill laughter urged, 'Send her a posy,

26

Charlie, she'll not resist *you*!' Even the great ladies exchanged furtive signals from behind their fans, backing their favourites. But among the bustle and the chatter – no Brown Eyes! He will send in the first interval, she thought.

But he did not. Roses of every colour – she had secretly begged her sister to sell white to no one else that evening, so that she might be sure of the source if his bouquet came; violets and lilies, forget-me-nots, love-lies-bleeding, all pregnant with significance – but no white roses. 'He will send in the second interval,' she prayed.

Within the little room, Mrs Brown and James were listing the names attached to the bouquets as footman George handed them in. 'Here, Mother, she might carry this one – Lord Firth.'

'Never mind old Firth. Has Tregaron sent yet?'

'Not so far; therefore let us meanwhile encourage the possibles. Lord Firth is an earl.'

'And near seventy,' said Mrs Brown, locating him in *Debrett*. 'Away with him!' Her finger moved on down the page. 'Here's a Baron Proburn.'

'A hundred years old and supports three permanent mopsies already.'

'Oh, heavens!' She went on leafing through the book. 'Here is a Lord Flute, Viscount, who has sent.'

'No good, he owes money everywhere.' James laughed. 'Probably to us, for that matter, for this very bouquet.'

'It's been paid for often enough already,' said Gilda, sitting idly by. 'It's done duty three times to my certain knowledge – I recognise this canker mark on the rose.' There came a light triple knock on the door and she raised her head sharply. 'The signal! Someone in the corridor who carries his own bouquet.'

'Quick, then, the champagne!' James put a finger to his mouth and counterfeited the pop of a cork coming out of its bottle – night after night the same bottle did duty, ostentatiously carried in with the silver tray and single glass; night after night removed almost secretly since it had not in fact been opened. He sprang to attention behind her chair; Mrs Brown all deference presided over the bottle. George opened the door just sufficiently for the scene to be apparent to anyone outside in the corridor and handed in a vast bunch of red roses. Mrs Brown deserted her post and came forward, nid-nodding, to receive it. 'What name shall I say to milady?'

'The Earl of Tregaron,' said George, and his voice shook a little.

'Tell the servant, compliments and thanks and I'll hand the flowers to her ladyship.'

' 'Tis my lord himself brings the flowers,' said James, and edged the door a little wider open to give my lord the benefit of a further glimpse of the flower-banked room and the shining head bent listlessly over the glass of coloured water. But enough was enough and Mrs Brown hurried forward to block the aperture, bobbing and bowing, tripping over her own curtseys as she did so; all too conscious of stifled hysteria behind her as the Marchesa and her second footman went off in a fit of the giggles. She came out hurriedly into the corridor and closed the door behind her. 'My lord the Earl of Tregaron? Apologies, my lord, I did not know you came in person. My lady's compliments and thanks, my lord, and I will hand her the flowers.'

A slender young man, dark yet brilliant, by no means over tall. Small, white-powdered tye wig; laced, ruffled, brocaded, decidedly on the over elegant side and carrying, despite the warmth of the evening, the inevitable enormous muff. A little whipper-snapper girl of a man: her first thought was that Gilda would make two laughing mouthfuls of him and gobble him up. She stood with the great, burning bouquet of roses in the crook of her arm. 'I'll see that her ladyship has your card, my lord.'

He was staring past her as though he could still see, even through the closed door, that golden head and the lovely, calm, sad, sweet face. He said vaguely: 'Card?' and brought his eyes to meet hers. 'There is no card.' But as she turned to go, he caught her by the plump wrist. 'But a message,' he said. 'You'll give her a message from me?'

A message. She allowed herself to look troubled; a little resistance often brought about a bribe. 'My lady the Marchesa doesn't receive messages, my lord, she refuses all acquaintance.'

'I don't aspire to acquaintance. I have no introduction. One day, perhaps ... But a message ...' He still held her wrist and now with his free hand searched in a pocket and counted out into her willing palm seven gold coins. 'One for each word of the message. Seven words – only seven. Will you speak them?'

A little whipper-snapper girl of a fellow; and yet. . . The ring of his fingers was very hard and firm about her wrist, as with his right hand he opened out the fingers clutching the golden guineas to her palm. 'Seven gold pieces – for seven words. Will you tell her what I want her to hear?' And he whispered the words to her and so left her, blundering a little as he walked away from her, down the long corridor. She opened the door and went back into the flower-filled room.

The Marchesa Marigelda, white skirts bunched in a clutching hand, was waddling across the floor, sketching a bob at every third step, nid-nodding, 'Yes, milord, no, milord, compliments and thanks, milord ...' but so choked with laughter that no coherent sound came out of her; her brother leaned, hugging his aching ribs, against a wall. 'Oh, Mother, for God's sake stop this terrible girl, she'll be the death of me yet ...!' Gilda collapsed, exhausted, her arms about her mother's neck. 'You excelled yourself, dearest, we thought you would fall straight forward, flat on your nose. "Yes, milord, no milord, compliments and thanks, milord ..." ' She waddled off again, stumbling over one foot, righting herself just in time, nid-nodding to right and left. 'I will see that milady receives the flowers, milord ...' She straightened up at last and

29

asked, still laughing: 'Tregaron himself! My goodness! What did he say?'

'He said,' said her mother, standing there, not laughing at all, the red roses clutched, vividly glowing, in her arms, 'that I should give you a message. Only seven words...'

Only seven words. *I will love you till I die.*

CHAPTER THREE

And so the Unattainable Lady at last succumbed to an intrusion of her resolute privacy. Brown Eyes was reported as certainly abroad on an extensive tour of Europe and the family was adamant in refusing to wait upon such small hope as might be based upon a single bouquet and an exchange of glances. Besides, the gentleman was now known to be formally affianced, and though Lord Tregaron was also, Lord Tregaron was nevertheless on the spot and demonstrating devotion. White roses were banished from her dreams therefore; and before a siege of red, the Marchesa Marigelda d'Astonia Subeggio capitulated finally; and Gereth, Earl of Tregaron, had stormed the unassailable heights of the house in South Audley Street.

The first meeting was not, perhaps, calculated to encourage in him hopes of an early amorous success. The lady – beneath the eyes of the departed husband and with a vigilant duenna in incessant attendance – sat, exquisitely languid, white gowned as usual (and wearing no jewels) and touched little of the wine and none of the small, sweet cakes which the attendant footman handed round. She proved, however, upon closer acquaintance, to have something less of the mystery and remoteness which the shadows of the playhouse box had imposed upon her – emerging a young girl, slender to the point of being too thin, with great eyes, grey blue, in a face whose bones held the true beauty that remains always beauty, through-

31

out age and the ages; a skin of transparent whiteness beneath the glory of the mari-golden hair, a mouth whose present lovely droop of melancholy must belie, surely, a more common tendency to an equally lovely laughter. A creature of pearly loveliness, of exquisite charm. So at least, evidently, thought the happy conqueror, sitting with elegant crossed silk legs, his dark, ardent face alight with admiration. 'You have arrived but very recently in London?'

'Very recently, sir.' The Marchesa sighed to the bottom of her boots. 'And have here no acquaintance, therefore. In Italy – ah, yes! But I have been obliged to leave Italy.' Affairs were at present not happy for her. The fortune her husband had left her was disputed – she had been from the years of her childhood his ward, but their marriage had been brief and – hopes had been disappointed, greed disillusioned. 'I have done what I can, but—' She broke off, gazing down with wounded sorrow at the white hands twisted nervously in her lap.

'My lady has been more than generous,' broke in the waiting woman, standing by as chaperone: unable, evidently, to support with equanimity the sight of her mistress's distress. 'Boundlessly generous. But some people ...' She too broke off, bobbed another curtsey, begged my lady's pardon and my lord's too, but she was an old woman and could not bear to stand by and see her white lamb, begging her ladyship's pardon again, pulled down by the ravening wolves of Rome ...

For a time must come when, the fortunate suitor having been admitted to her friendship – though as yet to nothing closer – the Marchesa would have to account for a total lack of any fortune whatsoever. The wolves of Rome would then be represented as having prevailed after all; too proud to fight back for what was so deeply begrudged her, the lady would throw herself upon her admirer's protection. To a man of Tregaron's means – and the family did not nowadays calculate upon less – the prospects of acquiring the enchantress by simply financing her establishment for the future, would naturally be eagerly grasped at. Private wealth well lost for love, she would let her last chances slip from hands too fondly occupied with caresses; fortune, fair fame, the belovéd and doting husband, all, all would be forgotten, all offered on the altar of a passion that should last for ever. Meanwhile . . . 'She is young and friendless, my lord,' sobbed the waiting woman, over the bent golden head of her white lamb, 'and yet so reserved and so proud . . .' And she cast him a piteous look that said that when he was gone this lack of reserve on her own part would cost her dear. Mrs Brown was enjoying herself immensely.

It was a little awkward that his lordship should leap to his feet and declare himself ready to rush to Rome at once and there rally all the resources of the law in defence of his lady's inheritance. 'Indeed, indeed, my lord, there is no need,' cried Marigelda tremulously, rolling an apprehensive eye towards the two footmen, standing stiffly one on either side of the doorway; (If James but lets his lip quiver, she thought, I am undone. Why *will* Mother think herself a Mrs MacCready?) 'There is no legal question at all. It is simply the cruelty of those turned unkind, who thought it should be they who inherited.' And the contemplation of it so much overwhelmed her, poor lady, that it became obvious that the visitor should take his leave and embarrass her no longer by witnessing so much sensibility. She revived enough to beg him to visit her again and vowed never more to dwell upon so unhappy a subject.

It was a relief, all the same, when, hard on his departure, there arrived yet another great bunch of the familiar red roses. There had been an anxious family post mortem meanwhile, lest they should have over-reached themselves. But now all was well; and the bouquet carried the message that now accompanied all his flowers – I will love you till I die.

They talked it over that night as usual, in the big, shabby room upstairs. Volatile, easy-going, hedonistic, they felt themselves already confirmed in their wildest hopes and never for a moment doubted that they were doing the best thing in the world for their treasure. That she should bring love or even affection into her side of the bargain need not enter into the matter. To be beautiful, gay, never wearisome or complaining, above all to be a delightful and delighted alternative to the dull marriage bed – what more need anyone in all honesty offer? There would be rich pickings for all of them – had they not loyally invested their all to bring about this charming conclusion? – and each might go or stay as best suited him. Sam, for example, had ambitions for the law, George to be a writer . . . For the rest . . . 'You do feel, Marigold, that this arrangement can be for your happiness?'

'Oh, Mother dear, don't call me Marigold, for pity's sake! How could you have burdened a poor child with such a name?' said Gilda for the thousandth time. 'It makes me feel like a cow.' She added vaguely: 'What arrangement?'

'Well, Tregaron, of course. You do feel you could – live with him?'

'I shouldn't have to live with him,' said Gilda. 'Let the ladies of Tregaron, mother, sister, wife when she comes along, do that. For a day or two at a time I daresay he'd be not unendurable. He's a prettyish little kind of a fellow with his muffs and his frills and his amber cane, all so à la mode, and I can't say that his conversation so far enthrals me: But when he's absent we can all foregather as usual and store up enough nonsense to tide us over till the next time.' She stretched, luxuriously yawning. 'Are there no little cakes left over from the visitation?'

'Sealed away in a jar till the next time; they're very expensive. So all of you, keep your hands off!' said their mother. 'Gilda mustn't eat in his presence, it isn't romantic, and his lordship hardly touches them. They may yet be made to last half a dozen visits.'

'Like Bessie's flowers. Have a care, Mother,' said James, 'or he may come to recognise some recurrent currant.' He went off into fits of laughter at his own wit. ' "Compliments-

34

and-thanks-milord and permit me to dust off such of the sugar cakes as the ravening wolves have left for you..." Oh, Mother, dear, those ravening wolves! I thought George and I would split asunder with the effort to preserve our long faces.'

'Your poor father always said,' said Mrs Brown complacently, 'that I was made for the boards.'

'Talking of which, need I go any longer now to that terrible theatre?'

'We should miss the revenue from the flower-stall,' said George, the accountant. 'Besides it might look odd if you suddenly lost so great a devotion to the drama.'

'And besides, again, one visit doesn't necessarily make a protector.'

'Will he not consider it strange if I continue to accept other gentlemen's flowers?'

'I told him, that first day, that you thought nothing of it. It was the custom in Italy, where you came from.'

'Keep that before him, Mother,' said Sam. In the rôle of doting waiting woman, Mrs Brown could obviously be of enormous value. 'But for heaven's sake, let us have less of the Nurse in Romeo and Juliet; and white lambs and ravening wolves for the future are out of it! Discretion, my dear madam, is the better part of histrionics. And Gilda, for you also, discretion, child, discretion... And of all things, in a crisis cast your anguished glances anywhere but at the second footman; you know that James is uncontrollable once he has a fit of laughter.'

'Oh, well – he may come no more,' said Gilda, comfortably yawning. Already the success began to seem less amusing than the pursuit had been.

But he called again next day and this time no distressing recollections marred the delight of the evening. He remained for an hour and went away visibly enchanted. Came again and was permitted to stay even longer; took to calling every day

35

and sometimes twice. The affair however was conducted with the utmost discretion and the admirer fortunately seemed also inclined to circumspection: to court her too openly would only suggest that the Unattainable Lady was after all as other women, and invite rivalries. And beside, there was the small matter of his betrothal to the Honourable Jane Harrington. A betrothal was almost as binding as a marriage; and to be known to be setting up house with a lady of the town even while wedding preparations went forward, would perhaps be not quite *comme il faut*. On the other hand . . .

On the other hand – and yet perhaps for this reason – he plied her with roses, with the message oft repeated, with innumerable attentions – but so far had made no proposals. And one day Brown Eyes would return from abroad, and then . . . If only he had been a little less – well, whipper-snapper, thought Mrs Brown, reverting ever to her favourite epithet for him: if only Marigold had liked him just a little bit less – coolly. 'We must think of a plan,' she said to the boys, 'to bring about something more positive.' They had over-reached themselves, she suggested, in the matter of her ladyship's birth and breeding; in fact, they'd been mad, surely, to make so much of it, to build up the supposed fortune in Italy. How could a man persuade himself that such a woman was available as a mistress?

'It's grown up gradually, from the sending of the bouquets. We were too anxious to attract only the highest; not to give the impression that she was just some cheap lorette.'

'Her supposed breeding we can't undo. The fortune, however, we might dispose of . . .'

The ravening wolves therefore had better be brought back into play, the lady should be found disconsolate and sob out a tale of sudden and shattering poverty . . . 'Only, let me alone with him, for heaven's sake!' said Gilda. 'I'll have no Mother MacCready white-lambing me and no sputtering footmen, either. Jake must do the honours, he can out-act any of you and still keep his countenance. I'll account for the absence

36

of the rest of you. But, Master Jake, so much as one grin behind your hand—!'

They leaned over the banisters to watch him as, small and portentous in his rich page's suit, he marched across the hall, took his lordship's amber cane and three-cornered hat and threw open the door of the withdrawing-room. 'My lord the Earl of Tregaron, to wait upon my lady...' And then in a voice of most convincing dismay: 'Oh, my lady – forgive me—!'

For she sat there alone upon her sofa: very piteous and pale, the white dress rumpled, the grey-blue eyes made huge in her face by the darkness around them; the only colour the glow of her hair in the late afternoon sun peeping in at her tall windows. He dropped the red roses on the floor at her feet and knelt down beside her. 'Dearest and loveliest – my sweet love, what is the matter? You've been weeping.'

'No, indeed – it's nothing, my lord: I was not expecting you; see, my dress is disordered. My servants are off duty for one reason or another; the child should not have admitted you...' But she made no attempt to run away and repair the damage, only drooped on the sofa still, and seemed not even to observe that his arms were around her. 'I am a little unhappy, my lord, but – it's nothing.'

'It's everything,' he said. 'To me it's everything – to see you for one moment sad, is an agony to me, to see these lovely eyes veiled with tears, to catch a sigh on this mouth that was made – was made only for kisses...' And he blanched and trembled and caught her in his arms and looked down on the beautiful upturned face and whispered at last: 'For my kisses!'

A prettyish little whipper-snapper kind of a fellow – but those arms were like bonds of steel about her, his mouth was hard on hers, his white teeth crushed her lips with a true man's rough passion. A flame rose in her in response such as she had never known or thought to know, the dream of white roses was a far away memory, the heavy scent of the crimson blossoms at their feet was all about her. And he murmured a question into her ear and half swooning, she dragged herself free from him and, spent with desire unfulfilled, stumbled to the door ...

She went up to her bedroom, alone: the bedroom that had long ago been prepared for this day, the satin and sandalwood, the frilled muslin draperies, all the delicious paraphernalia of the fashionable *poule de luxe*. The family had retreated before her and now huddled in a group in the doorway, almost scared by the blank, bemused look on her face, by the slowness, by the silence ... She stood by the high four-poster bed with its cupids, one at each corner, trailing ribbons of cerulean blue, and her shaking hands clung to the carved wooden spiral. Mrs Brown blurted out at last: 'For God's sake, child, speak! What has happened?'

She seemed to start awake – opened the grey eyes wide, clapped her hand to her mouth and spewed into it a sudden great hoot of laughter, still incredulous, utterly astounded. 'What on earth do you think?' she said. 'The very worst! He's asked me to *marry* him.'

CHAPTER FOUR

The page brought a silver tray with wine and glasses. 'And a message, my lord. Milady is with her maid and begs a few – a few moments of your lordship's patience—' stammered Jake, a little short on rehearsal; and added in a rush, '—while she composes herself.' He stood staring at his lordship with great round eyes. (The news had evidently already spread through the household. In that case, surely she must mean to accept him?) My lord, in his feverish uncertainty, caught at the first means of distraction and entered into conversation. 'Do you like sugar cakes?'

'Well – yes,' said Jake. '('When they're fresh,' he did not add, 'but we know now that you never touch them and these are two weeks old.')

'Well, then, put a few in your pocket. I can't bear sugar cakes myself,' confided the Earl, 'and yet don't care to offend Mrs Brown who so solicitously provides them for me.' He leaned in elegant ease, his hands languidly playing with a snuff-box of tortoiseshell and silver; but the child, alert and eager, saw that every muscle was tense, ears cocked for returning footsteps, bright dark eyes watching for the opening of the door. 'Don't go. Eat your sugar cakes and talk to me.' He cast about visibly for some subject of common interest. 'Have you been long in your position here?'

'Not long, my lord,' said Jake indifferently, diving into a

pocket and beginning unwillingly to nibble at a stale sugar cake.

'What next? A footman, I suppose? – one day a major domo? Is that a page's ambition?'

'Who – I? A major domo! I – I mean, my lord,' corrected Jake hurriedly, 'that that is not my ambition. I want to be something quite – well, quite different.'

'Come tell me then. Perhaps,' said the Earl, his eyes on the door, only half listening, 'I might help you to it.'

Jake laughed. Accustomed to the company of indulgent elders, the man, as a man, had no terrors for him; and as for his rank – after all, thought Jake grinning to himself, he's only my future brother-in-law. And he liked him; no sly, insinuating blade, handing out bribes for a peep through a lady's window, skulking in the shadow of bouquet-bearing footmen – but a real man (even though he might look somewhat womanish and dress a trifle over-foppish) who carried his own flowers and paid his own court honestly, riding up boldly to his lady's door: and sat his horse like a king what was more – Jake was sensitive to good horsemanship; back home in the Cotswold country all the family had been bred to the saddle: were as much at home on a horse as on their own feet. He grew confidential, drawing a little closer. 'I don't think your lordship could help me in *my* ambition.' And he leaned forward, almost whispering, his eyes bright with dreams of excitement and daring. 'I want to be a highwayman,' he said.

If the Earl looked a little startled, at least, unlike less intelligent adults, he did not burst into derisive laughter. 'What, ride the High Toby? You've been reading too much of the Weston brothers and Sixteen String Jack.'

'They say he wears a fine brocade suit laced with silver, and eight ribbons at each knee of his breeches. And at his execution, sir, a highwayman may commonly have as many as half-a-dozen fine ladies to sup with him in the prison, the night before he dies—'

40

'And so he dies,' said Lord Tregaron. He smiled rather wryly. 'If you're so hot after the women, young sir, there are other ways of dining with them than by inviting them to Newgate.' And he laughed and put on a quizzical air. 'But, come, I may yet be of use to you after all. We have a fine mob of just such villains operating from a lair close by to my home in Carmarthenshire. Y Cadno – The Fox – they call their leader, from the name of the hamlet where they have their den – a chapel and a smithy, no more, which in Welsh is called Cwrt y Cadno, that is to say The Court of the Fox or The Den of the Fox.' He laughed again. 'Shall I commend you to these gentry with a few handsome words of reference?'

'You smile, my lord; but one day—'

'One day you will swing from the Three-Legged Tree, my boy, if you cling to such visions as these; with friends paid to hang upon your legs as you dangle there, strangling, and so the sooner put an end to your agony. Who cares for the plaudits of a silly crowd? – that hears them only through ears muffled with laudanum (if he's fortunate) and clasping his own shroud and coffin – if he's rich. Do you know the average length of a highwayman's life? Twenty three years – and that's putting it high, I assure you. Isaac Darkin they accounted successful and famous, and he died before he was twenty-one. McLaine, the hero of them all was but twenty-six. Though I confess,' he added, 'that The Fox outlives most of his contemporaries and must by now, by five or six years at least, have outstayed his time.' But there came a step upon the stairs and he raised his head sharply, all else forgotten. 'Is that your lady?'

But it was the waiting woman. 'Oh, my lord – she's a little discomposed, as is but natural; lying down upon her bed and begs you will excuse her . . . Later, perhaps? If your lordship would call again this evening? She'll receive you this evening, my lord, and – and I know you will be made happy . . .' She turned and scuttled out again, pausing only for one of her nid-nodding curtseys. The would-be highwayman, hugely grin-

41

ning, conducted his lordship, willy nilly, to the door.

Upstairs, however, the heroine was by no means lying upon her bed but standing with her back to the fire in the old, familiar attic sitting-room, roundly declaring that nothing would induce her to become a countess. 'I've been a marchioness already for near three months, and the dullness of it is beyond enduring. What, sit all the rest of my life in a box at the playhouse—?'

'Once you're married, Gilda, you need never hear another murmer—'

'Pouff, that's all you know! The place is stiff with dowagers on the nights when the solemn pieces are played, sitting poker-faced, bored to a thousand tears. To go is an obligation, and to take along with them such poor, down-trodden daughters-in-law as they may have acquired. The only fun is in the boxes where the harlots entertain. Oh, who could have dreamed,' mourned Gilda, wringing her hands, her genuine despair tempered, as ever, by laughter, 'that he would want to make me an honest woman?'

'Child, you'll be rich beyond your wildest dreams.'

'What's the use of being rich if we may not spend our money as we wish to? He'll immure me down there in wild Wales, I shall moulder away in the damp till my hinges grow rusty, moss will grow over me, great cracks appear in my structure...' She made up her mind. 'I shall tell him the truth; if he loves me so much, he will still, surely, take me for his mistress?'

The family burst into protestations. A tiny house, a few jewels, an all-too-uncertain tenure – against lands and title as great as any in the Kingdom. 'Once he has a wife, of course the town house will be opened. Dear heaven, child, you'll be queen of society – Marigold, Countess of Tregaron—!'

'Marigold the Cow of Carmarthen,' said Gilda. 'For heaven's sake, Mother, don't call me by that name! Besides, what of the Honourable Harrington?' Hope rose in her. 'He is long ago formally affianced, he has no right to ask me.'

'That's between him and his family – and hers. He has

evidently made all right. You're sure, though,' said Sam, suddenly anxious, 'that it was a proposal of marriage? You didn't misunderstand?'

But she had not misunderstood. 'Do you think I don't know a proposal of marriage from the other kind? I've had one or the other, God knows, from every hickory-stick in Gloucestershire.' And that gave her fresh hope again. 'We could never get away with it. Once he's my husband he'll make it his business to investigate the fate of my fortune in the paws of the ravening wolves. He'll discover then the whole deception, from Gloucestershire onwards.'

'Once he's your husband,' said Mrs Brown tartly, 'what does it matter? He can't un-marry you because you were never in Italy.'

'He could leave her,' said Bess.

'But not unprovided for. She'll still be his countess. Whereas if she were merely his mistress—'

'An hour ago,' said Gilda, 'it was the height of your dream that I should be his mistress.'

Sam gave a warning glance at his mother. He sat down in the old, shabby armchair and pulled his sister on to his knee. 'Come, sweetheart, consider this thing calmly, there's no need for dissension: you fly off at the slightest word, like a sitting pheasant.' And he held her lightly, lovingly, in the old brotherly way and talked to her gently and quietly. 'No one wants you to do what is not for your happiness. What is it you're afraid of? As a man – don't you care for the fellow?'

'Oh, as to that . . .' She would have burst out into ridicule of the muff and the snuff-box and the clouded-amber cane, but the memory came flooding back over her, of those arms that had closed about her so passionately, of the fierce, hard lips pressing down, parting her own: of the fire that so utterly unexpectedly had blazed up within her, until it had all but consumed her . . . She knew that her cheeks were aflame and bent down her head to conceal it. 'As to that – he's too fond of a satin waistcoat to be quite what I take to be a man;

43

but he's well enough, I dare say.' His conversation, however, she insisted, appalled her with its dullness. 'And why not? What's there for him to talk of in this terrible Carmarthenshire, but sheep and cattle?'

'There are highwaymen,' said little Jake, eagerly. 'They live in a place called the Court of Foxes.'

'Oh, very well then, that settles it. If I'm to have foxes to converse with as well as sheep and cows, what more's to be desired for me?' And she burst into a fresh spate of laughter, tinged with hysteria now, at the thought of having left the wet wilds of the Cotswolds only to end up in the still wetter wilds of Wales, shivering in coronet and goatskin in some medieval keep in Carmarthenshire: and leapt up and thrust a cushion upon her head and clutched the worn hearth-rug about her in a wild parody of high living among the Welsh aristocracy . . .

But when he came that evening she told him – as she had all along known that she must tell him – that she would become the Earl of Tregaron's wife.

Now the Unattainable Lady appeared at the playhouse no more. The flower stall was closed, the gallants disconsolate; outside the little house in South Audley Street a footman replied to all those who in their extremity dared to call, that the Marchesa was indisposed. The flower girl, indeed, still full of initiative, had set up her little booth again at the street corner, for any who wished to leave messages of condolence for the invalid; but with the falling-away of all those who had cared more for the wagers than in fact for the lady, trade was not very brisk; and moreover in the cold light of day, the well-worn condition of the blossoms became so apparent as to force frequent renewal, which cut down the profits most depressingly – only his lordship remaining faithful in huge purchases of red roses. So funds were very low; and the sooner, decided the family, that the Earl made good his promise, the better it would be for all concerned. Moreover, he must some-

44

how be persuaded to keep the whole thing as private as possible. The expensive necessity of providing for a wedding had not been taken into consideration when their plans were laid.

So her ladyship sat in the little drawing-room with her lover's hand in hers and asked very prettily if when the time came, it might all be done very quietly; and raised her eyes to the portrait, smiling so tenderly down upon her, and said that for the sake of that dear friend (and he had been little more than a friend, she had been almost a child then – and *his* child, since he had brought her up, almost from babyhood – just a kind father) – for the sake of his memory she would prefer no outward parade of rejoicing . . .

He was disappointed. 'I wanted to show my prize to all the world. The Prince himself had promised to be there.'

'The Prince?'

'His Royal Highness is my intimate friend. He was the first I went to when I knew I was to be the happiest of men. He was delighted. He has never really cared for—' He broke off abruptly, bit his lip a little, shrugged it all off. 'The – er – the lady concerned was from the other set: there are two divisions in our present society, as no doubt you know, those who circle about the court and those who attach themselves to the Prince, who is of course not at present *persona grata* with his papa. So that – well, as I say, he would have undertaken to dance at my wedding; and confided to me, dearest, by the way, that it had been in his mind to send you flowers, but that you appeared so adamant in refusing all acquaintance that he dared not: for the Prince of Wales can hardly afford an open rebuff.' (Oh lord! reflected the Unattainable, there we went too far!) 'But he greatly admires you and would be more than happy to give our marriage his blessing.'

An inspiration struck her. 'Under the – circumstances: since you have now mentioned the other lady – would not a big wedding perhaps prove embarrassing?'

He shrugged again. 'A little. But as I have said – there are these two divisions in our present society. And my mother, of course, would wish it to be a great occasion.'

His mother! They had not, naturally, counted on interference from such a quarter; a man picked up a mistress without reference to his mama, but a daughter-in-law of course was different. Suppose the Countess of Tregaron were to be more scrupulous than her son in taking up references! 'Could we not,' suggested Gilda timidly, 'slip away by our two selves anyway – why?' He smiled at her fondly. 'Are you ashamed 'What – wed in secret? How could this be possible? – though it's true that my family are at present abroad. But anyway – why?' He smiled at her fondly. 'Are you ashamed of your bargain?'

A little ashamed, perhaps – though not as he meant it. And a little ashamed, also, of what she must do now. For the look in his eyes had been a prompting: there might be more ways of killing a cat than by filling it up with cream, but this cat looked very hungry for cream. Her life had been planned as the exploitation of her physical beauty and passion, for gain, and now the first step in that direction must be taken. She got up slowly and moved away a little and hung her head and drooped an adorable lower lip – so that he must as a matter of course, jump up and follow her, come close to her, catch at her hands and ask her what was the matter, did she really care so much to have their marriage kept private, did it mean such a lot to her ... ? And she, with her hands in his, bent her head till the bright hair brushed his lips and murmured that life was so sad and lonely, she had stood so long alone and undefended, it had been so wonderful that soon, soon, he would be always with her, she need no longer struggle on her own ... But now ... 'All this fuss and preparation – how long will it not take? Weeks and months – you're a man, my lord, you don't think of these things, but a great wedding can't be all arranged in the twinkling of an eye: I know for I've been through one already.' And on that occasion the bridegroom had at least – at least been anxious to have things

46

hurried forward . . . (Lest he die of old age, meantime, thought Gilda to herself, glancing up, all heaven in her eyes, at the portrait of the unknown octogenarian above the mantelshelf.)

'Do you think *I'm* not anxious? If I could marry you tomorrow—'

'Ah, but you can't marry me tomorrow. Your lady mother, the Tregaron family, his Royal Highness, all the rest of your world, my lord – they won't let you. So that, though you and I may wish it, we, though we're the principals, must wait.' And meanwhile, she added, giving in with a pretty grace, moving away from him, slipping her hands out of his, he must release her hand, she was a woman alone, it was not *comme il faut* that he should come so close; she didn't know what her duenna would say. And she'd be right to say it. Once they were married, of course—

He came after her, caught her to him again. 'Damn your duenna—!'

'With all my heart,' she said, almost laughing, looking up at him with a look very different from the look of pure maidenly love she had given the portrait. 'But as I say, after all she would be in the right.' And she gave him a little push, the palms of her hands against his breast. 'So let me go now, or I must call her in – for propriety's sake.' And she hung her head again and forced a blush – which came with a somewhat disconcerting ease, when she felt herself so close to him – and murmured that they did not want a repetition of – of what had happened when – when first he had kissed her . . .

His left arm held her fast, his right forced back her head till her mouth touched his, lip to lip. 'We'll be married tomorrow, next day, whenever you will. No one shall know. It shall be just as you say. Only never again, for God's sake, refuse me your kisses . . .' And his lips fastened down upon hers and triumph for a moment struggled with shame, and she thought: What an actress I am, what a sham it all is! And

47

then it was a sham no longer, there came again that leaping flame, that wild surge of excitement, her hands grasped his coat sleeves, she strained herself to him, gave her mouth to his, was lost – lost to all but the thrilling pain of his arms so fierce and hard about her, his mouth so mercilessly pressing down on hers; his face looming above her, gone so strange and pale. When at last he let her go, she leaned trembling against a chair while he flung across the room and cooled his burning forehead on the chill glass of the window pane. He said: 'I'll ride to Wales tomorrow. I must arrange things there. But I'll be back within the week. Meanwhile – I'll arrange a marriage licence. Today is Monday. Next Monday: will that do?'

She answered, too shaken inwardly for further triumph, humbly: 'Monday? Yes, my lord.'

'Say nothing to anyone. If the secret gets out, we're lost. Can you trust your servants?'

'My servants? – oh, yes, certainly.'

'To deflect suspicion, let your household here continue a little while, let your servants continue to say you are indisposed. That will throw any enquirers off the scent. Meanwhile, once married we'll go straight down to Carmarthenshire.'

She was stricken out of acquiescence. 'To Wales?'

'We shall hardly keep our secret by setting up home in the family house in Hanover Square.'

'I suppose not,' she said doubtfully. Once they were married, did it matter to her that the secret be kept at all? But then again, was not the whole thing too overwhelming altogether? It would be best to have time on her side. He said, rather edgily: 'You seem not over eager to come to Castell Cothi. But after all, this is to be your home.'

She pulled herself together. 'You must make allowance for me. I am but an urban creature, used only to cities. And—' She affected a rueful laughter, turning it all back upon herself, a deprecatory little joke. 'I can't help thinking of my duenna, as you call her. She will rot away in – I mean, she'll be quite

48

lost, without the familiar link lights and cobble-stones of town.'

'She'll be necessary here. You can't leave the business in the hands of your cook and your footman; if your woman shows herself, then none will doubt that you are really sick a-bed. I'll bring back a Welsh girl to attend you to Wales.'

'A Welsh girl?'

'Welsh girls are what we *have* in Wales,' he said, again with a sharp touch to his voice. But he controlled himself. 'Have no fear, the girl I think of is accustomed to this work, my sister employed her for some time.' He appeared to consider the matter as settled – and she dared not argue further. 'We'll be married as early as the priest is astir and, by using six horses, may lie that night at Cheltenham.'

'At Cheltenham? Drive off a hundred miles or more without so much as a wedding breakfast?'

'It was you who didn't wish for a wedding breakfast.'

'I have no objection to eating one myself,' she said crossly.

'We needn't go hungry; but by cutting short such ceremony we may reach Castell Cothi by the second night.' He looked at her, astonished. 'Does this plan not appeal to you? It was you that wished so much for discretion.'

'Discretion, yes. But not to creep out of bed, waken up some unshaven cleric to couple us up; and then rattle away in a carriage to Cheltenham.' What use, she had said to the family, a great fortune if they were not to enjoy the spending of it? – and what sort of start to the spending of it was this? 'Is that your notion of a wedding day, my lord?' He began to speak but she overrode him; despair and frustration raged within her, the Marchesa Marigelda acting outrage became Miss Marigold Brown in a genuine temper. 'Why not fly to the Fleet outright, where some unfrocked wretch may mumble our lines for a guinea and hustle us off? A fine marriage, I declare: and I in my servant's sac, I daresay, the better to disguise my identity? – creeping out of town as though I were – as though I were—' But she remembered what in fact she

49

was and, with all her indignation and despair, was hard put to it to prevent herself from bursting into laughter. A muffled sound, hastily hushed, from behind the door, reminded her that the footmen doubtless had their ears pressed against it, reporting all that went forward to the rest of the family, hanging over the banisters; and probably in much the same half-hysterical condition as herself.

Lord Tregaron stood staring at her in dismay. 'But – it's you who wished for discretion; and in my case – as in your case, for I think you little know how much talked about you are – discretion must involve absolute secrecy, or be useless.' He stood, indecisive. 'For my part I care nothing of the how or the where or who's present or who is absent – so that you marry me as soon as may be.' He came to her, holding out his hand. 'Come, tell me what it is you wish and it shall be as you say.'

'I wish nothing. A respectable church, a decent hour of the day, at least to wear my own gown—'

'Who suggested anything different? – be reasonable!'

'—and not to go jolting off like an escaping criminal to Cheltenham.' Let the newly coroneted head, she thought, at least lie one night upon the pillows of the mansion in town: by the time she returned to London, it was too likely that the truth would be out and she a pensioner on her husband's bounty, doled out because, she being his countess before all the world, he could do no less. 'Let the marriage be arranged for Monday evening – if you wish it so. I will sleep that night in Hanover Square and come with you next day to Carmarthenshire.' She had retreated to the cool remotion of the Unattainable, standing quiet and composed in the doorway, not taking his outstretched hand. It was, after all, for the Marchesa to make her own terms.

His hand dropped to his side. He bowed. 'As your ladyship commands.'

'You ride back to Wales tomorrow then?'

'And shall return by Monday.'

She was a little alarmed at the chill in his tone, afraid lest she had gone too far, betrayed herself perhaps, in the frankness of her outburst. She threw a new warmth into her voice. 'Not before then?'

He bowed again. 'You have warned me that until we are married I must – keep my distance.'

'But needn't do so literally?' she suggested, smiling.

'If I am to do the one, I had better do the other also,' he said, still coldly.

She left the door and came to him and stood close against him, not touching him, her hands behind her back: and lifted up her face to his. 'Perhaps you're wise. We are – neither of us – so strong that we should take foolish chances.' And as he remained stony-faced, braced back from her, she came closer, leant upon his breast but still with her hands behind her back, not touching him; and put her lips against his lips and whispered: 'But let us take just one more foolish chance, to say goodbye . . .'

And he caught her in his arms and held her close; and she knew, with a triumph tinged with shame, that there was a magic strong in her, that henceforward would work her will with him.

Upon the Wednesday evening after his departure a man came to the door, a messenger: a hard, brown, sturdy man, his Welsh accent so thick as hardly to be understood. He wore a sort of jerkin of natural coloured frieze, buttoned to the waist over trousers of the same rough wool, and a round black beaver hat: and he carried a vast bouquet of red roses. 'From the Earl of Tregaron.' He pushed them somewhat un-ceremoniously into the footman's arms.

James took the flowers. 'Is his lordship back in town?'

'No, no: sent up from Wales. I rode up from Castell Cothi; just arrived now.'

'Will you see my mistress? Have you any message for her?'

'No, no,' he said again. He shrugged. 'He's well. No trouble on the ride down. And to give her a package and tell her he returns on Sunday. And he said that if I had any trouble with the Gentry on the way up here, I should tell the lady's page. Well, and so, inform the young gentleman that I did. Waylaid by Y Cadno himself of whom it seems he spoke to the boy.' He laughed. 'I played him a trick after Y Cadno's own heart: feigned fear, let my eye and hand wander, as though in particular anxiety, to a certain saddle-bag, and at last contrived to slip it free and cast it into a thorn bush, as though to come back for it later, when he should have gone. And he, mightily amused, let it all go forward and then dismounted and made for the thorn bush. So when I had him in a fine tangle, caught up in the thorn bush and reaching for the bag – which by the way contained a change of stockings and little more – I set spurs to my pony; pausing only to deliver him a load of buck-shot which I think did him some injury. And so am able to deliver the package to the lady.' He handed it over, a small, hard, wrapped box, grinned broadly, biffed her ladyship's foot-man jovially in his fine plush ribs by way of farewell, and ambled off. So, thought James, is my lovely sister to be waited upon in the future! Still, in Aston-sub-Edge she had not been waited upon at all; and one way or another, they would soon have her back from Wales.

The package contained a ring set with a ruby as red as the roses themselves magnificently mounted in gold; and the now familiar legend: *I will love you till I die.*

And so the Monday came; and for the last time she put on the white gown of her theatre-going days and went with her little group – ('My servants shall be present, my lord; they are my friends, I have no others,') – to the small, care-fully obscure chapel where he awaited her. Within its shadows, a girl was standing. Gilda slipped her hand away. 'I want to speak to her.'

'It is only the flower girl who sells me roses.'

But she left him, uncertainly standing. 'Bess!' She led her

52

sister aside out of earshot. 'Oh, Bess – now that the moment has come – in God's name, what am I doing?'

Bess looked at her, terrified. 'Do you not now wish to go through with it?'

'A man I don't know, don't love ...'

'You've always believed, Gilda, that love didn't enter into it.' (Bess, nowadays, herself knew better.)

'That was for – those other plans. But this is marriage, this is for ever.'

'When he finds out the deception—'

'What if when he finds out the deception, he won't let me go?' In the background, music played softly, the Earl stood quietly but with an air of puzzlement, waiting. 'Oh, Bess, what am I doing? What am I doing?'

'Can you not like him, dearest? He's handsome, kind, charming—'

'And rich. You don't add, Bess, the most important thing of all – he's rich.'

'Riches are not all,' admitted Bess. She stood with her sister's hand in hers, holding her fast. 'We've been dazzled by this opportunity, we haven't stopped to think: it's all been so rushed and quick. But if you truly dislike him, Gilda, you know that even now, none of us will urge you forward. Say the word and it's all over; if need be we can go back to Gloucestershire – you shall not be made unhappy for our gain: not even for your own. If you don't like him—' And suddenly she dropped the two white hands. 'Oh, Gilda – it's not that you don't like *him*! It is that you like someone else. It's because of Brown Eyes ...?'

She turned swiftly and ran – back to where he waited, back to the folly, the wild, wicked folly of her chosen destiny. But walking up the brief aisle upon his arm, standing at the altar, walking down again, Countess of Tregaron, at her husband's side – the scent of white roses filled all the air for her.

The carriage, discreetly uncrested, which had brought them

to the chapel, took them home to the great mansion in Hanover Square, the Welsh maid he had brought back with him, perched respectfully upon the seat opposite, her eyes respectfully lowered: a slim, neat girl with a frizz of black hair, in the national black, beaver chimney-pot hat, worn over a frilled white bonnet; trim jacket and three-cornered shawl over a petticoat of brick-coloured wool. The Earl took the hand of his new Countess into his own. She remembered the thrill of that other hand, brushing against hers and was sick with the terror of what now, past reclaim, had been done. If it had been Brown Eyes who sat in the carriage with her now; if, to mansion or bijou, it had been Brown Eyes who was bringing her home . . . !

The carriage drew up with a rattle of iron-shod wheels upon cobblestones. Between fluted Doric columns, two footmen, white-powdered, plushy-breeched, stood already in waiting outside the high front door. She passed in, beneath the lovely glass fanlight to a hall as big as a garden, where upon the patterned marble floor beneath the painted ceiling, a majordomo bowed, a house-keeper curtseyed, murmuring a welcome. Everything was prepared, a meal would be in readiness when her ladyship should wish it . . . Gilda stifled a giggle as, bobbing and bowing, as so lately her own mother had bobbed and bowed to the gentlemen outside the box at the playhouse, the woman led the way upstairs.

A room which might have swallowed up her little bedroom in the bijou house round the corner; but not white and gold and cerulean blue as that room was, with billowy hangings held up by small naked cupids, peeking through to watch the sweet nonsense of love in the filmy white bed below . . . That bed which would never now be used, which was to have been the tumbling-place of so much naughtiness and fun – with a sovereign to be paid for every kiss, no doubt, but for kisses that would have been, tender and gay, for loves that were always new. Would not kisses grow stale that were given in this huge four-poster, year after matrimonial year? – caged in

54

by columns of carven mahogany and curtains of damask fringed with gold. Crimson damask; the whole great room was hung with crimson. Red roses in a room of crimson: no doxy to be bought and sold but a lady of title now, rich, powerful, adored, in this great room of crimson in this great house, as splendid as any in the land. And she would give it all, she knew, to be back in the little white room, in the little white house around the corner; with no wealth, no security, no future – only the promise that lay in a bunch of white roses, a pair of brown eyes. I can't go through with it, she thought. I'll tell him it's all been a trick, I'll tell him I repent of it. If I refuse to consummate the marriage, it can yet be annulled. Her heart shuddered at the thought of what her family would say; at the thought of the punishment that might come upon them all, if he revealed their deceptions to the law ... But she need not, after all, go to such lengths as these. She could simply tell him the truth. I'll tell him that I'm in love with another man; that in these past weeks my love has been stifled, forced down, half-forgotten and yet has been always there, always deep in my heart. I'll tell him I can't let him love me, I can't let him touch me – when all my heart and my body cry out for the love of another man ...

The woman had curtseyed herself out of the door, dismissed, and now he came into the room. Came up and stood behind her and put his arms around her, his hands on her breasts. She swung round to face him. 'My lord – one moment: one moment – listen to me! I want to tell you – to explain to you ... My lord, I repent of this marriage. I ... My own heart ...'

His arms closed around her, hard and strong, his mouth came down upon hers. She felt the sick surge of excitement that she had known on the first day he had kissed her, on all those other days of his controlled embracings; and fought against it, moving her head from side to side, repudiating him, trying with all her no small strength to thrust him away from her. But all the time, even as she fought, she knew that

55

the flame was burning up within her, growing bright within her, uncontrollable, a flame of pure physical passion, pure animal desire. His eyes were dark and brilliant, staring down into hers; one arm now sufficed to hold her, one hand struggled to pull aside the low bodice of her white gown; and, sick with angry shame at her own weakness, her own infidelity, she yet, unresistant, permitted, encouraged – half swooning against him in a sort of sick rapture as his hard brown fingers touched for the first time the sensitive tips of her breasts. He said nothing, spoke not a word; only violent, ruthless, relentless, in the grip of his own passion, imposed his will upon hers, ripping away her petticoats, silently cursing impeding cambric and corset, flinging her at last half naked across the width of the bed. Her arms fell lax, her lips acquiesced, accepted, responded: grew, in response as avid and demanding as his own. Her body arched to him, the flame was soft and lambent no longer but a flaring-up of ecstasy that flared at last into such a bonfire of consummation as burned away all other longings, all other desires – all other loves . . .

They sat through the long evening meal, one at either end of the mahogany table, polished through the years to the colour of old wine; speechless, exhausted, sick with passion consummated, desire fulfilled. The servants moved about them quietly, handing dish after dish, course after course, removing each almost untouched. They spoke not a word; what words, she thought, could two people have left to speak to one another, after such an hour as that? And yet . . . Had it been Brown Eyes – would there not have been a look, a sweetness, an exchange of glances, half-tender, half naughtily ashamed, under the silent, impersonal watchfulness of the attendant staff? What have I done? she thought; what have I done? For, heaven knew! – no one could claim the marriage unconsummated now; and with its consummation went all hope of ever finding her way to the arms of her own true love.

The meal reached its climax, the housekeeper reappeared and led the way to the vast withdrawing-room upstairs, proffered chairs, proposed the tea board at such and such a time ... Will she one day decide, thought Gilda, that we can find our way, without conduct, about our own house? – or am I to move through the rest of my life as though I were a dummy, incapable of decision or action on my own? And will every evening drag like this evening? she wondered, stifling the first yawn, half a silent hour later. Would there be nothing to look forward to ever again? – but the ending of an evening like this – which in turn would lead up to the great bed with its dark crimson hangings and its dark crimson blazing of animal matings with a man whom she never could love; and yet, it began to seem, never be able to resist. . . And she thought of her true love, of Brown Eyes, with his arms full of roses; and was sick with shame for that earlier loveless devouring that now had for ever ended her hope of his love. For something to say, she asked, for the third or fourth time, about arrangements for their journey on the following day, towards Wales; for the third or fourth time was told briefly, almost abruptly, that all was in train, a coach would be at the door by seven o'clock; a plain hired coach to preserve their secrecy, rather than the huge, crested family equippage. They were to sleep that night at Gloucester; with changes of horses they might be there by the evening; it was almost exactly half-way, they might be at Castell Cothi by dark the next night ...

'In that case, I must be up by six for my toilet; with your permission, my lord, I will retire.'

He jumped to his feet. 'Certainly. It will be best.' And he pulled on a bell rope and soon the woman came and there were more curtseyings, and a procession formed at last to conduct my lord and lady up the stairs to their rooms. Two footmen went ahead with candelabra held high, the housekeeper after them, walking crabwise looking backwards, alert lest a young woman of seventeen years be unable to mount a score of broad, shallow steps without a helping hand; behind her Catti Jones, the dark Welsh maid, stepped smartly with her skirts held up above her trim ankles. At Gilda's side Lord Tregaron kept a protective hand at the elbow of her right arm.

A man came to the top of the stairs and would have descended; but seeing the little cortège coming up, paused at the top and waited for them to come to the splendid curved landing of the first floor. The footmen moved a little to the side to avoid him as he stood silently, bowing, making way for the lady to pass. On Lord Tregaron's arm, she paused for a tiny moment to bow back an acknowledgement of his courtesy. He raised his head; and once again for one moment they looked back at one another, those two . . .

Fair hair and a quiet face, gentle yet strong. Brown Eyes.

CHAPTER FIVE

At the door of the bedroom she stopped. In front of them all she said to her husband, coolly: 'I will bid you goodnight, my lord. We have an early start tomorrow,' and bowed and went in; the maid Catti following her, closed the door behind her. She said sharply: 'Lock it; you can sleep on the sofa in here, with me.' Not for all the red roses in the world would she spend the night in that other man's arms; but her own vile flesh even now assured her that if he came to her, she might still be unable to refuse him.

The lady's maid was not much of a lady's maid; but Gilda after all was sufficiently capable of preparing herself for bed. She allowed the girl to brush out the marigold floss of her hair; the elaborate coiffure had been so tumbled that she had hardly been able to get it into some sort of shape for the supper hour and tomorrow might (with relief) resort to a simple knot of curls at the nape of her neck, tied back with a black velvet bow as was the habit when riding or travelling. Now, as the bristles slid their way through the silky floss she asked, secretly trembling: 'Who was the gentleman on the stairs? Do you know?'

'On the stairs? His lordship's brother, David of Llandovery. They were saying in the servants' hall that he is just this moment arrived, back from foreign parts much earlier than expected.'

Gilda sat astounded. 'His lordship's brother? Is *he* the Honourable David Llandovery?'

Catti misunderstood the emphasis; spelt out the lessons doubtless learned below-stairs. 'My lord your husband is the head of the family, Madam, is it not so? – his father being lately dead and he now Earl of Tregaron. And the other, being the younger brother, second son of the late Earl, is but an "honourable", with the family name of Llandovery. Dafydd – that's the Welsh for David and Dai the short form of it: Davidd bach of Carmarthen, we call him down in Wales, begging your ladyship's pardon, or Dai bach. There's no exact English for it: darling David you might say, or dear little David – a term, one might say, Madam, of a sort of loving disrespect – everybody loves him in Wales, so brave and gay he is, and kind . . .' But she broke off sharply as though she had said too much, been guilty perhaps of disloyalty. 'All but his lordship, that is: for you saw how the two brothers passed without a word – it's said they haven't spoken for years . . .'

Here in this house, her husband's house: the love of her life, her own husband's brother, her own brother-in-law! She said faintly, 'Does he – does David Llandovery live here in this house?'

'Oh, no, Madam, he has a home of his own in Carmarthenshire where he also has estates, my lord of Tregaron of course having far the largest share. But this is the family house with no mistress till now but my lady the Countess, their mother, and therefore available of course to all her family. And returning from abroad and believing Lord Tregaron in Carmarthenshire I dare say – which indeed he was until yesterday, milady – came here not expecting to meet him. Or came anyway, perhaps; the house is large enough, heaven knows, to accom-

Dafydd: the single f is pronounced like a v in Welsh, and the doubled like the hard th in 'the'. Roughly, then, Duv-ith, accent on the first syllable.
Bach: a gutteral sound, almost impossible to the English tongue – bar-ch, without any sounding of the r.
Dai: is pronounced to rhyme with 'dye'.

modate even two quarrelling brothers. And the staff here being forbidden to speak to anyone of your marriage, of Lord Tregaron's being in town . . . It has been difficult for them in the servants' hall, milady. A word was spoken to milord – to Lord Tregaron, my lady – when he arrived, as to his brother's being in town . . .'

That accounted perhaps for much of his abstraction during the evening; for the stilted conversation, the brief impersonal replies. But, meanwhile . . . She was shaken suddenly by a storm of temptation. 'Catti – I would like . . .' She broke off. She improvised : 'If I – now that I am married – were to speak with David Llandovery, were to hold out a – a hand of friendship to him, were to try to heal the breach . . . My position isn't easy, Catti, married secretly to my lord, without the knowledge or acceptance of his mother; how greatly it would ease matters if I might be the means of bringing her sons together again . . . !' And she urged the girl on. 'Run down, Catti, find out if he's still here; seek him out, ask him – ask him if I may – but secretly, Catti – have just one word with him.' The girl looked at her sharply, enquiringly, she was astonished no doubt at so fantastical a notion : that the unknown bride of an hour might patch up a quarrel of many years' standing; and Gilda recalled that this was a servant of her husband's, bound to him no doubt by long ties of family service in the half feudal conditions that would probably still continue in the ancient mists of Wales. But there was no time to be wise; here might be her last chance ever to speak to her belovéd . . . You are a married woman, her conscience said to her, a married woman for less than a day, and already planning treachery to your husband – and with his own brother. But she did not care. I loved him first. I have loved him only : my husband, whether he knows it or not, has bought me for money, I care nothing for him; he's seduced my virtue out of me by some magic of his own, but for the rest he is nothing, nothing to me . . . And she shoved the girl out. 'Run, run and find out! Find out if he has left the house and

61

if not, make an assignation with him for me . . . And secretly, secretly, Catti, I'll reward you well . . .'

It seemed a long time before Catti came back; in that time she had settled her dress, touched her face to new beauty with a shadow of paint here, a dusting of powder there; arranged the lovely sheen of her brushed-out hair into a very allurement of its own unrivalled beauty. I'm a traitor, she thought, a cheat and a liar and no better than a whore! But it was as nothing else that she and her family had embarked upon this adventure. In my husband's arms I'm no better than a whore indeed; but this other I love, in his arms I shall be pure and made whole again because I love him, I love him — not for what he has or may give me but for what he is. However I may come by it, my love with him will be pure . . .

But the maid came at last to the door and, silently curtseying, shook her head. David Llandovery had passed on down the stairs after their brief meeting; and not pausing to speak to anyone had walked out of the house and not come back.

She slept alone that night and undisturbed, Catti Jones curled up on the couch at the foot of the great bed. Next morning very early she was wakened and while she dressed, was brought a cup of chocolate and a hot roll. By seven the coach was at the door with more bobbings and bowings, the staff saw them off and the door of her new home closed after her. So this is greatness, she thought: this is grandeur! A moment of love without passion; an hour of passion without love — for the rest, an oasis of ponderous boredom, never free for a moment from servile eyes watching, respectful ears listening, from eager hands working at what one would very much rather do for oneself. With her husband she had exchanged no more than a perfunctory word of greeting as, in his three-caped great coat, he joined her in the hall and handed her down to the coach, Catti Jones scrambling in to perch on the seat opposite them, clasping milady's dressing-case since no jewel-box had been brought with her. From under white, lowered lids she flicked up a glance rather anxiously at their two faces. What might Catti have told him of that mad attempt last night to see his brother? Not for one moment, she thought, would my lord of Tregaron accept any nonsense about hopes of bringing about a reconcilement. He looked very grave, and for a moment she was afraid. But after all . . . You had but to go up close to him, stand with your hands behind your back, raise your lips to his, yet not kissing him . . . Shame filled her at the readiness with which the thought sprang to her mind, but it was not the shame that had come on that first occasion, in those first early days when she had discovered the power of her body over his senses; she knew that, little by little, that shame was dying, that shame would die. Such gifts, after all, were but weapons, put into a woman's hands.

The coach rolled and rumbled over the cobbles, every turn of the iron-shod wheels taking her further away from all those she knew and loved. Cold, aloof, withdrawn, her husband sat in silence; she looked over at Catti's face, and Catti was looking down with a hangdog air. Traitorous bitch! she thought; and was for a moment disconcerted when, as though in reply, the girl returned a look of dislike and resentment hardly less violent than her own. A fine pair, she thought, to be travelling with, two hundred miles.

At midday the coach drove off along a side road and at last stopped at an inn. There was a flutter and a flustering, a great deal of bowing and protesting, but the accommodation was villainous and the meal not much better. They ate in chill silence, broken only by necessary civilities; in silence resumed the drive. But at the Cheltenham inn that night he came to her room, dismissed the maid with a wordless gesture, threw himself across her body and began, at first violently and then with slow, sensuous mouthings that turned her bowels to a sickness of desire, to kiss her white shoulders and breast: possessed her briefly, rose and still with hardly a word spoken, was going to the door. Unsatisfied, filled with shame at her body's longing, she sought to conceal it in anger. She said:

'Your lordship has, I now perceive, but one use for a wife.'

He stopped, his hand on the door. 'Have you some complaint to make of my love-making?'

'I think only that there is very little love in it,' she said, and as he remained silent, ventured, almost timidly: 'I think that a man and his wife should be not only lovers but friends.'

He came back and stood over the bed. 'A man and his wife – and all his relations?'

'Having no family of my own, of course I – I hope yours will be my friends. Your mother; and your sister also—'

'And my brother?' he said. 'Is he also to be your friend?'

So now she knew. 'It was only that—' She stammered and faltered. 'The girl perhaps told you? May she not have misrepresented the situation? It was only that I thought the hand of a sister – of a new sister—'

'You had seen my brother once, I think, before this?'

'He sent me flowers—'

'He gave you flowers. Others sent them but from him alone you, personally, received them. And I saw the glance that passed between you: the same glance passed last night upon the stairs. I had thought it the thing of a moment, long forgotten; but last night I saw that look again. Well ...' She sat, almost cowering, huddled against the white pillows, looking up into the angry brilliance of his eyes. 'Well, Madam, Take heed! My brother and I, in spirit as well as in actuality, live apart. You'll not meet him again; and if you should, will do your husband the courtesy of ignoring his enemy. Moreover, since he is betrothed—'

'Betrothed?' she said, her heart sinking.

'To Lady Blanche Handley, daughter of the Earl of Trove. A binding engagement.'

She did not remind him that his own engagement had apparently proved less than imperatively binding. Her heart was too sick with a stab of jealousy, the first she had ever known, at thought of her belovéd affianced to another. Marriage was a humdrum business, she knew that already after

64

less than a day and a night of it: a jog-trot of boredom interspersed with taken-for-granted occasional violent moments of pleasure. But betrothal – a time for whisperings and kissings, for the murmurous pleadings, the slow, sweet, creeping-on of the intimacies of love. She made up her mind, from that moment, to detest the Lady Blanche Handley, daughter of the Earl of Trove.

It was a grey September day when, next morning, they set out on the last lap of their journey: keen and cold for the time of year but fine, with the leaves just here and there beginning to turn and the nuts on the hedgerows of hazel growing brown and fat. Within the coach it was dark and warm with the gleam of old black leather polished through the years by the rubbing and shifting of seats and shoulders, the clutching of hands as the wheels lurched over the ups and downs of the rutty roads. The straw at their feet smelt strong and sweet, the rumble of the wheels ground out a rough lullaby. They clattered through the narrow streets of Gloucester, past the white, glittering twin-towered hump of the cathedral, over the crook-backed Severn bridge and out again into the country. It was afternoon when Lord Tregaron said to her: 'We are passing into Wales.'

'It looks very much like the same England to me,' she said, not very agreeably; for with every turn of the wheels she came away, alone and dejected, from all the light-heartedness of the life she had lately known. Rogues we may be, the whole lot of us, she thought; but it seems there is but dullness in virtue. And if this be Wales, it is only that much further from all I love.

'Why, what did you expect?' he said. 'These are not the high mountains and great passes of North Wales. These are but the foothills of those mountains, a sweeter land to me by far, for all it has less of grandeur. But you will see soon how the roads twist and turn, with never an inch of flat land between the wild hills with their hanging forests of scrub oak, that have been here since the Romans and before them.' And sure enough, soon the roads ran only uphill or down. It was sundown when he said, as they clattered through a small townlet: 'This is Llandovery. In two hours we shall be home.'

Llandovery. At that name, her heart turned over. 'From which your brother takes his name?'

'It's the family name. The title comes from the great Bog of Tregaron, which lies in Cardiganshire, twenty miles northeast of Castell Cothi; five miles and more of bogland where the tall, pale grass that covers it all takes on, in sunshine, a sheen of gold—'

'And yet more pink than gold,' said Catti from her corner. She spoke dreamily, her mind so far away, that she omitted the respectful 'my lord'. But he appeared not to notice it; the formalities in Wales it seemed were less extreme than in the *haut monde* of London. I'll soon change all that, thought the new countess – she who had so lately railed at the empty obsequiousness of the inn-keepers; I've not come to the ends of the earth to be on terms of easy familiarity with serving girls. She listened in disdain as he answered, simple and friendly in the cool assumption of a superiority beyond necessity of condescension. 'You are right. And yet gold also, a pale gold – have you not seen it, Catti, when the sun lay on it? – miles and miles of it, moving a little, shifting a little as the wind blows over the grasses, as though there were ripples on a broad lake of gold. And there are creatures there, wild birds that you'll never see in any other part of Wales, and the great salmon come up the River Teifi to their spawning beds . . .' He said to Gilda: 'You shall see it some day.'

'Don't keep me too long waiting. Wild birds and spawning salmon,' she said, irritably scornful, 'have long been the passion of my life.'

They had come through a winding valley, and now struck off down a narrow path where to their right the river hurtled and tumbled to green fields eked out of spare soil by a farmer, far below. 'This way was hewn out by the Romans from the solid rock, in the building of the culvert which runs by a thousand tricks of land level and water pressure, from the waterfall behind us to the gold mines of Pumsaint, eight miles ahead. You may still see the mark of its progress through the fields, no tillage obliterates it.' As she remained indifferent, contemptuously bored, he added: 'We begin now the ascent through the forests of scrub oak that have been here since those days and for all the years before. Within half an hour we shall be in sight of home.'

Home. Some dreary castle in this dreary land of rock paths hewn out by Roman legions (and not much improved upon since, reflected Gilda, jolted this way and that by the rough riding of the iron-rimmed wheels over boulders and pot-holes) – of stark mountains, patched with gorse and heather, of stunted oak pouring down the mountain side to the green fields fringing the quiet-flowing river, dotted with grazing cattle, blurs now in the failing evening light . . . My home is not here, she thought; my home is a bijou house with frilled curtains and a white door leading in from the cobbled street where the coaches rattle and the link boys clatter and the watch-man cries out, All's well! My home is a four-poster bed with the one I love to hold me in his arms and be not violent and rough but tenderly kind . . . My home is where all is laughter and fun and gaiety and love, where the talk is a sputter and a sparkle, not this flat dull conning-over with a servant wench of whether some salmon-ridden bogland be pink or gold . . . And she leaned her head against the padded leather of the coach and listened for any sound above the rumble of the wheels; and heard nothing, nothing – only the eternal silences of the countryside, the stillness, the dullness, the nothingness, the hush of the evening . . .

The hush of the evening: slashed across suddenly, violently, by the high, shrill whinney of a horse, the clatter of hooves, the jingle of harness, the breaking of branches, the sound of men's voices yelling . . .

And a man's voice crying: 'Stand and deliver! Your money or your lives!'

67

CHAPTER SIX

The coach rocked with the sudden check, the rearing and stamping of frightened horses, brought too abruptly to a halt. She could hear the cursing of the coachman on his box, the yells of two outriders, unable to come near. ' 'Tis Y Cadno, my lord! 'Tis the Fox!'

'They won't harm us,' he said. 'They won't harm us. They only want our gold.' But as she caught at his arm, terrified, the muzzle of a pistol appeared in the window and a villainous face, half masked by a scarf pulled roughly across the mouth and chin. 'Crouch down, Gilda, don't let yourself be seen; and for God's sake, don't let them have a glimpse of your hair! They say that he has a – has a fancy for fair women . . .' He struggled blindly to pull forward the shawl she wore over her head, to block out the sight of her from the man at the window. Catti's strong arm shot up and pulled her roughly down to the floor of the coach.

The pistol gestured. 'Come – out, sir, out!' There was a clattering and slithering as he backed his pony away to allow for the opening of the door; but the Earl held his ground, still blocking the window with his body. Outside, the coachman struggled with his horses, pleading, 'Leave me be, lads, t'aint no fault of mine if they won't come to attention, I'm doing what I can.' All about there was noise and movement, the sound of horses' hooves scuffling the dead leaves beneath the

Y Cadno: pronounced Uh *Cadno*.

68

scrub oak, men swearing and shouting, laughing, cheering –
there must be a dozen or more of them, riding up along the
road behind them, down the forest slope, above them, climbing up from below – ringing them in. Lord Tregaron spoke a
word and the leader yelled out for silence, perhaps moved
closer, looked more carefully: cried out in Welsh, yet clearly
enough to be understood: 'It's the Earl, boys! Tregaron himself.'

And it muttered and rumbled about the coach, the sound of
rough voices: 'It's the Earl! From Castell Cothi! Tregaron
himself!' and the laughter and cheering were renewed. But the
first man said suspiciously: 'You travel very humble, for his
lordship. Where's the quarterings on your coach?'

'I travel incognito out of respect for – such very gentry as
yourselves. And for the same reason, carry no valuables.
Travelling from one home to another, why should I do so?
A handful of sovereigns for the journey and those already
spent but for a such few shillings as wouldn't be worth your
acceptance.'

'But which we will accept, however, my lord; being not so
proud as you credit us.'

'Are you Gareth y Cadno?' he said in a puzzled voice. 'I
had heard *he* was proud: proud as the devil.'

'Why as for devils, I am myself as it happens The Devil –
Dio y Diawl, second in command to Y Cadno. The Fox is
sick: wounded in an affray with a rider – who played him a
trick and left him shot in the body and helpless. Of which
rider you know something yourself, my lord, I believe?'

And it was true. Crouching on the floor of the coach with
Catti whispering rapid translations into her ear – for the man
spoke for the most part in Welsh – she recalled how the
Earl's messenger had told her little brother of his wayside
adventure. 'Wherefore, my lord, Y Cadno craves a word
with you. I am to bring you to the Cwrt.'

Well – he was a brave man, for all his foppishness: she had
to acknowledge that. He stepped down immediately, closing

the door of the coach quickly behind him. 'Very well, I'll come with you. Let my men take the coach on to Castell Cothi and I can follow when the Fox has done with me.'

The man laughed, a great rolling ho-ho-ho! Beneath his pony's hooves, the dry twigs snapped, and crackled as he backed away to allow for the opening door. 'What – send the coach on? – and all your gold with it!'

'I have told you and I swear it – I carry no gold.'

But the hooves slipped and scuffled again on the leaves mouldering, ever renewed, beneath the small stunted scrub oaks, and over his protests a voice cried, 'Move aside then, and let me see!' and the light from the window was blotted out again. Petrified into quietness she crouched with Catti, on the floor in the blackness keeping her head bent low beneath its dark, covering shawl: and raised it sharply, in startled terror as a torch was thrust in and the whole interior blazed into light. And the shawl slipped back and the lovely hair fell all about her shoulders: and the voice said slowly, huge with triumph: 'Well, but my lord, it seems you lie – when you say that you carry no gold.'

No gags were necessary. In all those bleak, wild mountains, who would hear them however loud they might cry out? Sick with terror she felt herself hauled out, rough arms lifted her across the pommel of a pony, rough arms held her there. Beside her, she knew that Catti was carried also, screaming and struggling amidst the laughter and cursing of those who had her in their charge – somewhere behind them, Lord Tregaron followed. Down through the forest of oaks, fording the little river, sore with the jolting jog-trot of the pony over the tussocky ground she gave herself over to the merciful darkness of oblivion; and woke to find that the jog-trot had ceased, that there were lights, the flickering of torches in approaching darkness, an outline of black shapes towering above her as of rugged buildings. Whimpering she struggled into a sitting position, the rider still holding her round the

70

waist with one arm, as with the other he reined in the stubby little pony to quietness. In the smokey dusk, all about her men were descending from their mounts. She cried out: 'Where's his lordship? Where's my husband?'

She saw him released, set free to stumble over towards her, rubbing his arms where the bonds had cut into him. 'Hush, Gilda, make no outcry, be quiet, do what they tell you.' His face was patched with shadows in the flicker of the torchlight. 'It's Cwrt y Cadno, the Court of the Fox – the lair, the den of this footpad, this Gareth y Cadno.'

'Oh, God!' she sobbed. 'What will they do to us?'

'I think they won't harm us. I think they mean to hold us to ransom.'

'To ransom! Then very soon—? But in the meantime . . . ?'

'In the meantime they'll house us, I suppose, in some sort. They seem to have a rough kind of fortress here among the caves between these great boulders.' And indeed the massive blocks now revealed themselves, to eyes growing accustomed to the new light, as great rocks, tumbled thousands of years since into this narrow valley; through which the hand of man had threaded walls and reinforcements till the whole thing resembled one vast, nightmare, armed encampment, filling the little valley and spreading away up the hillside. Above and beyond them and all about them, the rough, low mountains of Carmarthenshire ringed them in, dark against the darkling sky; blotting out all hope, all thought, almost all memory of civilisation. She burst into a torrent of helpless weeping.

Catti Jones had ceased her screeching and now came to her mistress, rubbing stiff arms also, but miraculously restored to courage and good cheer again. 'Come Madam, come, my lady! My lord, I'll take her.' She put about Gilda's heaving shoulders an arm which – unlike his own – trembled not at all; and led her towards lights that flared at the black mouth of an entrance to the caves. ' 'Tis not too bad, my lady, no harm will come to us, since they hold us to ransom. And

Cwrt y Cadno – pronounced (roughly) Coort-uh-*Cad*no, sounding the r.

71

meanwhile my orders are to wait upon your ladyship and see that you don't suffer.' And she went before her down the dark tunnel-mouth of the over-hanging rocks and emerging, urged: 'Come – lift your head and see!'

A room as huge and high as the huge, high hall of the mansion in Hanover Square; and in its wild, crude way almost as magnificent. The plunderings of a hundred rich wagon loads had gone to the furnishing of this great room; the tables might be of young ash-plants lashed tightly together, but they were covered with such cloths of damask and brocade as had graced the hangings of Hanover Square itself; the floor might be covered largely with rushes, but one end was spread with a carpet of the finest Turkey, brilliantly glowing in the light of the torches thrust into sconces in the rough-hewn rock walls. And a chair stood at this same end, draped over with fox skins: a sort of throne, perhaps, for it was set a little apart from the roughly made benches – which were strewn nevertheless with small rugs and mats, each man perhaps choosing and making fine some place of his own. Light, in daytime, would filter in through slits and crevices in the rocks; for the rest the black walls were hung with tapestries as fine, no doubt, as any in Castell Cothi – some possibly having, indeed, been designed to hang there and never reached their destiny. And strangest of all, laid out upon the long central table, patterned with care as though for a stall in some grand charity bazaar in town, an assortment of valuables as motley as at any bazaar – and yet which no bazaar could ever have boasted of: firearms, chased with silver at their barrels, carved and inlaid boxes holding cups and cutlery of silver; dressing cases of gentlemen and ladies' jewel cases, writing cases, exquisitely furnished; a heap of ornamental buckles torn from belts and shoes, a heap of embroidered shawls, of furs, of the rich hand-made lace of Brussels, of Honiton and Ireland ... Fans, watches, trinkets, gew-gaws of fashionable women; silver chains, chains of gold, a small heap of jewellery set with precious stones, a small heap of sovereigns, gleaming, butter-

72

yellow in the torchlight... The gleanings of the rich mer-
chants, carrying their wares, alert and anxious but of necessity,
to the new, thriving towns of the newly thriving land of
Wales: of the gentry passing to and fro between this grand
house and that, where to carry none of one's splendours would
make the visit not worth the undertaking (for how should a
lady from the fashionable metropolis appear in the society of
the great country land-owners without her diamonds, her
jewelled trinkets, all the comforts of her gold-mounted beauty
box, her wardrobe of splendid furs and rich dresses and
cloaks and shawls ... ?): of the cattle drovers, returning from
the long, slow trek to the London market, their beasts driven
patiently before them – coming home with the profit stowed
away in saddle-bag or pocket, because there was no other means
of transferring it. Laid out here upon a table: measured,
counted, belonging to all and so belonging to none – watched
by the finest of all guard-dogs: the jealous eyes of a community
who, together and severally, owned it.

Two women appeared from an inner cave; rough, unkempt,
but handsome in their brilliant Welsh way with the lovely
complexions of a land of soft rains, bright-eyed, the dark
hair, uncombed, tumbling in black tendrils from crown to
shoulders; the strong, sturdy figures decked out in what had
been the finery of rich women plundered – once lovely petticoats of cambric and lace, now bedraggled and clinging to
sturdy brown legs. They spoke to Catti in Welsh. 'They say,
milady, there's a place, a – a cave – where you may sleep:
Y Cadno's woman will give it up to you. And you shall have
food.'

But a few hours ago, mine host had scraped and cavorted
and offered of his best to her ladyship; the night before that,
it had required a whole retinue to see her up to bed. And
now ... All the planning and the scheming, in long-ago
Gloucestershire, all the hours of anxiety, all the daring of
it! – and for this ... A cave where she might sleep; and she
should have food. She could not help a small giggle at the

73

thought of it, the topsy-turvy absurdity of it; and had suddenly a vision of her dear mother nid-nodding and bobbing, compliments-and-thanks-my-lady and there's a cave where your ladyship may sleep – and went off into outright laughter, peal upon peal of it ringing through the barbaric splendours of the great cavern, out to where in the flare of the torches, the men thronged, shouting aloud their triumphant news . . .

Outside, in the broadening out of the little valley before its final embracement of the fall of rocks, a sort of foreground had been stamped by the tread of horses and men, and here the gang were assembled, the women running out to their men with tankards of ale or wine, with wild kisses and bursts of triumphant, capering dancing as, in incomprehensible Welsh, they tossed the good news to one another – the Earl himself taken and his lady, and brought to ransom, coach, coachman, horses and all (Willie-bach was bringing the coach round by the roadway.) It was like a stage set, thought Marigelda, running back from the great hall to the tunnel mouth, standing there, watching it: the young boys humping the saddles from the ponies, sliding the bits from their mouths, giving them a friendly whack on the rump, to send them trotting off gratefully to their own quarters, the women all laughing and dancing, a rabble of children scampering about amongst them; the men shouting to and fro their boasts of riches to come, half in Welsh, half in English, in either hardly to be understood. In their midst stood Dio y Diawl – Dio the Devil, stout and jovial, with a big handsome head and heavy body, fat yet muscular, with huge shoulders and arms; and laughed and touched tankards with reeling admirers and broke at last into a velvety tenor, singing a hymn of praise. All around him the song was taken up, the deep sweet music bell-like and clear in the hubbub of laughter and shouting, rising up in a crescendo of sound to the palely appearing stars in the quiet sky. And suddenly, from around a corner three men appeared. And the music died and the voices were hushed: and silence fell.

Two of the men supported between them the third. His head seemed fallen forward, his whole body drooped forward, so that she caught only a glimpse of the white face; without their hold on his arms, he could hardly have stood at all. He wore a cloak clutched about him and a sort of cap, a strip of reddy-brown fox fur, with the bushy tail hanging to his shoulder, over one ear. As they moved slowly forward, the crowd as slowly turned, so that all faces constantly looked to him. When he stook, all stood motionless.

He seemed to speak; but the effort was too much, the murmur so low that no sound intelligibly reached the listeners. One of his two supporters bent an ear, attentively; cried aloud a message in Welsh. Dio y Diawl stepped a little forward from among the men; there was a mumbled exchange. He swung back and in his turn spoke to the rest. Though she could not understand the Welsh, Gilda guessed that he told them that The Fox was pleased with their exploit; that till he was well enough to lead them again, they should continue under his, Dio's, leadership ... The men growled acceptance. As their sick leader turned to creep away again, they raised a respectful cheer and as soon as he was gone, broke out into chatter and laughter and song once more. Here and there on the ridges of the brooding mountains that ringed them in, a horse and rider, sentinel, were silhouetted against a gleam of light in the evening sky.

Catti Jones was in ecstasies. 'It was Gareth y Cadno himself! The Fox himself!'

'What of it? This low footpad, this highwayman—'

'My lady, he's famous. Not since Twm Shon Catti—'

'Twm Shon Catti?'

'—the greatest of them all, milady. Two hundred years ago he rode these valleys, Twm Shon Catti, Tom, son of Catherine, "the wild wag of Wales". And here now is Y Cadno, as famous already—'

'I hope he's famous for his hospitality at least,' said Gilda shortly. 'Since we have to endure it. And that it won't be for long.' She looked round at the girls. 'Ask them where I am to sleep.'

Into a rock at the far end of the hall, steps had been cut. They climbed, the two girls and Catti nipping up nimbly as cats, Gilda scrambling, putting out a hand to save herself, scuffing the cloth of her dress as she fell to one knee. The steps led to a passage, the divisions filled in between tumbled rocks, an opening here and there into smaller caves, which however they passed by. But there came at last a mat of plaited rushes hung like a curtain; and one of the two girls pushed it aside and ushered the lady in.

A fire burned in a brazier and gave a golden glow to the tapestries which covered the walls from the low ceiling to rock floor; on which floor were thrown down fur carriage rugs that had no doubt once served to keep warm some voyager's silk-stockinged knees. On a table, damask covered, stood a lady's dressing case, fitted in tortoiseshell and gold, a lovely gilt mirror to one side of it. There was a stool before it and a sort of rack had been fashioned where fine clothes might be hung; on another table stood a little china basin with a tiny jug, filched from a travelling toilet set. And against the centre of one wall was a bed, hugely piled with straw, softened at the top with hay, the whole covered with the finest of linen sheets, the warmest of fleecy rugs, with an overlay of fur. No lady of quality need lie more softly, sleep more sweetly tonight than the Countess of Tregaron, should she so choose, between the sweet cool linen of the sheets in her scented nest of hay.

And tomorrow my lord would send messengers to Castell Cothi for the ransom money and they could proceed upon their way. Would she be more content than this, she wondered, when the crimson and gold magnificence of her second home closed in upon her? Would a bed of down rest her more deeply, would light burn more brightly, could water be more soft and cool than this in which she now bathed her white hands? She said to Catti: 'How can this be?'

'It's the room of Y Cadno's woman, milady, they say; which she now gives up to your ladyship.'

Willy nilly, thought her ladyship; and reflected that it was perhaps a good thing for her own comfort at the hands of Y Cadno's woman, that by tomorrow the affair would be settled and she would be gone.

Lord Tregaron came to her in the little room. 'Thank heaven you're safe! I've been anxious about you – but they kept me, dragged me to the presence of Y Cadno. He's a sick man.'

'I've seen him,' she said; sick he might be, hardly able to stand, but could yet hold in command all these rough men and women.

He reflected her thought. 'Sick he may be, yet still, he drives a hard bargain. I've agreed of course; the sum is enormous but it must be paid, we won't remain one hour here more than may be avoided.' He roamed restlessly about the little room, blind to its beauties, bent only on their ultimate safety. 'The trouble is . . .' He broke off anxiously. 'My bankers will never, upon a mere note from me, release so huge a sum; indeed I doubt if, without much complicated business, I can produce it. My mother's abroad and so would my brother be, but that he returned early. And my brother . . .' He shrugged rather hopelessly. 'I've written off letters already, to my lawyers, they smuggle them somehow out of this place; but I've been obliged to apply also to him. I wonder . . .' He stopped pacing, he faced her, gloomily. 'I wonder if he's capable of – refusing.'

'Of course he won't refuse,' she said sharply.

'You don't know him,' he said. 'He's a man very sweet-tempered with those he loves; but also very implacable in his hatreds.'

'If he knows *I'm* here—' she began.

'If he knows . . . Ah!' he said. 'That's it, isn't it? What he wouldn't do for his brother, he'd do for his brother's wife – wouldn't he?'

'Your brother is a gentleman: he wouldn't leave any woman in such a place as this.'

'You know nothing about him,' he said shortly.

'One has only to look at him—'

'Ay, and you *have* looked at him, haven't you?' He caught her arm roughly; the little, dandified, dancing master fellow, who could yet show cool courage in the face of dangerous men and, heaven knew, a stern face to a woman who offended against his honour. 'And would have looked at him again and not looked only, if a servant girl hadn't been keen-witted enough to prevent you.' And he swore a filthy oath. 'By g— and by God, he works fast, my little brother of Llandovery! And you too, bitch and whore that you are, with your tricksy wiles that I've fallen for often enough myself, poor doting fool that I was – to be half cuckolded upon the very day of my wedding and with my own brother... And now am to pay out half my fortune to get you out of the hands of these ruffians.'

'Pay no ransom. I like it here,' she said, jauntily, looking round the little room.

'Like it here! *Like* it here! You'll like it, I warrant you, when he gets his foxy pads upon you! – you with your flame of hair to draw any man's eyes to you, you'll like it when The Fox wants his prey and you're dragged willy nilly, like a white goose fluttering, to his den...'

'Poof, the man is too ill to stand upon his feet,' she said disdainfully. 'By the time he's well enough to put into practice all these dire prognostications, we shall be gone from here.'

'*If* your admirer foots the bill for you,' he said. 'He'll not do it for me and the more so since I've apparently stolen the woman he fancies, from under his nose.' And now he did look round the room. 'It's as well you're so comfortably accommodated, my dear, for you won't be leaving tomorrow, I fear, nor the next day nor the next. And in your prayers tonight I advise you to include one that'll keep Master Fox in his present reduced state of health. He's said to have a partic-

78

ular taste for fair-headed women as I told you; and an ugly way with all of them.'

'And not the only one,' said Gilda, looking into his face.

He lifted the rush curtain and went out without another word. A pity, she thought, he should not evince so fine a display of temper upon more practical occasions: with those *canaille* outside, for example . . . But at least tonight it seemed likely that she might sleep alone and undisturbed and dream such dreams as she cared to. All the same . . .

All the same – if in her dreams she could go back to that night, that night at the playhouse when first Brown Eyes had brought her white roses and touched her hand with his – would he not find a very different girl from the girl she then had been? Then she had been sweet and easy, readily controlled and directed by a loving hand: having known no other. Now . . . If her family could see her now, she thought, turned all in an hour to a wildcat, fighting for her own interests, spitting fire and contempt, and with this welling-up in her of a sort of – courage – she had never known before (having had no need of it) would they recognise their Marigold, their little sister, their pet and pride? And she thought about life and circumstances and of what it might bring about in those who, untouched by experience, might never know it existed. What am I? she thought. Who am I? From this strange experience, this danger, this beginning of hate for the one sole being to whom I should turn in reliance and love – what sort of woman is going to emerge? Of only one thing she was certain: that woman would remain steadfast in her heart and mind, if not in the rebellious flesh, to her only one true love.

With the morning came anxieties again, the more so as her husband deserted her – closeted in argument with the Fox, said Catti; and sent no word to her. She wandered out at last, a rabble of women and children following her, gaping at her fine clothes, exclaiming at the fair skin and shining hair. Down

79

by the stream, girls crouched washing their linen, beating with flat wooden spatulas at the home-spun woollens; small boys were scrubbing down the strong little mountain ponies, caught and trained for the work of the hide-out here among the rocks (where no stolen, town-accustomed horse would have been sure-footed enough) and for the night work on the high toby. Now in daylight, she could catch glimpses of the sentries, one at each end of the valley on the mountain tops above them; from the forests at their lower slopes came the voices of men and the barking of dogs, out hunting; in the far away valley, old men stood patiently fishing. Above in the clear September sky kite and kestrel wheeled and hovered, lazily, effortless: from some improvised farm came the gentle lowing of dairy cows, the cluck of chickens, the grunting of pigs. Dio y Diawl sat out in the sunshine, perched upon a boulder surrounded by a small group of men, holding a large sheet of paper and all earnestly talking. Everyone seems occupied and busy, thought Gilda, as though in some perfectly normal community; but the cows had been driven off by night, no doubt, from a neighbouring farmyard by men with a nice fat hen tucked under each arm for good measure, or a squealing piglet, hurriedly hushed; and the clothes the women washed had come from plundered coaches and the sportsmen, not a doubt of it, were poaching woods and rivers, an offence punishable by long imprisonment. And the paper would be a rough, home-drawn map of some cutting or crossroads where in the near future rich cargo was due to pass by . . .

A red-headed young woman approached, bobbed her a curtsey and offered: 'Would you wish for a drink of milk, Madam? Fresh drawn it is from the cow.'

She had to strain her ears to catch the words in their heavily inflected south Welsh accent, very different from the more familiar sing-song of the north as she had heard it mimicked upon the London stage. She accepted the milk, sat down on the moss beneath a little tree, growing up, crooked and spindly, between two rocks. The girl sat at her feet, her rough brown legs curled up under her. 'You speak English then?'

'I was in service at Lampeter, Madam, with a lady who taught me the English. But Y Cadno set about her carriage one day and she was killed by a stray ball; if the women wish to be safe, they should stay in the coaches. And so I came back with them here.' She nodded to where a group sat with Dio the Devil. 'My man's over there; Tom the Scar they call him.'

'Your mistress killed?' said Gilda, horrified, '—and you came away with her murderers?'

The girl shrugged. 'What was I to do? I ran and was caught – by this same Twm, as we say the name here. And from struggling he turned to kissing and from kissing to something more; and so since he had made me his woman, I could but go with him.' She laughed. 'I told you – the women should stay in the coaches if they wish to be safe.' She dismissed the subject. 'My name is Jenny, my lady: Jenny Coch, they call me, which is to say Jenny the Red, because of my hair.'

To learn a little Welsh would occupy her time and might yet come in useful. 'What colour would you call *my* hair?'

'Your hair – ah, Madam, no hair is like yours that I ever have seen. It is the true Melyn Mair, the marigold.'

'And so they call me: Marigelda or Marigold. Well, and so tell me another Welsh word, Jenny—'

'I will tell you the loveliest word in Welsh or in any other language, my lady. It is Cariad.'

'Which means Dearest. You forget,' said Gilda, not without some bitterness, 'that I have a Welsh husband.' And she wondered if he would ever call her Cariad again; and doubted it. Well, what do I care? I know him now and he knows me. Let him accept, she thought, that she was in love with his brother, let him put her aside and be done with it. He wanted my body, that was all; well, that he has had and shall have no more. For the rest, rich or poor, I don't care; I've had little enough amusement out of being a titled lady of wealth...

81

He came to her that afternoon as she sat down at the common table with its long centre-piece of high-piled treasures of the gang; bending over her, urgently whispering. 'For God's sake, Gilda – what are you doing here?'

'Dining,' she said briefly.

'The women don't eat with the men. Don't you see how they stare at you? To flaunt yourself in this way—'

'Nonsense, they're intent upon their dinners!'

'They are ugly and vicious men who'll rape a woman as readily as they'll kill a man. Only the fact that Gareth y Cadno may want you—'

'He may have me and welcome,' said Gilda, 'since my own husband deserts me – and in such a place as this.'

'Desert you? I've spent the whole morning chaffering with that creature for your safety, God damn you for the silly bitch you are! For let me inform you, dear Madam, that sick he may be but he misses nothing – do you think he didn't spy you out last night, peering forth from the entrance while he was talking to the men? Do you think this damned hair of yours didn't take his fancy? – why else, indeed, did the Devil drag us back here, but that you might make a nice offering for this ogre? And do you suppose it makes my bargaining any the easier? I tell you, if my precious brother doesn't agree with the lawyers soon, some way to arrange to raise the money—'

'He may take his time,' she said negligently. 'I'm quite happy. I spent a delightful morning, sight-seeing.'

'You'd better have spent it praying,' he said, 'that one of your admirers finds the money before, at the hands of the other, you become not worth paying for.'

It struck an ugly note; and yet . . . She thought of Gareth y Cadno as she had seen him, a man helpless in sickness, who could yet still command an absolute authority over such men and women as now surrounded her. Such a man . . . Love was easy, after all: she had given herself in passion, in an ecstasy of passion, to one she cared not a fig for, and while she loved another. What difference if the man be Gareth the Fox or the Earl of Tregaron? Or any other, for that matter. To Brown Eyes she would come, if ever she did come to him, pure in heart, loving no other, having loved no other. What did it matter what her body did, if her heart remained purely his? For a wicked moment she thought that it would at least relieve the tedium of waiting if the Fox indeed called up the white goose to his lair. And she shook her bright locks and cared not at all for the glances of these rough vile creatures, staring across their laden plates at her white bosom, pushed up by the busks of her corset, beneath the green cloth of her habit. She was safe from them, as long as the chance remained that their leader might want her; and Tregaron had taught her this, if nothing else, that she had the power to make any man want her.

The days passed. Her lessons in the colloquial Welsh progressed. Now she knew the little farm and every calf and bottle-fed lamb, every foal, every puppy and kitten; knew the girls by their names, went with the children gathering the strands of wool stripped by the hedgerows from a passing flock of sheep; smiled at the older women, tried her new Welsh words on them; laughed with the men over their triumphs in the hunting field, in the battle with a fat brown trout or sewen, even in their jubilant return one night with a sackful of silver. But from David of Llandovery no answer came, not a word. My lord's men of business wrote that every effort should be made, but that without his own presence and his brother's co-operation it was impossible to raise ready money on family property. He came to her at last, deeply despondent; and the thunderbolt fell. Time was passing, every day Y Cadno's strength improved and she was in increasing danger from him. And so – 'I am helpless but – you are rich. Could you not do something yourself, towards your own ransom?'

She stood absolutely stricken. Tell him now? But, knowing the truth of her deceptions, might he not then simply abandon her, leave her here to her fate? What chance that the outside world would ever discover what had happened? – the marriage had been kept strictly secret, the very few who knew of it could doubtless be easily bribed – her own family, discredited, would have but an unlikely tale to put forward. She made up her mind quickly. 'Oh, certainly! I will write for the money to be paid at once. It was stupid of me not to have thought of it before – why should *you* pay for me?'

'I have been working day and night to arrange it,' he said resentfully.

'But so curiously unsuccessfully.' And she scribbled off a letter addressed to 'The Staff' at South Audley Street, explaining her plight, begging them to apply to her men of business; full of veiled references, however, to the wolves of Rome (who might surely be relied upon to prevent her from receiving the money.) And she signed herself for the first time Countess of Tregaron; and was overwhelmed with the knowledge, all over again, that it was actually true; and with rueful amusement at the thought of how little good it had so far done to herself or any of them.

Five days later a letter arrived via the corn chandler of Caio, larded with respectful compliments that made her bite hard on her lip at the vision of her dear family sitting down solemnly to compose them; of more sincere exclamations as to the dangers and anxieties of her plight. She summoned Lord Tregaron to her room, the only place of privacy available. 'I see now, my lord, that you haven't after all exaggerated the difficulties.'

He looked troubled; almost angry. 'I also have had letters; my case seems for the moment hopeless. I can only advise you to write again and with the utmost urgency.' She began to be afraid that in hopes of her succeeding, he would relax his own efforts to get her released, and to wish that she had antagonised him less. She went up close to him. 'In view of all this, my lord – I must take back words that I spoke last time we discussed the matter. I know that in truth you grudge

84

me nothing, would give all you have to get me out of this horrible danger.' And smiled at him wistfully and said that though she tried to put a brave face on it, tried to seem bold and – and careless, rough perhaps – she was in truth anxious and frightened, sick with hope of an early release; and growing weary, weary of the company of none but serving maids and doxies . . .

'You might have had that of your husband,' he said stiffly, 'if you had cared for it.'

'Might I?' she said innocently. 'I began to doubt it.' And she turned angelic eyes to the huge, soft couch of linen and hay. 'Of all the nights of my marriage, my lord, I've spent all but one alone.'

'I am glad to hear it,' he said bowing, 'since I have not been present to make sure of it myself.'

She went scarlet. She said sharply: 'Your absence has been of your own making.'

'Do you think I should wish to lie in arms that ache only to hold another man, and that my own brother?' Fop and whipper-snapper, yes, she thought, but in these moods at least he was a man; and it vastly became him. And seeing the dark face grow darker, the bright eye brighter, the thin, hard lips grow grim with anger at the memory of her offence against him, she felt her own blood rise, felt within her the first piercing stab of that now familiar surrender, half slavish, half arrogant, to this same manliness. A pang of shame assailed her, but after all – what had this to do with love? Her own love was not there to take her; in these other arms she had found, if not happiness, at least a very abandonment of pleasure. She went up close to him, putting her hands behind her back, leaning her white breast against his breast, lifting her lovely face to his. 'But your brother is not here,' she said. 'And after all – are you not my lord and husband . . .?'

The face growing white, the pinched nostrils, the strong hands gripping her arms, forcing her away – only to catch her back close against his body . . . Excitement rose in her, excite-

85

ment and triumph: tumbling down under him to the yielding nest of the bed, shaking loose the soft wild silk of her yellow hair so that he buried his fingers in it, holding her head in both hands, his hard mouth brutal with kisses. And he took her briefly, violently, so that she almost screamed with the pleasure and pain of it; and lay not a moment more but rose and pulled her up roughly, to stand in front of him . . .

And slapped her once across her face, still sick with the satiation of his embraces; and went out of the room.

CHAPTER SEVEN

The afternoon was balmy and fair, the day far lighter and warmer than had been the evening of their arrival, now more than a week ago. Tables had been dragged out and placed end to end upon the open patch before the great division between two boulders which served as a front entrance to the rock fortress; with benches placed along their length and a few wooden chairs, carved in hours of idleness into things of beauty. The women were busy laying out a feast in prospect of a triumph. Tonight a group of drovers would be passing along the road from Cilycwm.

Each year in spring and autumn, from innumerable small farms scattered about the three western counties, the beef cattle were bought and assembled into great herds, to be driven at last to the few great markets whence they could be again distributed – London, Barnet, Rugby and the rest. Fattened up for the long journey, driven by devious ways over the mountains to avoid the heavy fares at the toll gates across the roads – which later the Rebecca Riots would help to abolish – hastening to catch the right moment for crossing the River Wye at Erwood, when the water would be low enough for fording, without the great expense of ferrying the beasts across; and so on to Paincastle where the soft hooves must be shod for the roads of England. Slowly, slowly, browsing as they went, the great herds moved forward, caked in mud, or cloudy with dust if the roads were dry; to be fattened up again at a ha'penny per beast, in the grazing grounds before town. And so to Smithfield and long days of bartering, arguing, haggling, chaffering all over again in the evenings at the Lock and Key; and the two or three weeks of rest at last, before the long trek home.

At twelve pounds a beast or more, the sums accumulated were large: the profits of a whole year of hard work, breeding, selecting, fattening and at last delivering. They travelled usually, for safety, in large groups, sufficient to out-match any lone footpad or highwayman – and most worked alone. But by the time they reached Llandovery, many would have peeled off and taken more direct routes to their own homes, and those that made for Lampeter and further west must pass through Cilycwm and the narrow valley leading on to Pumsaint, by way of Cwrt y Cadno. The Fox's gang was their last hazard and their worst.

And tonight they came.

The women worked gaily, their children running at their skirts. Crusty loaves were being baked in the big brick ovens, filled with burning wood, scooped out when the oven was hot enough to take the risen dough; there were joints of mutton from sheep rustled from their grazing grounds on the mountain tops with the aid of the clever, shaggy sheep dogs, hams from the farms of more distant neighbours – it was wise policy to keep on good terms with those closer to them – great mounds of their own salty butter and home-churned cheese; wines and delicacies from intended picnic meals of travellers left to go hungry. The Countess of Tregaron entered into it with the rest, decorating the table with great bowls of gorse, coconut-scented and as blazing with gold as her own bright head. Lord Tregaron came upon her there. 'For God's sake – must you bring yourself down to the level of a scullion?'

They allowed him to go riding now, for exercise, though always with an armed guard; she had watched him with envy, ambling off on one of the brave little ponies, born wild on these bare mountain tops, caught and trained for the work of the gang. 'You have something to do with your time. I have nothing but this. It amuses me.'

'Will it amuse you when your maid spreads the news at Castell Cothi? – how you ran to and fro laying dishes for this scum of the countryside.'

'She runs to and fro pretty merrily herself,' said Marigelda. 'A fine waiting woman your sister has trained up! I saw her exchanging embraces with the Devil himself, with Dio, before the men rode off.'

'I hope they ride to some purpose,' he said, changing the subject. 'The Fox is uneasy about the whole business, it makes him irritable and therefore dangerous. It is to our interest, I fear, that they do well.'

Vain hope. They came trit-trotting back at last, by no means triumphant, for the gold had indeed been well guarded it seemed, and many of those who actually carried it had escaped with their store. And one of their own number had been wounded and left to die or be captured, as luck befell him. But to die would be best. 'He'll be strung up, sure,' said Dio gloomily, throwing himself down upon a bench and snapping his fingers for a child to come and drag off his boots, 'and left to swing and his hand lopped off, as like as not, as he hangs there, and a hank of his hair, to make a Hand of Glory. They thrust wicks in under the nails,' he explained to an open-mouthed Gilda, 'made from the man's own hair and soaked in grease from his body – it must be no other; and carry it blazing, for a sort of charm. They say none stirs in a rifled house when the thieves light their way by a Hand of Glory.'

'Dear God, how disgusting!'

He shrugged. 'What matter, if one's dead? And so, I say, I wish poor Twm may be dead, for his own sake.'

'But couldn't you,' she said, horrified, 'have brought your friend away?'

'What and risk the same fate, Madam fach?' He repeated her question in Welsh and they all burst out into laughter; a too ready laughter, she thought, as though no pitiful, pitiless joke were too small to catch on to: as though a shudder ran through them all which said: His turn today – tomorrow mine.

Nor was their unease without reason. The Fox, it seemed, had dragged himself from his sick-bed and summoned the men to the council rock – that boulder on which she had seen Dio perched, planning this very adventure. He was enraged, Tregaron had told her, at the failure of the foray and the loss of a man. They stood together and watched from a respectful distance as he came out, painfully limping, supported on either side by Dio and another of the elders, Huw the Harp – wrapped in a rough blanket held about him like a cloak, wearing the cap of red fox-skin; and stood swaying, spitting out at them what seemed to her but a very few half-whispered words, to have sent them all away so hang-dog and shameful. The scared girls, running after them, anxiously questioning, were told angrily to cut the gabble and bring something of better comfort than quacking and kisses. Very soon the meal was in progress, and, stuffed to capacity at last, they turned to drowning their sorrows in drinking, growing ever more wild and uproarious as their cares fell away into oblivion; and against the sunset sky, the first star appeared, a sentinel rider was lit for a moment to a tiny statue of gold.

Gilda sat at the top of the long table, solitary; repelled yet fascinated, her husband, as solitary, at the far end of it. And so might we be sitting, she thought, at this very moment, languid, bored, speechless one at either end of a table as long, ringed round by servants, in some great, gloomy dining-hall at Castell Cothi: just as we sat, for that matter, at our wedding dinner in Hanover Square. All about her the women drank almost equally with the men and soon were half intoxicated

Madam fach: the single f is pronounced like a v. This is the feminine of 'bach', an endearment robbed of any hint of disrespect by the 'Madam'. The word rhymes roughly with the German 'Bach' as in Johann Sebastian.

at least, running about, noisy and abandoned as children; like anything but children in the direction of their abandonment. Three girls ran back to their quarters and reappeared, dressed in the traditional costume of the county, the ankle-length brick-red striped petticoats under the turned-back skirts, the trim jackets, the little fringed shawls, the black chimney-pot hats lined with white frilling: and were lifted up on to the table and there danced, jigging and tripping, the country dances of their childhood in more innocent places – the men tossing up the red petticoats as they danced to peer at the nakedness underneath, falling to fisticuffs with such of their companions as, drunkenly aggressive, took exception, or with their own women. And the women were fit for it, strong in wrist and arm and not too particular how they used elbows and knees. Now and again a man fell heavily, groaning and, struggling up, laid about his girl in good earnest until he was set upon by other women and she was pulled out of harm's way ... As night fell, the new lit torches blazed up upon what had so far been concealed in the shadows and Gilda, scandalised, curious, shamefully titillated, turned her head away from one scene of wild wantonness, only to encounter another. Her own maid, Catti Jones, had given up all pretence of attending her mistress, having now apparently lost her head and her heart entirely to Dio y Diawl; and not only heart and head it seemed – nor any of it too recently, if her familiar acceptance of his far from surreptitious fondlings were any indication ...

Down the long length of the table, Lord Tregaron sprawled in a chair – half drunk, she thought disgustedly – his slight body all relaxed for once from its habitual springy tension, slender legs stretched out before him, ankles crossed: blissfully, foolishly smiling; and a woman came up behind and leaned across him so that his head lay heavily against her half-naked bosom. He lifted a languid hand, pushed aside the last remnant of concealing bodice and turned his head lazily so that his mouth was against her breast.

Rage rose in Gilda's heart. So had his lips caressed her and

91

she, poor fool, thrilled with an exquisite rapture, given herself up to him in a swoon of desire. And now – to this coarse creature, publicly, oafishly, hardly knowing what he did – the same sweet, intimate, deeply possessive caress . . . She sat with both hands gripping the arms of her chair, willing herself to control, to remaining as though unaware, unmoved, uncaring – and suddenly was up and out of it and flying down the length of the improvised table and had her hands in the woman's hair and was yanking her head back, dragging her off him, pushing her with wild punches at the naked shoulders to stumble before her fury down the slope of the grass, away from them . . . A bold, bright-eyed huzzy of a woman, ever indolently smiling; dressed habitually in a gown of scarlet, laced in tightly to show the luscious bosom above a tiny waist, the big breasts boiling over the scooped-out neckline: Gilda had marked her, hitherto felt, without much wondering about it, that she in some sort avoided her; now knew why . . . For the woman screamed out, 'Let me be! He's mine! He's my man – has been from the beginning . . .'

From the beginning . . . Night after night alone in the bed of cool linen and soft-heaped hay; while he . . . The whole crowd had risen to their feet, the men spilling the girls off their knees, loosing hold in the shadowy corners beneath the trees, coming forward to stand, roaring with laughter, in Welsh and English cheering them on. 'Go to it, Madam fach!' 'Fight back at her, Blodwen . . . !' 'Dal ati!' 'Rho iddo hi! Tear her hair, Madam Countess, gouge her black eyes from her, let's see those long nails of yours put to some use after all . . .' And the woman fought back indeed, hands reaching out like talons to grasp at the candy-floss marigold hair and tear it out by its roots, strong brown arms flailing, calloused feet kicking out hard and hurtful at the slender white legs beneath the impeding petticoats. But the petticoats were protective also and bare feet no match for vicious little leather-shod toes and heels. One last final shove and Blodwen tumbled backwards once and for all, did a half somersault, picked

92

herself up and ran, hugging her naked breasts, screeching of vengeance to come, into the maze of the scrub oaks beyond.

She stood for a moment, panting, slowly gathering herself together; and turned and faced them.

Out of the throng, a man – she never knew who – walked down the small slope, deliberately, yet reeling as he came, in drink; and gathered her to him and tossed her up like a child, caught her again, disorientated, bewildered and, dropping her feet to the ground so that she still stood tumbled against him in the ring of his arms, bent his face over hers. She struggled violently but his hot, reeking kisses were all over her; and now other men came running down the slope to join him, she felt herself pulled aside and into another pair of arms, torn away from these in turn, bounced against a huge chest, her bodice torn, vile hands fumbling at her bosom, lifting up her skirts ... Voices cried out commands to stop, to release her, but they shouted back, laughing, that if she was good enough to fight with their women she was good enough to love with themselves. Women's voices yelled, laughing encouragement or shrieking out jealous disapproval, small brown feminine hands joined in now, trying to tear her from the bear-hug embraces; buffeted, bewildered, half out of her senses, she knew that in a very little while her struggling arms would have no strength left to defend herself; that her torn clothes already left her half naked to vilest assault. Sobbing and gasping she fought, struggled, prayed for deliverance. And almost as she reached the last ounce of strength and spirit, deliverance came. A voice called out, laughter and screaming suddenly died, hands dropped from her, the drunken, struggling crowd fell back and away and there was silence.

A voice crying out in Welsh and in English: 'Leave her alone! Swine, fools, insolents! – don't you know that she is reserved for *me*?'

Wrapped cloak, fur cap, swaying on his feet yet yelling it out in a voice of black fury: the Fox himself, Gareth y Cadno.

*   *   *

She slept ill, a prey to nightmares. Catti Jones was banished, red-haired Jenny lay at her feet on a couch of dried bracken, improvised for the night. Lord Tregaron came to her there in the morning. He looked very pale and worn. 'Are you recovered? I've been anxious about you.'

'Anxious about what?' she said, viciously. 'My health or my beauty? For with my beauty impaired, I shan't be so good a bargaining point for you, shall I, my lord?'

'What do you mean?' he said, his face growing cold.

'Those long hours with Y Cadno while he haggled over our ransom! When you haggled with him over your safety, don't you rather mean? – since you can't get the money, your wife's body, for your freedom: your safe conduct at the price of her virtue.'

'Of her *what*?' he said.

She shrieked at him, blazing. 'My virtue, I said. Do you deny me even this? Who has ever possessed me but you who are my own husband? Isn't that good enough? – to give myself in marriage to my husband . . . ?'

'To two husbands,' he reminded her coolly. 'And to neither in love. For one was too old, and the other unfortunate in his choice of brothers. Is that virtue? In cold blood to give yourself to any man: married or unmarried.'

'And so you will sell me to this monster, this brigand, this filthy, cut-throat toby-man, sell me for the price of your miserable life and into the vilest of beds. But what care you for vile or not vile, who would tumble that bitch of a sloe-eyed slut with her bosom half out of her bodice for any man to fondle; only that she keeps herself for you, for my husband, and offers herself, forsooth, in the face of all the company . . .' And as he, but twenty-four hours ago, had slapped her across the face, so she now hit out, violently, bruising with the gold and ruby ring against the sharp cheekbone. 'Get out, begone from my sight! – and only as you value your safety leave that woman alone, for she'll not share your favours with me, my dear lord, even though mine shall be given you never more.'

94

He turned and was gone, making no sign, giving no answer; and she threw herself down on her bed again, bitterly weeping, sick with the battering and bruising of the night before, with the fear of the future – with the bitter pangs of an utterly unreasonable, utterly unlooked-for passion of jealousy.

All next day she kept her bed. Catti came to her abject in apology, confessed her wantonness, begged for forgiveness; but Gilda knew that though she might fear to lose her place, in Miss Jones servility was now lacking; that Castell Cothi once attained would ring with the recital of last night's doings at the Court of Foxes. She pretended a grudging pardon, turned to purposeful gossiping. My lord—? My lord, it seemed, said Catti, had kept his room, worn out, no doubt, by the fight with the drunken mob for her ladyship's safety . . . ('Did he fight?' said her ladyship, astonished.) From London no word had come; nor, strange to say, had anything been forthcoming either as to financial dickerings with the wolves of Rome. And Jenny, joining them, reported that already the Fox was again in earnest counsel about a new expedition. A spy was set in Cheltenham to send him regular information of those booking accommodation in advance at the coaching inns; travellers gave false names and details, trying to keep the facts of their journeyings secret until they should be safely accomplished. But the extent of the arrangements could not be concealed, and now he sent messages that in the finest inn, rooms had been set apart for the following night but one, for a lady and her maid, and others for two gentlemen; and since the messenger making the arrangements had spoken with a Welsh accent, he had made particular enquiries; they were headed for Carmarthenshire. With coachman, footmen, perhaps an outrider or two for their further safety, this would comprise half a dozen men at least, and all doubtless armed. The gang had been long withdrawn into Y Cadno's apartments, said Jenny, where from his bed the sick man raged at the inefficiencies of the night before . . . And Blodwen, by the way, no longer wore her languorous smile but combed out her torn locks and mended her rent petticoats and was swearing an ugly vengeance; and moreover finding backers amongst the women. 'But don't they understand,' said Gilda, 'that this after all is my husband whom she is coquetting with?'

'What is marriage to us here, Madam? She has been his woman all this time, and—'

'All this time. We have been here hardly more than a matter of days—'

Jenny looked a little foolish. 'A week, two weeks in our lives – if a man stays so much with one woman, why then she has a right to consider him her own. It is like a – a betrothal. And such women as he had before that, must give way without argument.'

'All this time!' From the very beginning – from that first night, no doubt, when he had said: 'By heaven, he works fast, my little brother of Llandovery.' You work pretty fast yourself, my dear, she said to him savagely in her sore heart, jealous and angry. And yet how be jealous of one whom you so bitterly despised and detested . . . ?

They kept themselves very quiet after that, he and Madam Blodwen; very quiet and very discreet. But that night she saw them (and understood now those rides 'under guard': Blodwen, armed, was guard enough for any man) – slipping away separately from the rock fortress to where two ponies were tethered at the fringe of the oak forest; riding off into the deep, dark privacy, no doubt, of some bed on the rustling leaves under the starlit trees. And the next night they went again. Very well, she thought: next time I shall follow you and when I come at last to your precious Castell Cothi, my lord of Tregaron, what a scandal will not then rend the ears of your fine high society, unless you pay out and pay and pay . . . ! But she knew that she went, not for the gew-gaws and gold she might extract from him, but for some other reason she could not herself clearly understand.

She laid her plans carefully, took no one into her confidence, was quiet and circumspect, kept out of Blodwen's way and preserved at least an armed truce with the woman's friends. In the bustle of preparation for that night's foray, intensified by the brooding, unseen presence of The Fox in the background, her occupations were not much remarked upon; and when, the rest having departed, she saw her husband slip off to join his partner down by the river side – she herself had a pony hidden away in the scrub land, and was ready to follow them.

It was dark that night. The moon, which had shone so brightly over the feastings and fightings three evenings ago, now was cloud-covered, there was a faint drizzle, mist rose up from the stream and obscured the pathway. But she rode the stubby pony, rolling fluidly in the saddle to the rhythm of its pecking struggle up the hillside, sitting astride, her petticoats pulled up to her crutch, for there was no one to see her. His sure feet found out a path he well knew and she was content to leave it to him, moving on up, and ever uphill, stealthily, holding aside the branches to save her face from scratches, releasing them whippily, rejoicing in a freedom of movement she had not known since the old happy, out-door, too-much-despised old days in Gloucestershire. Far ahead came an occasional crackle of twigs that ceased at last; and she thought of their shocked surprise when she came upon them there in their secret nest, of the rage of the woman, of the wretched self-abasement of the erring husband; the slow dawn of his realisation as to her adamant intention – exposure to the whole outside world of his vile surrender of herself for his safety; of himself to this slut and whore. And adamant it should be: no touch, no caress, no keen brown face deliquescing into the surrender of passion, ever again should turn her from her purpose. One only should play at that game now; *he* might be not proof against her magic for him – she, forewarned, would be as ice now, against his magic for her.

And, so vengefully dreaming, she sat the little pony and he brought her to the edge of the tree line – and out on to a

97

road that led upwards from her left to her right, between the hanging forests. And suddenly . . .

Suddenly a shout of men's voices, a clattering of hooves, a rattling of coach wheels, the shrill screams of terrified women; and out of the darkness carriage lights looming, the flare of torches and a mêlée of riders crashing down from out of the scrub. And a voice crying out: 'Stand and deliver! Your money or your lives!'

The pony had followed his fellows to the hold-up of the coach.

The mist had been left behind, hanging low over the valley; in the course of the long, uphill, dreaming ride, the clouds had drifted and now let through a pale moonshine with a twinkle of far away stars. In the shaft of light cutting through the narrow defile between the oak trees, she could see the rocking of the splendid carriage with its family quarterings, the uniformed coachmen sitting up, great-coated, on their box, the six fine horses rearing with rolling eyes and tossing heads, nipping at one another with a baring of white teeth in their unrest and alarm. Out of the window poked a head crowned with a black tricorne hat; a voice cried out: 'It's Y Cadno's gang!' and the head disappeared again. She heard the wild yells of the highwaymen reining in their ponies after the steep dash down through the forest, closing in, ringing the coach about, as so short a time ago, they had closed about her own; and sitting there stricken motionless on her pony, watched how the gang broke up, two men taking charge of one outrider, two of another, dragging them down from their horses, resistant, disarming them; two more keeping their firearms trained upon the men on the box, the rest clustering about the coach trying to squeeze their ponies past it along the narrow roadway or make a detour through the scrub oak on either side, to come close up to the windows and threaten those within.

But the neighing of the horses excited her own pony; it

began to call back, nervous and restless, and she came to her senses, slipped down off its back, forced it hindways into the shelter of the trees and there left it with its bridle hanging free. To have ridden it away, with a scudding of hooves down the mountainside and the giveaway crashing of branches, would have been to invite pursuit, since they would suppose one of the coach party escaping. She crept back up to the road. A pistol, jerked no doubt out of the hand of one of the outriders, lay there, its silver chasing gleaming in the moonlight, and she picked it up and held it cocked as she crouched back into the shadow of the undergrowth. The country pursuits of her native home had made her an excellent shot; and whose side she might be on in this struggle must be problematical but it might yet be that a firearm would come in useful.

From within the coach came the wailing of women; and, one from either side, two men now leapt out and began firing into the scrub forest, working their way slowly crabwise, forward to the horses' heads. Let them but disarm those who kept the coachman in subjection and he might, by driving relentlessly forward, force a passage between the three or four marauders left on the road ahead of them, and they two leaping on as it passed them, contrive a getaway. And indeed, Sam the Saddle, taken unaware from behind, was caught in the wrist and dropped his pistol screaming out in agony, a second man cried out and tumbled from his pony; only two were left in the path of the coach. Those riding past to fire in at the windows, seeing what was happening and trying to turn back, were caught and mazed in the low branches of the oak trees; it began to look as though, for all their outnumbering, the strategy of the two creeping figures, stealing with cocked pistols to the horses' heads, might yet succeed.

And out of the roadside shadows a man's figure rose up and moved quietly to stand in front of Marigelda, looking down the roadway towards the struggle going on around the coach; with pistol also cocked but seeming to take no part in it. She kept very still, crouching in the shadows almost touching his cloak; and he made no move to look down at her but after a moment spoke in a rapid whisper. 'Gilda! Keep quiet – it's I, Tregaron. They caught up with me in the woods and brought me here at pistol point, telling me to keep silent or it would be the worse for me. We must try to help these people; but meanwhile keep absolutely still, keep absolutely quiet and only, for God's sake, cover your head. Don't you know that that hair of yours is like a flame where the moonlight catches it? I knew it in a moment.'

The two travellers now had joined forces, shooting their way to the very heads of the leading horses. One cried up to the coachman: 'Be ready! Drive forward with all your might. Take heed of nothing in your way. We will give you the signal.' They stood side by side, swivelling their guns to cover any lingering opposition at the wayside ahead of them. One moment and they would be gone. Gilda, beside herself with excitement, whispered triumphantly: 'They've won!'

And must have jerked back her head and let the dark covering fall; for one man cried out: 'What's there?' and both pistols swung to point directly towards her; directly towards Lord Tregaron, standing immediately before her.

In one moment they would see him: at this range, could not miss. She leapt up, levelled her own pistol and fired point blank at the first man's heart. In the same moment her husband also fired and cried out: 'Got him!'

For one startled, terrible second all was silence. Then the shouting began anew, horsemen burst forth from the shelter of the scrub, from the coach the wailing and screaming were redoubled; and as both men fell, Lord Tregaron ran forward and with Gilda almost at his shoulder, looked down at them.

For one moment he stood there; and then he turned to her, caught at her hand, tore from her finger the heavy gold and ruby ring of their betrothal. Dio came running and he spoke a rapid word to him, grasped at the bridle of the nearest horse, swung himself into the saddle and was galloping like a madman off into the darkness.

100

All about her, Gilda was conscious of noise and movement. She knew that the coachman crawled down from his box in abject surrender, that Dio y Diawl was shouting out orders, that out from the coach two women were being dragged in a terror of weeping. But she knelt between the two fallen men and saw that they were desperately wounded; one cried out indeed at this moment: 'Oh, God help me! I'm dying.'

It diverted her attention from the other. She whispered: 'No, no, you shall have succour, you shall be cared for,' but he only cried out again, 'I'm dying!' and fell to a sick and feverish muttering. She caught the words, 'Gereth . . . Earl of Tregaron . . .'

At her left hand the other lay, softly moaning; white face turned up to the moonlit sky, a spreading stain above the heart, fair hair all blotched with blood; and choked out, 'My brother? Is my brother hurt . . . ?' and moved his head towards where the dying man lay, opening upon her piteous, questioning eyes; and unanswered, let the heavy lids fall again and slid back into oblivion . . .

But not before she had seen that look, as brief now as upon those two other, ever belovéd, ever recollected occasions.

The Honourable David Llandovery: Brown Eyes.

And she looked up and saw the great coach with its blazon of arms, as once she had seen it when a man who was now her husband leaned against the door, watching her smile down upon a gift of white roses; and cried to the dying man whom David Llandovery this moment had called his brother: 'Then, for God's sake – who are *you*?'

And he whispered again: 'Earl of Tregaron,' and fell back again to his mumbling and muttering: 'The Fox . . . I am killed by Gareth y Cadno, Gareth the Fox . . .'

Gareth y Cadno: no Earl of Tregaron any more than she had been Marchesa D'Astonia Subeggio, but a penniless adventurer who had married her for the ransom she would pay over to him and his gang before he turned her loose

101

again: who would find himself, however, having been out-witted by as penniless an adventurer as himself.

Gareth y Cadno! Her wedded husband, who now had shot and killed a man and ridden off into the darkness with only her ruby ring for his fortune, and a price upon his head.

CHAPTER EIGHT

The true Earl of Tregaron had died in her arms; the new Earl of Tregaron lay helplessly injured, his head in her lap. The false Earl of Tregaron had ridden off into the night. She called peremptorily to a man. 'Send Dio y Diawl to me and quickly!' and while he ran off began to wriggle out of her petticoats, to tear them into strips for the bandaging of the heavily bleeding wounds.

Dio came and stood over her. Even now in the midst of his anxieties, his big face was – a little quizzically – smiling. 'So, Madam fach – now you know all?'

'I know that I've been made a fool of. I know now who my husband is.'

'He is Gareth y Cadno, Madam; whose woman, it seems, is already issuing orders.'

'The Fox's woman is a slut named Blodwen,' she said. 'I am his wife.'

He gave a small rueful assenting nod of his head. 'Well, that's true enough. So – your orders, Madam Vixen?'

'This man is badly wounded; if he doesn't have care, he'll die. And the other is already gone, we've trouble enough without a second. Besides with his brother's death he becomes the new earl, he's a man of great importance now. Better get him back into the coach and send him home.'

'What and lose a fine carriage and six horses?'

'What good are they to you? Such horses are useless on

the mountains? And the coach too – best be quit of it all with the women and servants . . .' To have him here in her arms, and to send him away, perhaps for ever! But all that mattered to her was his safety. She urged: 'Let him go! We're in trouble deep enough already.'

'We?' he said. 'Do you then remain one of us?'

It occurred to her for the first time – so intent had she been upon his welfare – that here lay her own chance of escape. She tried to speak unconcernedly. 'Why, no: why should I remain with you?'

He stood looking down at her as she sat in the roadway, the wounded man held in her arms. 'That's not quite what I said, Madam fach. Of course you remain *with* us.'

'But why? What am I to you?'

His bright eyes widened in his big, round face. 'Well – are you not a ransom?' he said.

A ransom! She opened her mouth to reply that she could pay none, that her whole story was as false as Gareth y Cadno's own. But she closed it again. The hope of ransom might yet preserve in them some respect for her; and it was deeply necessary that they heed her opinion and advice. 'Very well. But you're a fool if you don't let *him* go.'

He considered again, humping his huge shoulders in the effort to think it all over; pausing now and then to shout orders to his men – who, however, were efficiently employed in plundering the coach, the women meanwhile standing alongside, one white and silent, the other pitifully moaning. He nodded at last. 'Ay, better be rid of him.'

'Very well.' And having won the first round, she took swift advantage. She said, and made it an order: 'Send the women here to me.'

'From the coach?'

'Yes, I must have help.' But she glanced at the dead man lying in the road beside her. 'First best move him elsewhere; he'll only distract them and I shall need all their attention.' She sat with the unconscious body held close against her as with her free hand she pressed a swab of linen against his shoulder to stem the bleeding, while two fellows came forward and lugged the body away. 'Send it back in the coach,' she said to Dio, 'or you'll have the place overrun with his people, searching for it.' And as soon as it was out of sight: 'Now, call the women.'

They came hastening, weeping. 'A woman! Thank God!' And they threw themselves on their knees beside her. 'Oh, he's wounded! Yes, it's true, he's wounded. And the Earl? – can it be true also that his lordship is dead? – can you tell us, Madam—?'

An elderly woman in a mob cap, a sober dress beneath a travelling cloak; a sort of upper-class servant, apparently sufficient duenna for a young lady alone in a coach with two gentlemen. The other – young and very lovely, a skin like white velvet, thick and matt, unlike Gilda's own white skin beneath which the colour came and went; a nose exquisitely chiselled, hair very blonde, no match for Gilda's own lambent flame but the colour of corn in sunshine, fallen now from beneath the frilled white cap and tumbling to her waist in a ripple of gold. And the tapering fingers might flutter but they were capable enough, taking up the linen squares that Gilda had torn from her petticoat, dabbling them in water brought by one of the men from the little stream that ran down the mountain side and across the road to join the river below; tenderly bathing the wound with it. The ball had taken him in the shoulder; the blood in his hair must have come from his hand, for there was no wound there – but his arm and sleeve were soaked in it. Lost to all about them, now, but the need to staunch the bleeding which, after ceasing a little under Gilda's pressure, had now started off afresh, they knelt one on either side of him, the servant holding a lantern brought to them from the coach. There was a ragged wound of entry and, high up behind the shoulder, a bulge and bruising with the skin not quite broken, where the bullet must have lodged against the shoulder blade. The girl said, awe-stricken: 'Should we try to remove it?'

To remove the ball! To penetrate that fair skin, probe in, search through the welling-up of the blood . . . 'Dear God, I could not do it . . .'

'I don't know . . . If we leave it . . . I know nothing about such things; but with the jolting of the coach between here and the castle, might not the bullet shift and do further damage? – perhaps break through the skin and start a bleeding which we would then be powerless to deal with?' Across the unconscious body, they stared into one another's eyes. 'If you are brave enough to hold him,' said the girl at last, 'I will try to be brave enough to do it.'

The maid had a small penknife, pearl-handled; washed it in the blood-stained water, passed it, shuddering. Gilda held him in her arms, a pad of wet linen pressed hard against the major wound, the discoloured shoulder turned outward. The girl said: 'One moment while I steady myself; my hand is shaking,' and was still, her right hand holding the little knife, the left pressed across her eyes as though, thought Gilda, she might be praying. Then with a swift movement, giving herself no time to think, she made a shallow slash in the skin across the bulging bruise and almost before the blood could spring, had delved in with the tip of the knife and scooped the bullet out into her hand. And cried out: 'Oh, God! – thank God!' and fainted.

One hand still pressed against the entrance wound, Gilda dabbed at the other with linen and water; but it was nothing; the blood gushed for a moment, trickled and soon ceased to flow at all. The woman, meanwhile bent over the swooning girl, slapping at her face with wet hands, imploring recognition. 'Come, my lady, wake my lamb, all is well, my darling! Come, Miss Blanche—!'

Come, Miss Blanche . . . Gilda sat up with the fair head cradled in her lap, her arm aching with the sustained pressure upon the bleeding. She said, 'What was that name you spoke? Who is this lady?'

'Who is she? Why, my Lady Blanche Handley, Madam, daughter of the Earl of—'

'Don't tell me,' said Gilda. 'Daughter of the Earl of Trove. I know it!' And she leaned across the unconscious body between them and slapped vigorously at the girl's white, upturned face. 'Come, enough of this fooling! Wake up, stand up, I have need of you!' As the girl, bewildered, came-to and began struggling to her feet, she said: 'I must have more cloths, I must have bandages. Off with your petticoats!'

She stood there helpless, astonished at the sudden change, her hands still bloodied, gaping. 'My – my petticoats? I don't understand.' And the woman cried out: 'My lady's petticoats?'

'Why, certainly, I've given up my own, let *her* now contribute!' And she leaned forward, one hand still pressed to the wound, and tossed up the girl's skirt into the air, so that her underskirts were exposed. 'Come, waste no more time, undress her, take off her petticoats!'

A man, who stood holding the horses' heads, looked back over his shoulder, laughing; called to his companion standing guard over the two coachmen. The maid stammered: 'In front of *them*? Take off her petticoats in front of *them*?'

'One moment more and I'll call to them to come and do it for you,' swore Gilda. 'Come, hold up your skirts, Madam, so that she can get at your waist band . . .' (The Lady Blanche Handley, forsooth, daughter of the Earl of Trove!) 'Where is Dio?' she called to the men. 'Tell him to have a stretcher constructed. We'll take this man home after all, to Cwrt y Cadno.' The girl stood, utterly taken aback, the stuff of her outer skirt clinging forlornly to her legs as the maid heaped the white petticoats beside the wounded man. 'Now, take the knife and you, woman, take your scissors, cut across the hems and slit all this up into decent bandages. The whole lot; where I'm taking him, I shall need all you can give me; we boast of no such refinements.' And she took the first strips that, subdued, silently weeping, they handed to her and padded out the wounds anew, and clumsily but efficiently bandaged

107

them. They stood by staring with all their eyes, not daring to expostulate as two men came up with an improvised stretcher and she saw him lifted on to it. 'Now, back to the coach with you and sit there mum till it's ready to drive off; and be thankful you go with your skins intact.' And she gave the girl a shove that sent her flying, tripping over her own feet, stumbling towards the coach; and then called her back again. 'Before you go – that's a very fine ring you wear!'

She pulled it off, silently, handed it over: a ring with great diamonds burning blue-white in the light of the newly arisen moon. Pulled off her gold chain, brooch of wrought gold and sapphires: wordlessly unhooked her ear-rings. Gilda said to the woman : 'What's that you conceal in the pocket of your skirt, beneath the cloak?'

A soft leather pouch: an Aladdin's cave indeed, emerald, sapphire, ruby, pearl . . . Gilda held out her hand for the pouch, balanced it: considered – flung it down, spilling its contents into the rutty road. 'On second thoughts, no – I'll take nothing personal from *you*. Pick them up and be gone!' As Blanche hesitated, staring down through terror-filled, tear-blinded eyes, she raised her small fist again as though to strike her. 'Come, do what I say, down on your knees and pick up your rubbish and depart with it.' And she stood over her as the girl knelt and gathered the jewels together from the blood-stained mud and dirt of the roadway. 'Now go; and take my advice, return for good and all to the noble Earl your father and your London home, for there is not room in Wales for thee and me. And if he asks who sent you: why tell him you had the misfortune to meet upon the road the wife of the Fox, the Vixen of Cwrt y Cadno . . .'

Little Marigold Brown of Aston-sub-Edge in the county of Gloucestershire: Marigelda, Marchesa d'Astonia Subeggio; her high and mighty ladyship the Countess of Tregaron . . . She had come a short road but an eventful one, to be the wife of a common highwayman with a price upon his head: Gilda, the Vixen of the Court of Foxes.

CHAPTER NINE

She walked beside him the whole way, slipping and slithering down the mountain side, through the leafy mould that lay beneath the scrubby trees, the two men carrying the stretcher, sure-footed beside her, others following with their own two wounded men. After a little while, Dio y Diawl came up alongside, dismounted his pony and walked with her. 'Well, my pretty one, I must say you accept it all very well: this trick he played on you. Perhaps after all it suits you better to be Madam Vixen than to be a grand lady, so readily do you take to our ways. How you set about that poor wretch, for example!'

'I had supposed she was, if I thought of it at all, some Honourable Harrington or some such name, affianced to Gereth of Tregaron. But she is Blanche, daughter of the Earl of Trove.'

'What harm has she ever done to you, then, this Blanche?'

'Simply, I did not care for her,' said Gilda, briefly.

'Then heaven help all poor girls you take a real dislike to! They had better look to themselves.'

'Including Madam Blodwen,' said Gilda.

'Ah, poor Blod! Yet you must realise, she had been his woman for – I forget: many months, what amounts with us to a marriage – before you came into it.'

'He is my husband,' said Gilda, briefly again.

'*If* he is your husband. But no, no,' he said laughing, 'you need have no doubts there. If it came to legalities, he wanted to make all things watertight – the first time ever, I think, The Fox tangled with the law. May it be the last! – considering his situation now.'

If it had not been truly a marriage . . . ? Her glance went to the still figure on the stretcher. 'He married me as Earl of Tregaron.'

He laughed again. 'Have no fear – or no hope, which ever way you care to look at it. He took all that into consideration. I tell you, it's watertight. If not,' he added with that old rueful smile, 'do you think I should be treating you as a familiar? Until Gareth comes back, I am leader once again.'

'I hope you make less hash of it,' she said, 'than you did last time, in the affair of the drovers.'

He went off into roars of laughter, standing bent double for a moment, helpless. 'Oh, well done, my little Madam Spitfire! Splendid! By God, there's spirit in the wildcat! No wonder he—' He broke off, shrugging. 'Well, never mind that.'

'No wonder – what?' she said curiously. Not that it mattered.

He shrugged again. 'It's the way he watches you. I never saw him look at a woman as he looks at you. And all this play with Blod – ay, he played it and hard, but I know him pretty well and sometimes since you have been with us, I used to think it – disgusted him.'

'It disgusted me,' she said. 'And if he didn't want it, why succumb to her?'

'Why, to drive you away; you were settling in far too well at the Cwrt, you seemed too much contented. And while you were contented why should you expedite your ransom?'

'But riding off with her each night into the forest . . . And then again this evening . . .' Understanding began to dawn, great thudding blows of it against a mind that seemed suddenly filled with cotton-wadding, looking back over the incomprehensible past. 'Of course! He couldn't show himself to

110

me – he was supposed to be my husband, the Earl of Tregaron. But when you all went out on the high toby – then he disappeared with Blodwen and left her somewhere and made his way to join you—'

'So it was not after all poor Dio who made such a hash of it among the twenty rich drovers,' said Dio, delighted.

'—and that time, that first evening – it was he who appeared, supposed to be so sick, and half-carried, falling forward so that I might not too closely observe his face – made white with chalk, no doubt, the better to deceive me. But – that other time, after the matter of the drovers: my – husband – was with me while we watched Y Cadno at the council rocks.'

'Any man if he be the right height and keep a good distance may wrap himself up in a blanket and fur hat and utter a few half-heard words—'

'And that same night – that horrible evening of the feast, when he cried out that I was reserved for himself—'

'Well, so you were,' said Dio. 'Weren't you?'

'But afterwards, that other one – the same – call him what you will – he'd been injured, he'd fought for me, Catti told me so—'

'Why as to that, anyone may put on a pallid air and nurse his arm a little. And as for Catti – well, Catti is the word! We've all played cat and mouse with you, Madam fach,' he said, laughing. '*And* had a few tricky moments. That fool Blodwen, squeaking out that he'd been her man "from the beginning" . . .'

On the stretcher, the wounded man had ceased even his occasional light moaning; she bent to him and saw that his breathing was normal and he in the blessed peace of total unconsciousness. 'But in London – oh, Dio, the fool he has made of me!' And she couldn't help laughing also, fell into a very paroxysm of laughter, let even the precious stretcher go on a little way without her as she clung to his arm for support, bent double with it, holding her aching ribs, peal after peal ringing through the whispering sound and movement that is

111

part of a night forest; laughing at the grandeur of his deception, the sheer impertinence of it, the ingenuity of it
– at the huge secret joke of her own impudent deception of
him . . .

And why not, indeed, laugh? True, her husband was gone,
ridden off into heaven knew what danger, and her heart must
give a small lurch at the thought of it: a little, whipper-
snapper dancing-master of a fellow; with hands that were like
steel, however, and a will of steel also, and a courage, a
daring, a humour – and a passion – to outstrip her own . . .
But he whom she really loved was now in her keeping; and
she would bring him back to health and so weld him to her
and make him hers for ever. And all this wild place should be
her home until she chose to go away with him (for when the
truth of her poverty was known, who would prevent her?)
and, married already, she must perforce be left to the bijou
house – and all that stuffy boredom of wealth and society and
stodgy, staid matrimony was over for ever. My mother shall
live with me, and little Jake; and Bess will be near us and my
brothers all about me; and there need be no deception between
us. He'll marry, no doubt, must marry, in his position as head
of the family, but let him, who cares? – since these great
society folk have to do so. (Only let her keep out of my way!
– nor shall it be his present beauty, my Lady Blanche Handley:
some other 'suitable match' must be found – I'll not have *her*.)
But his love will be for me; and all his gaiety and all his
happiness shall be found in my little white house with its
frilly white bed; and all the rooms shall be filled, always
filled, with white roses . . .

They caught up with the stretcher but still he lay quiet, his
bandages held, there was no sign of new bleeding. 'Come, Dio,
tell me all! That night he first saw me at the play?
Did he come up especially to town to seek out some rich
woman—'

'No, no, Madam Vixen, you mustn't think ransom a part of
our usual work. No such idea was in his mind!' She slipped

112

on the mouldering carpet of leaves and he put out a hand to grab her, held her safe from further accident, and so they progressed, now slithering down the steep slope of the forest, now toiling up again, in the pleasant companionship of a man, admiring, respectful, with the wife of his leader; and he told her the whole story. Y Cadno was not unacquainted with the metropolis; his up-bringing had not been that of a common footpad; now and again, after an exceptional haul, he would borrow some clothes from the wardrobes of plundered travellers and ride up to try for a better price from London fences than could be obtained through their representatives down here. 'All that we get, we need, Madam Vixen, fach, at the Court of Foxes. You won't suppose all our lives spent in such high adventure as what 'as happened this evening? A few sovereigns, that's our usual night's haul, and personal trinkum-trankums – fobs, snuff-boxes and so on. And we've forty men and women at the Cwrt or more and children unnumbered, and these come and go: and those that go must be paid off. Some are wounded and forced to retire – Y Cadno will carry no passengers, he's a hard man, your husband, Madam Vixen. And some won't serve under a leader and break away to set up on their own – which they usually come to regret; some are cozened by their women, who grow sick of the hard life and the danger, expecially when they have children; and some of the men themselves grow tired of it. But all when they go must be paid, and justly according to their work while they've been with the gang – otherwise we'd soon have informers, and the military down upon us, knowing our secret approaches, the disposition of our sentries, the timing of our exploits.'

'Yes, I see,' she said, 'that this all takes money.'

'Ay, and rich pickings or not, the jewels and gewgaws must be sold in a market that can make its own terms. But in London, as I say, prices are better; so to London, now and again, he goes, and a few weeks ago decides upon it once again, and rides off – and while there betakes himself to the playhouse, simply for his own entertainment and there observes that all eyes are turned to one particular spot; but is so placed that he can't see the object of so much interest. And half-way through, wanders out hoping to glean information; and dodges back again, out of sight, lest he be recognised and denounced as a highwayman. For who should be standing there, on his last night in England before leaving for the Continent, but his brother, Master Dafydd of Llandovery; the gentleman who now goes with us on his way – which is somewhat ironical – to the hospitality of the Court of Foxes.'

'His brother?' cried Gilda.

'Ah, yes, of course you don't yet know all. But you must have recognised some family likeness? – and the similarity of the name. For Gareth Y Cadno made not quite so wild a claim as you'd think, when he called himself lord of Tregaron. The old Earl, their father, was no miracle of virtue it seems, where the sins of the flesh were in question: half the pretty girls in Carmarthenshire, a generation or so ago, could testify to that – and among them Gareth's mother. He was born a week or two in advance of the legal little lordship; and, the heir being christened Gereth, the old man had the bastard the next day, and at the same font, christened Gareth – to remind him, I daresay, while his family, owned and unowned, grew up about him, that here in fact was the first born of the house of Tregaron.' He laughed out his great ho! ho! 'I think that to play this half-real rôle has given Y Cadno more positive pleasure than any other part of the whole adventure.'

The lady took leave to doubt it – but privately. They had come now to the lower edge of the forest and turned along a valley pathway made intricate, and deliberately so, by a hundred twists and turns, a dozen dividings into other paths that in fact led nowhere. 'But that night at the play-house—?'

'He stood in concealment and heard for the first time of the wonderful lady, very rich, a widow, unfriended, alone, after whom none but servants and a few men of business would

114

enquire; and so conceived the idea of wooing her and bringing her back here for ransom. Whether there was in this a touch of malice at the thought of going into competition with Dafydd bach, his half brother (wrong side of the blanket) who shall say? And other considerations also may have played a part: you can tell me that, better than I.'

'Who can say?' she said; but it was all bemusement, she could not yet sort out the real from the histrionic. 'He became – all in that moment – the pretended Earl of Tregaron? But ... The carriage – the family carriage, with its coat of arms – I saw him mount up into it; with my own eyes I saw him.'

'You saw him stand beside it as though about to mount.' He flung up his big hands to heaven. 'Diw, diw, the luck he had all along the way! There stood the coach awaiting, presumably, David of Llandovery; who, however, was running about with a great bundle of flowers, says Gareth, with no eyes in his head for anything but the beauty from Italy. So he marches himself over and stands by the carriage, casually, one hand on the emblazoned door, and lets you see him there as though about to enter it; nipping away with an exchange of goodnights with the footmen as soon as the true owner approaches it—'

'—having already formed the intention of impersonating Lord Tregaron?'

'Ay, well – having heard that evening that both brothers were to go abroad the following day; and having this ready-made likeness.'

'And it was all a nonsense, of course, that there was bad blood between the brothers?'

'To account for their not meeting. and conversing, outside the playhouse. For the rest – there's some family likeness, as I say, and the real earl was not much known in London, he spent most of his time at Castell Cothi, minding his estates. And so – he waited for their departure, both brothers, mother and sister; and behold! – "the Earl of Tregaron" begins to lay

115

siege to the citadel.' He went off again into one of his great guffaws.

'Very well, you may spare me his account of the wooing,' said Gilda. 'Looking back, I am not very proud of it myself.' And she thought of her one or two moments of delicacy and of how she had felt a small pang when he had asked her, 'Are you ashamed of your bargain?' and she had indeed for a moment felt a little ashamed . . . And all the time . . . 'He's a rogue and a villain,' she said; and still couldn't help laughing.

He laughed too, trudging along happily by her side. 'And so the arrangements went forward. Imagine his joy when you insisted upon secrecy: secrecy and dispatch. He'd been mortally afraid that the brothers might come back from their travels early, as indeed one of them, at least, seems to have done – and find a second Earl of Tregaron disporting himself, however discreetly, in London; and some other anxiety I believe he had, also – he thought you a little fancied this very gentleman now present. But it seemed not so after all, for you insisted upon an early and quiet wedding. He made haste down here to have all ready for a fake hold-up on the second night, following the marriage; and one of the boys rode back with a ring – our finest treasure, there was some argument among us as to giving it up to you; but after all, as he said, it would be coming straight back to us.'

'He was very sure of himself,' she said; the more bitterly that he had not known that it would not be for his charms that she would succumb to him. But light was still breaking. 'Then this story of the road – of Y Cadno tricked and shot up and the ring preserved, as told to my little bro – as told to my page boy—?'

'A tale to please the lad, to whom Gareth took some fancy since he prattled about highwaymen – to Y Cadno's immense amusement. But it came in handy later – accounted for the non-appearance of our "wounded" leader.'

'Oh, dear: poor deluded me, how I have been tricked and deceived by the lot of you!' And how I have deceived you in

116

turn, she thought smugly – who still expect so much of me. Let the sick man be made well and returned to safety, and with what glorious satisfaction would she tell them how the tables had been turned on them! But then... 'Why, the house! The night in Hanover Square! Will you tell me next that this was all a forgery?'

'No, no, how could he have contrived another such mansion? And with all the arms and emblazonments, the family uniforms for the lackeys, the crested silver?' He shook his great head and his black eyes sparkled with glee. 'Still you nearly had him there! – insisting upon at least one night there. How to refuse you? You were kittle-kattle; deny you, he says, and you might have been off any minute, at any rate delay the marriage and bring all to disaster. So – the family being abroad – he simply sent a note signed "Tregaron" instructing the staff that his nephew, his cousin, I know not who – my Lord Howden or Hillden or some such name, it's no matter – would come for one night and must be treated with all hospitality: the family being unfortunately from home but relying upon the major-domo's discretion. So the place was thrown open, but hurriedly, for he gave them no time to run gossiping with neighbours and discovering the non-existence of any such Lord and Lady Hillden or Howden among the family relations – and it was "milord" and "milady" – for what servants, he says, will address the great folk by their full titles, will use their actual names? Gareth knows these things; the old Earl was not so reticent of his bastard offspring as to entirely neglect those to whom he took a fancy and Gareth being the oldest, he believes that his father had a secret feeling of some shame towards him, that he should have no name nor title. At any rate he treated him kindly, came often to his mother's cottage and talked with him, and so taught him no little of the bearing and ways of the gentry; took him sometimes with him to London (but secretly), and had him well educated by a good master.'

'He needed no lessons in roguery, I fear,' she said; and

117

could not help laughing anew, at the risks he had taken, the spicey daring of it all. 'He must have had an anxious time when I wished to bring my – my waiting woman, to Hanover Square.'

'Why, yes, for she'd soon have learned from the servants that they didn't know him for Lord Tregaron. Catti, on the other hand, being in the secret, could cozen them and you, at one and the same time. And as to bringing the maid away with you, well he was ready with some plan to prevent it; a message was to have arrived saying she was too unwell to travel, some story – but . . .'

'But he found another way to avoid it,' she said, not now so much amused.

'You can believe it was a shock to him when Dafydd Llandovery made his appearance – having just that moment arrived back in England!'

'Yes, good heavens! But he, I suppose, had been told that we were there at Lord Tregaron's invitation – friends not among his personal acquaintance . . . And yet, he would recognise *me*.'

'You were understood in the servants' hall to be newly married: a remote cousin (and Gareth's likeness to these, his half-brothers, would allay any suspicion) and his bride, spending a night at the house on the way to a honeymoon abroad. No doubt it was a surprise to Lord Llandovery when he saw who the bride was; but he knew you for a widow, and for the rest – as I say, why should he question it?'

'And the inns upon the road – this accounts of course for their low standard; he couldn't go to the well-patronised hostels where other travellers might recognise him, where the landlords would know the real Tregaron, so long accustomed to use these roads and, I suppose, the same coaching inns . . . And Catti! – now I see, Dio, why Catti – why Catti looked so fierce upon me . . .' Her voice faltered: Catti had looked at her with anger because of the attempt to meet David of Llandovery; because of the attempt to cheat the belovéd leader.

She slanted the subject hurriedly. 'And I see also why – ah, Dio, I see also that I must after all absolve Catti of naughtiness!'

'She is my woman,' said Dio. 'Just as you are his.'

'I am his *wife*,' said Gilda.

Back at Cwrt y Cadno they showed a general tendency to regard her in this light, the men especially: Blodwen, only, putting up any great resistance. She arranged a room where the sick man could be nursed and sat by him all that night, drooping with weariness and sleep but adamant that she alone should care for him. A foolish resolution, for by the next morning she was utterly exhausted and his first waking hours were spent in the hands of another Blodwen (Blod the Bruises she was known as, to distinguish her from Blod Black-eyes) commonly accepted as nurse and doctor to the gang and therefore expert in treating injuries. It was Blod who told him, unemotionally, of the occurrences on the road and of the death of his brother: thus sparing him much anguish of explanation and tender sympathy, and depriving Gilda of the opportunity to administer the same. She said coldly when she heard of it: 'This should have been left to me.'

'I don't understand what you say,' said Blodwen in Welsh; perfectly understanding, however. She was a friend of the other Blodwen.

But what cared Gilda? – who now might sit all day with her belovéd's hand in hers, leaping up only to wait upon him (the more unlovely tasks of nursing, however, being deputed to others: romance must be preserved at all costs) – bathing his aching head, dressing his sore wounds, tempting him with eggs and cream rather peremptorily demanded from the girls who managed the farmyard. 'How can they grudge it to him?' she said to Red Jenny, nowadays her sole friend and confidante, and, 'They think that you should ask more humbly, Madam fach,' said Jenny, frankly; 'they think it is not for you to give orders.'

119

'I am the wife of their leader,' she said: absurd that she should actually say it with pride.

'But as the wife of Y Cadno – forgive me, Madam, but they say that you make too much of this gentleman here. Catti – well, Catti tells tales. She is Dio's woman but she's devoted heart and soul to Y Cadno. She won't say much to Y Diawl, since he seems so much your friend (and this also will hardly recommend you to her) – but she speaks among the women and they work upon their men. They fear that you'll purposely delay your ransom until Dafydd Llandovery is well enough to leave here . . .' And next evening she whispered that a council was called to discuss it, was that moment assembling.

'I'll go there,' said Gilda.

'My lady, for heaven's sake—'

'I'll go; but secretly. Take care of my patient for me, Jenny.' And with shrinking heart but head – at least as long as Jenny was in sight – held high, she crept out, bright hair covered with a dark shawl – that lesson at least had been learned – and stole in among the rocks of the small clearing on the slope down to the stream, a little way from the main building where, well away from the women, the men held their meetings.

The skin of a red fox had been thrown down upon the highest of the boulders which ringed the site, and this place was left empty. To its right sat Dio y Diawl, the rest all grouped about him. The wisdom or otherwise of kidnapping for ransom was evidently under discussion. '. . . it was Y Cadno himself who brought *her* here,' Dio was saying.

'Ay, but a woman – and was she not well chosen, what a man it is! – no friends, in all England and Wales but a handful of servants and a lawyer and banker. Who will enquire after *her*?'

'Yet it seems true enough after all – as Y Cadno has pretended to her – that these great folk for all their wealth may not just dip their hands into their own coffers.'

'She can dip hers well enough,' said the lame man they

120

called Hal the Hop. 'Y Cadno forgot when she put him off with excuses, that she has jewels, an Aladdin's cave of them, he was told up in London. Those she may surely lay hands on without lawyers or bankers?'

'And will do so fast enough now that she no longer has her "husband the Earl" here to rely upon. As for Dafydd of Llandovery,' said Twm the Scar, 'his home and affairs are close at hand, let him produce such sum as we agree—'

'The old mother arrives back tomorrow evening; she'll do the business for him,' said Dai Thomas. His brother Tegwyn was corn chandler in the neighbouring village of Caio, just over the mountain; an old member of the gang, lamed and now pensioned off in return for his services as disposer of stolen property and general spy in the world outside. 'Teg has news that she comes posting back day and night, from France.'

'Then agreed?' said Dio. 'Between him and his mother, let them produce the ransom, and as soon as he's mended and fit to travel the distance, pack him back home. None will come after him here in the meantime, if that's understood.'

Sam the Saddle sat nursing his right wrist and in his heart there was no love for the new Lord Tregaron whose bullet had shattered it. 'Dafydd of Llandovery you call him still, but he's Earl now. From the moment of his brother's death he inherits, titles, estates, fortunes, all. None greater or richer or more powerful, in the country. And do you think that the moment he's mended and strong again, and set free, he'll not bring all Wales about our ears like a hornets' nest, in revenge for his brother's death?'

'What then? Keep him here? The hornets will be upon us indeed, if we do that.'

'Give out that he's dead,' said one of the border men, Tom Jones of Salop: these men spoke only English and for their sake, conversation, though conducted in Welsh, was so larded with English phrases and pauses for translation, that Gilda had little difficulty in getting the gist of it. 'We've killed one.

If they think we've killed two it can make no great difference. Give out that he died in the shooting – was wounded and has now died.'

Dio turned his big head from one to another. He said: 'Well, come Sam – is this what you mean? We can't keep him here caged up for the rest of his life – he would have to be guarded, the thing's impossible. So if we're not to send him back – what is it you propose?'

What Sam proposed – nursing his wounded wrist, which for the rest of his life might impede him in the quick draw of a firearm, the aim, the re-loading – angry, revengeful and withal genuinely anxious for the safety of the gang and their leader: what Sam proposed was – murder.

CHAPTER TEN

She waited to hear no more; fled back to David's room and there, dispossessing Jenny, took the drowsy head in her arms and cradled him like a child, as though with her very body to protect him from harm. What to do? What to do? She dared not confide even in Jenny: for this would be an edict of the gang and none dare raise a voice against it. She could not possibly get him away, weak and helpless as he was, even could she have eluded the sentries, and she had no money for bribes; the only possession of value she had ever owned in her life was the gold and ruby ring, and that Gareth y Cadno had taken with him.

She had yet a little time. An assault was planned for the morrow on the Lampeter road, had in fact been initiated by Y Cadno himself before his abrupt departure. An Englishman calling himself The Black Toby-man, or Black Toby, had lately come to those parts and was making himself troublesome. Teach him a lesson, Y Cadno had decided; but Y Cadno was not here now and though determined to go through with it, the men were uneasy, knowing the project not sufficiently planned, not sure just what had been in their leader's mind, and moreover in some dread for the Black Toby had a fearsome reputation. They won't give their minds tomorrow to this business of David, she decided, wishfully thinking; and besides they'll wait a little while yet, in case Y Cadno turns up with a different opinion. So I have until tomorrow night at least, and then the night itself . . .

Tomorrow night . . .

Tomorrow night something was to happen. Something had been said that suggested that tomorrow night something was to happen. She groped for it, groped for the memory. Something about – somebody. Somebody travelling. Somebody travelling post haste . . .

And that was it! The old woman, the old Countess, with special horses, travelling post haste down to Castell Cothi to deal with the terrible events whose news by now had reached her abroad. Her ladyship of Tregaron: David's mother.

She calculated the hour: an early start, a change of horses no doubt at least twice upon the way, making very good time . . . At twilight the gang clattered off, having as she had expected, not troubled themselves with her or her affairs. As dark fell she handed over her charge to Jenny and Blodwen, declared that she was going, for once, to have a full night's rest, and retired to her quarters, begging to remain undisturbed. She had filched from among the heaped wardrobe of plundered clothes, a pair of velvet breeches, top boots which sufficiently fitted her, having belonged perhaps to some page boy in attendance; a frilled shirt, a waistcoat and a dark brocade coat. The night was warm and she would not trouble with the impeding capes of a great coat. She had kept the silver-chased pistol which she had picked up in the roadway on the night of the shooting, and this she thrust into her belt and strode up and down a little with a swashbuckling air; and laughed to herself, even in her deep anxiety, at the thought of how her brothers would roar could they but see her – the Marchesa d'Astonia Subeggio, courtesan-very-much-in-waiting.

In the foreground, the women were calling their children in from play, or sitting nursing their babies, waiting, anxious yet careless, for their men to come home. She slipped out

124

through a side entrance in a crevice of the rocks, rounded up without trouble a pony, dreaming and taken unawares, in the fenced-in paddock behind the sleeping farmyard; thrust a bit into his mouth and, not waiting for a saddle, flung a breeched leg across his bare back – the heaven of being out of petticoats! – and trotted away across the soundless grass and up into the safe concealment of the stunted oaks. It was pure good fortune that the gang, for this once, should have ridden in the opposite direction and taken the main Lampeter road, the real high toby.

It was eerie in the forest, in its mystery and movement, with no moonlight filtering through the close lacing overhead of the twisted branches; but the pony picked its way up sturdily, following the well-known trail, and brought her out at last to the very spot where, on that other night, she had crouched with the moonlight gleaming down upon the give-away brightness of her hair. She had brushed it back into a smoothness now, tied at the nape of her neck with a black ribbon like a man's hair; and concealed its shining with a man's black tricorne. She threw a leg across the pony's neck, sat for a moment with both feet dangling; slid down and, leading it back a little, hitched its rein to a branch. It fell into a dreaming doze at once, head gently dropping further and further downward. Once it's asleep, she thought, only I shall be awake: only I and the unseen creatures that start and tremble at my presence, that creep and call in the night air of the hanging woods. Only I and they.

Here, in this patch of mud, he had died, here in this ditch his body had lain concealed until they had loaded it into his own coach for the last drive home – Gereth Earl of Tregaron who, with so much dash and courage, had fought off, with only his brother at his side, a gang of men vastly outnumbering them. It was a stupid place for the gang to have chosen, that was the truth of it – they hadn't allowed for the huge size of the coach, the road had been too narrow to give them space to manoeuvre their ponies. But for her purpose, it was perfect. The branch of an ash tree hung half-way across the road, one of the few tall trees in this stunted forest. She had marked it, though idly, at the time; today had built her plan upon it. Then the gang had been almost a score against four; this time she would be one against half a dozen or more. You couldn't hold up coachmen if outriders were able to creep up behind you; you couldn't deal with those inside the coach, while those outside remained uncovered. And, for good or ill, she must hold up the old woman inside this coach.

Hold her up at gun point; force her to listen. 'Your son is in the hands of Y Cadno's gang. You must raise half an army, you must split it into three parts, one part must come one way, one another way, one a third – and by doing so you may take his captors by surprise. But you can do it only by recourse to these maps I've drawn out for you – knowing what little I do of the locality; here at least you will see the strength and weaknesses of their fortifications . . . And above all you must act soon, act immediately – even by sundown tomorrow I can't swear that he'll still be safe. I'll go back to him now and guard him with my life; but both his and mine are forfeit if you don't believe me, if you don't act soon . . . She had made within herself sundry subsidiary plans – to secure, hide, destroy perhaps – at any rate in some way to reduce the gang's store of ammunition; to scatter the ponies, to light fires if possible for the guidance of the approaching troops; above all to barricade herself in with him when all her arrangements should be made and with firearms, fists, feet, teeth, nails, defend him, lying there helpless, to the death. If only . . . If only the old woman came this way tonight. If only she could be made to listen and believe – and act.

She hitched up the silk scarf which was tied loosely about her neck, until it covered mouth and chin, leaving only her nostrils free to breathe; and began with small, helpless kickings and clingings to fight her way inch by inch up to the overhanging branch of the tree.

Far away, far, far away, the faint clip-clop, clip-clop of hooves; far away but drawing ever nearer, the jingle of harness, the rumble of iron-shod wheels on the pitted road. Down the narrow defile past the waterfall, through the ford in the broad valley below the old farm of Aberbranddu; the slower ascent of the hill up the roadway cut through the hanging forest – nearer and nearer. Her heart thudded in her breast till she thought sheer terror would suffocate her. She lay like a snake along the branch, perilously swaying with her weight, and watched two armed men ride beneath her in advance of the carriage. It was a post chaise, chosen presumably for even greater speed; far smaller and lighter than a coach and controlled not by a driver upon the box but by the rider of one of a pair of horses. She saw him now pass under the branch, gathered herself to spring – and as the shining black hump of the roof came directly below her, jumped – rolled, scrambled, fell, grasped at a rail, leapt to her feet at last and standing, legs wide apart to balance herself, cried out high and triumphant: 'Stand and deliver!'

The rider reined in his horses, confounded, not knowing whence the voice had come; the mounted guard doubled back but, as the gang had been on that other occasion, were impeded by the branches of trees growing close to the road's edge and, also mystified as to the source of the danger, milled about, arms at the ready, looking helplessly around them. She flung herself flat on the hump of the roof, slithered forward on her stomach till she hung over the side and, head downwards, could look in at the open window; and thrust in a small hand, clutching the cocked pistol; and cried out again: 'I have you covered!'

And the black hat fell off, the mop of marigold hair tumbled all about her face as she hung there, head downwards: staring, petrified across the dark interior of the carriage to the window opposite. Framed in its square outline, lit by the swinging lantern inside the coach – the muzzle of a second pistol, pointing directly at her; and behind the muzzle, a small, strong

127

hand, very steady; and behind both, a face with a scarf pulled up till she could see only a pair of eyes, brilliantly dark. A pair of bright, dark eyes that too well she knew.

Gareth y Cadno. And he was laughing.

How long she hung there, gazing back at him, the blood slowly mounting to her head, she would never know; but suddenly, close by, branches crackled and she had scrambled back to lie on her elbow on the roof of the carriage and was firing into the scrub beyond it. A man's voice cursed: the voice of the Fox cried, 'Splendid! Keep at them! I'll attend to the coachman.' In the chaise the old woman cackled out, commanding, 'James! Drive on! Drive *on!*' but nobody heeded.

Behind her the trees moved and creaked again and she swung round on her stomach and saw a hand with a firearm pointing directly up and towards her; and fired and heard a man curse again and a horse's wild whinneying as it scrambled and skidded with brightly shod hooves, unaccustomed, on the leaf-mould of the forest floor. And the rider was down from his horse and another man up; and a gay voice yelled: 'Hold fast!' and the pretty, shining thing rocked into motion. Men fell back as the two horses lunged forward, and they were away – tearing up the slope of the hill, leaving the outriders wounded, dismounted, paralysed with astonishment, standing feebly staring. She slipped and rolled, fell against the light rail that fenced the roof in, crawled up to her knees and, as the horses flagged, toiling more slowly up the steep hill and the men showed signs of mounted pursuit – clinging with one hand to the rail, fired back into the night behind her. They left their horses and dodged back into the shelter of the trees. Others might have crippled their beasts, but she would not; and anyway they were at the crest of the hill now and the carriage horses wildly galloping with stumbling feet down the rutted road towards the valley.

At the cross roads, he pulled up the beasts to a trot, turned into a narrow lane so deeply rutted as to be almost impassable; brought them to a halt and, quick as his namesake, had leapt down from his mount, run round to the side of the chaise and commanded: 'Down!' And he held out his arms for her and she scrambled and slithered across the rail and over the side of the vehicle, swinging feet feeling for the rim of the high rear wheel. He caught her round the waist and lifted her to the ground, dumped her down unceremoniously and left her by the side of the lane, pushed his head in at the window and demanded: 'Come now, ladies, quick! I have no time to lose – your valuables!'

No squawking and squealing here! But as they rolled and tumbled along the road, the women must have been stripping off such personal jewellery as they wore, and now wordlessly placed it, wrapped in a handkerchief, into the outstretched hand. 'Is this all?' he said, examining it with disgust.

'We are travelling,' said the older of the three women, 'not going to a rout.'

He acknowledged it, ruefully – perhaps respectfully – laughing; flung open the door, raked at their feet – a whimpering maid drawing up hers, not daring to cry out however while her ladies sat so straight and indomitable – threw out into the grass by the wayside dressing chests, writing cases, a basket of eatables. 'Unfasten the box,' he said briefly to Gilda, 'we may as well have that also.' She ran to the platform in front and tugged at the leather straps securing the trunk, as black and humped as the roof of the chaise itself. As she worked, a memory came back to her and she called to him: 'She arrives from abroad; has been posting all day and last night. She must carry a sufficiency of money.'

'Good wench!' he said; and to the old woman: 'Come – hand over!'

'How do you know this? How do you know that I come from across the water?' But she fumbled in her skirts and from some deep pocket pulled out and stonily handed over a small soft-leather bagful of gold. 'Now – you have it all. Let me be on my way, for my errand is urgent. I have nothing more to give you.'

'You, Madam, however—?' he said to the younger woman.

'My mother has told you; it's all we have. Let us go on now, sir, I beg of you ... Have we travelled like furies these three days and nights,' she said wretchedly to the older woman, 'to be held up now, indefinitely delayed, by these – people? – the very same, for all we know, the very gang of assailants who set upon my poor brothers.'

'I know nothing of your brothers,' said Gareth quickly. 'We're no gang, as you see for yourself. This woman is my doxy; we work together and alone.' And he drew away from the chaise and slammed the door to, and bowed with a flourish of the black tricorne hat. 'You are free to continue on your way, ladies, as soon as your henchmen have courage to rejoin you. I, at least, will no longer detain you. Come,' he said to Gilda, 'we will withdraw from this scene of much ado, I fear, about very little,' and he gave her a shove down the bank to the untilled fields where, ahead of them now, a line of trees, hazel and elder, edged the gentle stream of the river Cothi. 'Let their men catch up with them, the booty will be safe enough – they'll not wait to take the boxes with them. We'll go down to the river's edge and – after a short interval which I hope, my dear, may prove sweet to both of us – collect it and so back along the road and find our ponies and ride off whence we came.' And he took her hand and ran with her across the broken ground till they came to the gleam of the river and there without further ado, threw her down upon the grassy bank and with wild kisses flung himself across her body. 'Oh, my love! Oh, my love! All these hungry days and nights, how starved have I been for you!'

She fought with him, struggling like a wildcat. Now, with her true love after all attainable, with the vigils of her attendance upon his helplessness so strong and sweet in her memory – now she was proof against the seduction, the desire and the

130

melting. Now his hot, seeking mouth and ravaging hands only hurt and enraged her; his white teeth cut against her lips, his hard fingers bruised her tender breasts, she wondered how she could have come unscathed out of those other rough tumblings, what magic lay in the response to passion, that protected one from pain and the outward evidences of pain. But he cared nothing for her resistance, perhaps in his passion of desire at last to be fulfilled, was hardly aware of it. Only when he lay at last relaxed, did he say, half sullenly yet always with a touch of his own cool irony: 'What change is here? The violence of your struggles on other occasions, has been matched at least by the ardour of your succumbing. Not this time, however.'

She had leapt to her feet, was furiously pulling together her disordered clothes, hoisting up the boy's velvet breeches, fastening the wrenched buttons of shirt and waistcoat. 'You outrage me! I am not a slut and wanton, to be flung down on to my back in an open field, for you to take your pleasure of.'

'You deceive yourself,' he said. 'Slut and wanton is just what you are, and most deliciously so; only you're too much of a silly little prude to admit it.'

She stood towering over him as he lay, looking up at her, now laughing. 'I a wanton? When have I ever let you come to me without a struggle?'

'Ah,' he said, laughing still, 'but nothing to the struggles before you let me leave you! That night at the inn...' And he caught at her hand and gave her arm a jerk that brought her, half sitting, half kneeling by his side as he lay on the green bank, looking up, teasing, in the moonlight. 'You had me near exhausted...'

'I was a married woman in the matrimonial bed,' she said haughtily, interrupting. 'And you supposed to be my noble husband.'

'Are the embraces of a peer of the realm, then, supposed to be superior to those of a poor common highwayman? Who has, in this case, however, the very self-same attributes: the self-same arms, the self-same lips—'

'Very well, don't continue, I have no desire to list your anatomical perfections—'

'Why no: being well aware of them already. But tonight, my love, seemed less than usually appreciative; fought and snarled and used teeth and claws like a vixen—'

'Well, and so I am a vixen,' she said, glad to leave an argument that might lead dangerously close to the subject of her love for David of Llandovery. ' "Lluinoges", they call me now at the Court of Foxes – Madam Vixen.'

'Madame Vixen!' He sat upright, dark eyes shining with delight. 'A good name for you – who, after all, are the consort of the Fox. And fit consort too! What a piece of work was here with the post chaise, what despatch, what execution! Who taught you this trick, Madam Vixen, of attack from above? – and by the same token, who sent you alone upon this errand? Where is Dio, where is Sam? – ah, Sam was wounded, I recollect now – but where's Willie-bach and James and Ivor and Huw Peg-leg and the rest of them?.'

'Ridden out towards Lampeter,' she said and added sullenly, for now all the point of her desperate excursion was lost – and what would become of them? 'I am alone.'

'Alone? But why? For what purpose?'

'To rob the coach,' she said. God forbid that he ever suspect the reality, with all her intended treachery towards himself and the gang!

'But alone? Why alone?' He caught her by the wrist, violently. 'Come, answer me! What are you hiding?'

Away across the field, the coachmen and outriders had rejoined their charge and the chaise was in motion again, rumbling towards Pumsaint and the security of Castell Cothi. The distant movement deflected his attention, gave her breathing space. She made up her mind. She said: 'If I must tell

Lluinoges, a vixen: hluin-oh-gess, the g hard, accent on the oh.

132

you, why then – I was trying to gather together sufficient money for bribery.'

'For bribery? Of my people?'

'They're afraid: afraid at having taken back to the Cwrt, David of Llandovery – Lord Tregaron. They think there may be trouble. They're planning to – get rid of him.'

'David of Llandovery – my little brother Dafydd!' And he turned suddenly, swinging viciously round upon her and his eyes were as cold and bright as black stars. 'Ah! – so that's it, isn't it? For the moment I'd forgotten, so hot was I for you: but that's why your struggles in my arms were not quite like the old struggles, nor the succumbing at all like the old succumbing. It's Dafydd of Llandovery, my lord Earl of Tregaron whose embraces now sicken you for mine.'

'I've never touched him, not in the way of love—'

'And yet would risk your life to plunder a coach ... By the same token,' he said, getting up to his feet, 'we had better collect the booty and find our mounts again. I have a long ride before me.' He made no effort to assist her to her feet, simply started off walking across the moonlit field towards where the coach had been robbed, leaving her to follow, manfully striding after him across the rough, ridged surface, in the unaccustomed riding boots. 'You don't understand,' she said, catching up with him, walking alongside him, clutching his unresponsive arm. 'They want to – make away with him.'

'And so?' he said coolly.

'For God's sake, Gareth! He is your brother.'

'T'other side of the blanket. And would see me hanged a dozen times, wicked toby-man that I am, and never turn a fraternal hair. At least we'd give him a burial and not leave him to dance on a gibbet by the wayside, stripped of his hands and his tallow by the Glory men.'

They had come to the place and there, sure enough, was the trunk, a black hump in the moonlight, with the boxes and cases. He kicked out an ungracious foot towards them.

'That lot you may have and welcome; send men to pick them up in the morning. Women's finery, I daresay, with which you may at least buy a little kindness from the ladies at the Cwrt. For the rest...' He delved his hands into his pockets and produced the handkerchief wrapping the jewellery and the bag of sovereigns. 'Not much. Good pieces but few, such as sensible women would wear upon a journey. But there's quite a little gold.' He counted it over, appraising it. 'I'll make equal division, I keeping the gold since disposal of jewels isn't easy in my present condition. You may have the gew-gaws.' His cold face relaxed a little as he watched her stow away the bag in her breeches pocket, bending her leg, knee forward, to get at it, like a boy. But he started off immediately, again without ceremony, along the road to where their ponies dozed and dreamed in the darkness. She followed, trotting anxiously after him. 'In this matter of Lord Tregaron—'

'It's all nothing to me,' he said, walking steadily on.

But she persisted. 'And yet it *is* something to you; or you wouldn't be so angry. But – I don't understand why. You and I have never loved one another, have been nothing to one another—'

'I'd hardly say that,' he said. 'But as to love...' And now he did come to a halt, standing facing her in the narrow, rutty roadway as it ran between the little scrub oaks. 'As to love – why, Madam, if I may ask you so – why did you marry me? For my part there were other reasons, which by now you doubtless appreciate. But you – rich, highly born, free of other entanglements – loving me so little as you do, and make no secret of it – why did *you* marry *me?*' He added with deliberate brutality: 'The more so as you had already cast your lecherous eye upon this other.'

And indeed, short of telling him the truth, it was difficult to explain. She essayed a little shrug. 'He was promised elsewhere.'

'So was I supposed to be.'

'You appeared to make nothing of it. He,' she could not

help adding with a flick of scorn, 'was evidently a true gentleman: he would not go back upon a betrothal.'

'And is so still, no doubt. And you a married woman, like it or not. So what do you now propose, if – as your husband – I may enquire? You can hardly set up, a young lady of title and wealth as you are, in your house in South Audley Street, as this honourable gentleman's lorette.'

She could hardly keep from laughing outright at his continued ignorance of her true origins. 'Any more than I can continue at the court,' she said, however, 'as yours; for wife or no wife, what else should I be? – sharing your favours with that sloe-eyed quean . . .' Not that all that mattered to her. If once she were away . . . 'Let me go,' she begged, standing there looking up at him, and put out her hand again in a gesture of supplication, touching his arm. 'Let him go! Exact a ransom if you will, he's rich, what does it mean to him? – but let him go, let us both go.' She felt the hardening of the muscle under her hand, the tautening of his whole body in swift repudiation, and lied outright: 'He's nothing to me, not really; I felt a little sentimentality towards him once, it's true, but a sickbed cures the nurse of romanticism.' One set of the vapours, she added, laughing, deliberately debasing the loveliness of her love, soon cancelled out another. 'But – marriage or no marriage, love or no love – he can take me back into the world I know.' And she pleaded: 'You must let him go in the end, you dare not do otherwise. And when he goes – let me go too!'

'What prevents you?' he said. 'Who wants to keep you? – once your ransom money is paid.'

The ransom. She said, beginning to tremble: 'Is this really all? It's only for the money that you keep me?'

Again in his eyes that look of black brilliance, cruel and chill. 'Of course,' he said. 'What else could I want you for?'

And so it had come at last. She stood facing him, her face lifted to his, pale in the moonlight as a misted pearl. She said: 'There is no ransom money.'

'No money?'

'No money – none. And no title, no Italian husband, no Aladdin's cave. I am a penniless adventuress, who married you for your supposed fortune, just as you married me for mine.' And as he stood there, speechless, confounded, staring back at her, she tried to say jauntily: 'So you may as well let me go after all,' and waited, sick and trembling, for the cold fury of his reaction and wondered if it would not utterly annihilate her. It will be like a storm, she thought, the thunder and the lightning and the terrifying, drenching rain of his pitiless rage . . . And as there is silence before a storm, so there was silence now as she waited for it to break.

And it broke – in peal upon peal of laughter. 'Oh, marvellous, oh, incredible, oh, exquisite irony! How is the biter bit, how wonderful are the ways of providence, my vixen, that should bring together two such as you and I!' And he went off into great rolling roars of laughter again so that the sleeping birds woke to a startled shrilling and the dozy ponies lifted their soft noses and shifted on their feet before dropping off to sleep again. 'And the playhouse? And the portrait of the old gentleman? And the little sugar cakes and – oh, preserve me, or I die of laughing! – the wolves of Italy who would prevent the lamb from enjoyment of her patrimony...!' And he rolled and rocked again, holding his aching sides, mopping at his streaming eyes, spent with it, exhausted . . . 'Oh, Gilda, my Gilda, you'll be the death of me yet! Great lady – village bumpkin now it seems: vicious wildcat, doughty toby-man, and withal the most passionate prude that ever sent a man mad with longing . . . My lluinoges! – my doxy, my darling, my Vixen!' And he pulled from his pocket the gold and ruby ring that he had given her as a token of their betrothal promises. 'Here, put this back upon your finger where in all truth it belongs . . .' In the night sky the stars were fading; faintly, faintly and far away came the first pale promise of a new day. He glanced up at it, caught with one hand at his pony's bridle, with the other yanked her to him

136

and, as she began as ever to struggle, head held back to avoid his kisses, looked into her face and spoke the old message, the old, discredited message of a hundred, a thousand red roses... 'No use, Madam Vixen, for you to fight against it; or for me.' And he held her close and murmured it into her ear and so let her go, slung himself up on to his pony's back and rode away out of her sight.

The old discredited message, designed long ago for her intriguement, her enchantment, her enslavement – and surely for nothing more?

I will love you till I die.

CHAPTER ELEVEN

She sat for a long time after he had left her, thinking deeply over what she must now do; rose at last and led the pony, but slowly, still deep in thought, down the slippery mountain side, trusting him to ignore the misleading paths and take her back to the Cwrt. Dawn was breaking when they came there at last. As she had calculated, they did not arrive unobserved. 'Fetch Dio,' she said to the men who ran out to apprehend her; and to him when he arrived she said briefly, holding out her hand with the great ruby ring on it: 'I have been with Y Cadno.'

'With Gareth? Then,' he said eagerly, ignoring all the rest, 'where is he?'

'Gone back whence he came. He wouldn't tell me where. Meanwhile . . .' She held out the ringed hand to him again. 'Meanwhile, his message is this: that I am his wife, Madam Vixen as you yourself christened me. And that as his wife . . .' She took a deep breath. 'As his wife, Dio – these were his words to me: my orders are his orders and to be obeyed as such. Until he comes back – I am to be your leader.'

He thought it over doubtfully, silently. He said at last: 'You had better tell the rest of them. See what they say.'

'I will,' she promised, grimly. '*And* see what they say. *And* see what Gareth y Cadno says when he returns – if meanwhile any deny me.' A few of the gang standing about them stood, staring, trying to overhear. To them she called out:

'Assemble at the council rock in two hours from this! I have a message for you all from the Fox. And meanwhile, go call down the sentries. And send no one to replace them.'

'No one to—?'

'No one. Every man of you must be present to hear what I have to tell you. And these sentries are a waste of your manpower, nothing but a formality – in themselves a danger, for their presence on the sky line in a ring round the Cwrt only points to the enemy where we lie—'

'Well,' Dio said thoughtfully, 'there's some truth in that.'

'Of course there is. I've long recognised it. What's more, one of them ambushed and destroyed and we may be invaded unawares because of our reliance on his warning. Go call them down!' And with the swashbuckling stride she had a few hours ago practised, laughing, in the privacy of her own cell, she marched off into the fortress of rocks. She knew that they looked after her with a new respect as she went.

This time not only men came to the council rock. Jenny's red head was missing but for the rest every woman and child was present, ringing round the great central circle where the men already sat. Only the greatest of the boulders was unoccupied, save for the fox's pelt lying on it. She went up to it boldly but did not sit down. Instead she stood on the small rise in front of it and raised her hand and held it out for all to see the great ruby ring glowing there. And she called out: 'By this sign I am the Vixen, wife of the Fox; and by his word, until he comes back to order otherwise – your leader.'

They all knew of it already; she had carefully left time for Dio to accustom them to the thought, to declare that the presence of the ring proved that she had indeed been with Y Cadno last night. So they were roused only to a little angry muttering, a growl of repudiation. Before anyone could outwardly protest, she created a diversion. 'You men went out last night upon the road to Lampeter? Before I tell you how I fared, tell me how you did? What is your tale of good fortune on the Lampeter road?' And as they were silent,

139

sulkily glowering – for it proved that the Englishman, the Black Toby, had anticipated them once again and the travellers been found empty-handed – she cried out triumphantly: 'Very well – listen to mine!'

She told them the truth; or half the truth. 'Lord Tregaron was in danger from you: you don't know that yesterday I listened to your councils here at the rock – while you thought me milk-and-water drooping over his sick-bed. I had no money, no ransom having come for me, to bribe or buy his way out. I went out on the road to hold up a coach and obtain some. And I did hold up a coach – single-handed I brought it to a halt and had its coachmen and armed guard all helpless. True, Y Cadno came upon the scene; but by that time I had it under control and if when he comes he tells you otherwise, you may have my life for it. He assisted me then, true; if you go to the lane leading a little downhill from the crossroads, you may find the boxes we took from them – they are mine: what we took we divided between us since upon this occasion we worked alone and not for the gang; and those boxes are mine. And these also are mine . . .' She bent sideways again, knee crook'd to fish into her pockets like a boy, and one by one held up the looted jewels before them. 'But this bag of gold – this is yours. He has sent it to you in payment for the ring he gives me: and which I now wear as a sign that I am his wife – and your leader.' And she spread out her hands again before them, the left third finger wearing the huge thing of ruby and gold; and cried out: 'My hand bears his ring; and in these two hands, he has placed your fortunes.'

The muttering and growling rose but it had changed in significance. Dio said: 'They ask what lies behind this? Why should you *wish* to lead us? What are we to you?'

She wished it because what she said must be law until she had David, Lord Tregaron safe out of their hands. But she said: 'Y Cadno is my husband: you are his people.'

'Your husband!' said Dio. 'He tricked you, deceived you, courted you for your money alone. When your ransom is

140

paid, no such marriage will hold you: you'll be gone as fast as you may.'

'By then he'll be back and my trust will be over.'

'You change very suddenly. Only last night you were, by your own word, trying to bribe your way out of the Court of Foxes.'

She protested: 'Not my way out – David, Lord Tregaron's. This was madness, this plan to keep him here, kill him off, bury him away out of sight, deny knowledge of him. With such great folk as this, all this foolery with ransoms is too dangerous. You'd best just get him well enough to travel, and pack him back home.'

The growl rose again, protesting, threatening. She laughed in their faces. 'You're like children, you think out nothing to its proper conclusion. The solution to all this is simple.' And as they still muttered on, she shouted out suddenly, loud and clear at the top of her voice: 'I am telling you the way out of your danger and Y Cadno's. Will you hear me or not?'

'No,' shouted a woman's voice.

She had not prepared for this – for Blodwen. All the rest had been predictable but she had forgotten Blodwen. She felt herself beginning to tremble. Among the women one or two more voices cried out, though less decisively: 'Don't listen to her! No!'

And once again, for the second time, sheer rage came to her aid. She thought of the blowsy white bosom with the dark head lolling back against it – her husband, love him or love him not, with this insolent, opulent, sloe-eyed slut of a mopsy... And she was down from the throne of Y Cadno and running round the circle of boulders and had caught the woman by the wrist and with her open right hand slapped her twice across the face. Blodwen tore herself away, struck back but struck only at the air; for Gilda, blessedly free of hampering skirts, had stepped aside and now came in again smartly with a blow which left a red weal down the brown cheek where the gold and ruby ring had struck it. And she

141

stepped aside again deftly, like a boxer, danced round till she came behind the woman and caught her by the heavy dark twist of her hair, yanked her head back and stood, a clenched fist showing the rough ring on her knuckle. 'One more squawk out of you, Madam Blodwen, and you feel this ring down the side of your face in good earnest and your beauty gone for ever! And if you do, not Y Cadno nor any man again ever, I warrant you, will take you for doxy or wife or anything else. So say your say!' And as the woman squealed and struggled in her hold she cried out to the gaping throng: 'See how she flutters; the fat, ruffled brown hen in the grip of the vixen!' and heard, with relief and an unutterable triumph, how they all burst out, like children, laughing.

Sullen, resentful, Blodwen lifted up her hands in surrender. Gilda did not immediately let her go. 'Before all these people gathered here – an oath! What is there that you all hold sacred? – riff-raff that you are?' And she looked about her, the girl's head still bent backward with her grip on the coil of hair at the nape of her neck. 'The fox's skin – lying up there on the rock, the symbol of his leadership. Swear on the fox's skin that from this day until I go my ways from here I shall have no more trouble from you!' And as Blodwen still feebly struggled, she brought down her fist so that the heavy ring pressed into the flesh of her face. 'Speak, and quickly! Here is a language you understand: reply! I have no time for silly sluts, I have Y Cadno's work to do. Your oath on it!'

They heard the resentful spitting out of a half promise. She let go of the thick coil of hair, was turning away, relieved and thankful, when on an impulse, she turned back. 'Come, Blodwen – give me your hand now and let's have an end of enmity.'

But with Blodwen you loved or you hated; no such thing as a friendly truce could exist for her. Released now and still beyond control of resentment and rage, she swung round upon her aggressor and once more launched into attack. Gilda, taken unawares, flung out both hands to defend herself, caught

142

the girl's face with her ringed left hand and saw with utter horror how a great gash opened up bloodily from cheekbone to jaw across one smooth brown cheek.

For a long moment there was silence, while she stood, appalled. Then a voice cried out: 'She's done it!' and a voice cried, 'Serve you right, Blod, she told you she would!' and a voice cried, 'Diw, diw, there's a vixen it is indeed!' She collected herself. She said with chill nonchalance: 'I warned you,' and went back to her place slowly and from that place said: 'Now any man may have her – including my husband – if he wants her. For the rest, let this be a lesson. He has given me authority and I won't be denied in it.'

Voices muttered but now it was with awe. And calmly, with not a glance to where Blod the Bruises led away the other Blodwen, bloody hands clutched to her face, still shrieking – she put forth her suggestions. 'I've considered this matter of the prisoner. The Earl of Tregaron is dead, the new earl is in our hands . . .' But the muttering began again. Sam the Saddle's voice rose above the rest. 'Don't listen to her! It's a trick to get him out of our hands. She's soft upon him, anyone can see that.'

'Well, send messages for ransom, then. His mother is now at Castell Cothi—'

'We've been over all that. Once set him free and he'd have all Wales about our ears. Do you think they'll so easily forgive the death of his brother?'

She tried a tack that she should have tried sooner. 'It's Y Cadno himself who commands it. He said I should tell you—'

'Don't believe her,' cried Sam again. 'If Y Cadno had ordered it, these would have been her first words.'

'Nor would he send orders, Madam Vixen fach,' said Dio. 'While the leader's on the run, he may advise but he'll not give orders. That's for the man on the spot.'

'Or the woman,' said Gilda.

There was a silence. It was true that last night they had

143

failed in their venture, that since Y Cadno's disappearance there had been but little success. Dio y Diawl was a perfect lieutenant but as a leader lacked Y Cadno's confidence and dash. Dio said, speaking out of his thoughts: 'There's been too little work this way. Travellers grow wary since news of the earl's killing, they're not using our roads.'

'Then move further afield. If they daren't use the road through Pumsaint, they must go by Llanwrda. Intercept them there.'

'That part's commanded by the Black Toby as we found out last night.'

'What right has this Englishman to ride in Wales?'

'He's not particular as to his rights, Madam fach,' said Hal the Hop. 'He rides.'

'Then drive him away!'

Drive him away! The Black Toby had brought with him from his metropolitan origins, a fearsome reputation. 'No such devil ever rode, girl!' said Dio, shrugging his great shoulders up to his ears, looking round at the rest of them. Diw, diw, his look said, what will this wild woman think of next?

It was just what she wanted, an aura of daring to augment the good common sense with which she had lectured them on the subject of their sentries, to make the idea of her leadership seem an inspiration. 'What of it? Drive him off!'

But ... He's a very fiend for cleverness ... Shoots on sight ... And his horse is black and he cloaked all in black and his very firearms painted over so that no gleam of light may give him away ... And his horse is the best in the country, twenty hands or more, no man ever kept up with him ... And he has the strength of a bull, so they say ...

'But we should have a score of men and therefore the strength of twenty bulls. Or rather,' she suggested disdainfully with a glance of deliberate provocation, 'of twenty bull-calves?' She sat coolly, perched up on the rock, very small and brilliant with her white, white skin and the grey-blue eyes, the lovely face alight with eagerness beneath the marigold gleam.

'Or doesn't even that amount to the strength of this one solitary bull?'

There were ugly oaths all round her but she was used by now to filthy language; only sat there laughing at them, with an air of amused contempt. The smile however rather quickly disappeared as a man shouted suddenly: 'What price the strength of one solitary cow?'

She gave herself not an instant for uncomfortable foreboding. 'You mean you would send a woman to meet him? Very well, I'll go: and bring back an undertaking that he rides from hence and returns no more – and a bag of gold into the bargain.' Unless they would rather have his carcase than his promise? she added; it was all one to her.

It was a challenge: the test. She knew it and they all knew it. But – to send her out alone, a woman, a frail, small creature for all her boy's dress and proud boasting . . . The heart of Dio y Diawl failed as he thought of what his leader might say to this. 'When the Fox comes back—'

'When the Fox comes back he'll find himself master of his territories once again.' And she snapped her fingers. 'Dai Thomas – you hear me? Find out for me when the Black Toby comes this way again—'

'No need,' said Dai. 'He comes this very night. There's a farmer riding from Lampeter back to Llanwrda, carrying the gold for six or eight others – who are to ride ahead in a band carrying only a little and pretending it's the whole. They think it all a secret; but the Englishman has guessed it a plot and made some enquiries. He rides tonight.'

'Oh,' said Gilda rather glumly; not at all delighted at so swift a taking-up of her boastings. 'Tonight's rather soon. I've had little sleep in the past twenty-four hours.'

'We may never again have a forward information of his doings. It was only by the merest chance that Tegwyn the Corn heard rumour in Caio of the questions he was asking.'

'Well, well,' she said quickly, 'I said nothing but that I should need some rest. So let's count that as settled – one or

145

two of you had better ride with me to show me the road and from then on I act alone. Now to other matters. Your funds are low: for one reason or another – no fault of anyone's ... And yet at this time, with the winter approaching, surely you should be well prepared? I've thought this over. With the accession of the new earl, it seems to me, and the old woman now re-established at Castell Cothi, there must be much coming and going of visitors – men of law, sympathisers, relatives, all the rest of it. Moreover, there's a young woman there now, whom we spared on the last occasion; she must go home one day and must somehow carry back all she brought with her—'

'Her home is in these parts,' said Dai Thomas. 'She is daughter of—'

'The Earl of Trove,' said Gilda; ever illogically irritated by the very name.

'—and the Earl's land marches with Tregaron land; on the far side, towards Lampeter. It's thus that the families have planned a marriage, to bring the two estates together, she having no brother ...'

'Well, we won't trouble about her marital affairs. She has jewels, at least and must some day carry them to London; and next time won't be so lucky. Dai Thomas, keep your ears open. And by this same token – no more of these narrow roads between the oak forests! In that matter of the Earl's coach, there was no room to manoeuvre the ponies – as I saw for myself, being present on the spot – not like all these women, comfortably asleep at home. In future, we must move further down the valley, we'll attack at the ford across the Cothi by Aberbranddu, where we're not closed in by silly low-growing trees ...' Not but what a low-growing tree might have its advantages, she added, laughing, and described to them, perched there on the rock now, easy and unconcerned as a boy recounting an adventure in bird's-nesting, her use of the bough that grew across the road, the leap on to the roof of the chaise: the upside-down meeting with Gareth y Cadno.

146

And they laughed with her: and she knew that she had won them over and so, risking nothing further, rose and easily stretched herself and said that she had better go to rest now in preparation for their ride tonight, and strolled off towards the rock castle, leaving them to what discussion might ensue. But in a moment she turned back: 'One thing: of all this – no word of my leadership must reach the ears of our prisoner!' For after all, she said, laughing again, one day she too must be released to the outer world; and a fine thing if his lordship should spread abroad that she, a great lady of wealth and title – 'such wealth as I have left, after you have robbed me of my ransom, wretches that you are!' – had played such a part as this. She knew well enough that they had no intention of ever releasing her; that they accepted the present condition because they believed her likely to be for the rest of her days, their prisoner here and wife of their leader – as long as he cared to have her; but now she pleaded with them prettily, and they indulged her in it. 'Not a word to his lordship – for him I'll climb back into my petticoats and play the poor lady, as much at your mercy as he is ...' And she did a little caper, kicking up her heels in their masculine riding boots, over the tight-fitting breeches, and laughed and went off, swaggering. But her heart was in the boots as she went.

An hour at David's bedside and she returned to her own room and lay down to catch what sleep she might before the ordeal – and she knew it to be the supreme test, which would make or mar her lover's chances and her own – with the Black Toby.

They rode out at dusk with Dio and two other men – of similar character, she gathered, being called respectively John Jones Tomorrow and Ianto Next Week. They showed no evidence now of procrastination, however, alas! – but rode with her smartly up over the mountain, singing as they went, and down on to the high toby itself, the Llanwrda-Lampeter road. There, having been directed, she left them and rode off gaily with a joke on her lips and cold terror in her heart; and

147

prayed to such gods as she knew to guide her in what she should do.

A ruined chapel stood by the wayside. If I slip in there, she thought, and hide when he goes by, this desperado need never discover me, and I can pretend to them that he never came. But then he'd be bound to have passed the men as they lay concealed by the roadside, and they would know that he could not but have caught up with her. On the other hand . . . She recollected now a little turning up into the mountains, just before the chapel. Let me hide and once he is gone I'll ride back and up the lane and create some commotion – will they not believe that he turned off there and never reached me? And she slipped down from her pony and, leading him into the small copse beside the chapel, left him there, once again drowsing; and stepped in through the ruined doorway. It will prove nothing: neither my courage nor my cowardice, but at least it will seem no fault of mine, they must admire me for riding so boldly out to try . . .

It was chill in the chapel and eerie. Tonight the moonlight was cold as it had not been last night – last night when she had lain on the river bank and suffered the embraces of Gareth the Fox and this time, safe in her love for David, felt no shaming up-flare of passion, so that it must have been from without, not from within, that the night had been balmy and warm . . .

And clip-clop, clip-clop, hooves approached her along the narrow, rutted road that in Wales was the King's High Road; clip-clop, clip-clop . . .

The farmer riding out from Lampeter to join his friends in Llanwrda. And the thought leapt to her heart: If I could jump out on him now, if I could anticipate the Black Toby – as they failed to do last night – and ride back with the gold, triumphant: might I not then tell any story I cared to, of a skirmish with this wretch they're all so frightened of, a disarming, promises of good behaviour in the future, of leaving our territory, going back to England, anything I choose.

If the promises be not kept – is that my fault? And anyway, shall I not be free of the Cwrt and away, before the reckoning comes? She started to the door—

And clip-clop, clip-clop – from far, far away in the still, chill night, the sound of hooves coming in the other direction. The marauder, riding from Llanwrda as planned, to intercept his prey.

The farmer's horse was suddenly reined in, for a moment all was still save for that far distant clip-clop: she could imagine the frightened man sitting his pony listening, listening ... Then the sound of his hooves began again, rapidly, slowed when he neared the chapel, were still again. There was the clatter of a man dismounting, the sound of quick footsteps. Dear God, she thought, he's coming in here!

A small gallery ran across one end, of which a few pillars still stood and a tumbled stairway. It would hold no greater weight than her own, but it might yet hold hers. She crept up the broken steps and was there to peer, like a mouse, over the gallery edge as the farmer entered. She watched him dart across to a heap of hay tumbled into a corner, thrust something in and, hastily covering it over, rush back out of the chapel again. A moment later the sound of his pony's hooves once more clattered on their way.

She crouched and listened; deduced that as one set of hooves receded the other advanced; both paused an appreciable while – she imagined the hold-up, the blank denials, the pockets and saddle-bags turned inside-out and proved to be empty. The farmer's hooves clattered off joyfully, the highwayman's came slowly on, disappointed.

So again – what to do? If she were to let him go on, pass the chapel, ride on, then nip down and possess herself of the bag hidden by the farmer – why, could she not tell the same tale as she had planned in her then hopes of robbing the farmer himself? (She wondered if the men would have heard the hooves also, and could be induced to interpret them to uphold her story.) Or – to encounter him? – to bribe him with

149

the farmer's gold and go back to her men without it, but at least with a promise ...

Her distractions were settled by forces outside her control. The sound of hooves ceased as before they had ceased; for the second time footsteps approached – and a very different man entered the chapel.

A tall man: a very tall man, dressed all in black, wearing a black mask through which, however, his eyes shone with a steely brilliance of glittering blue. A mouth cut hard and straight across a firm jaw: a brave man, a ruthless man, a man of sheer braggadocian daring who rode the high toby for love of the game, who rode it alone because he liked his own company and none other; a man who would not sleep safe in a bed if he could ... He strode into the little room, the moonlight flooding through the broken windows and roof on to a face devoid of anything but a cool, uncaring purpose; glanced about him, began with a casual toe to turn over the heap of hay, as the most obvious hiding place for a man in haste ... Found the small bag of gold, lifted it, hefted it in his hand, brushed away the dust – and turned to see a pistol's eye pointing down at him from the low gallery; to hear a trembling voice pipe out: 'Your money or your life!'

In one movement the bag of gold was in his left hand, a firearm in his right. He stood, long legs astride, and called up: 'What boy hides there?'

She kept her bright head low, the pistol, still poking over the gallery's edge. 'One whose arm keeps you covered, sir!' And she cried out again, trying to keep her voice hard and low: 'Your money or your life! Throw down the bag of gold!'

He let out a great roar of laughter. 'Keeps me covered! Why, child, you see nothing while you crouch so low; this toy of yours wavers with the trembling of your hand, pointing anywhere but at me.' And he almost coaxed: 'Come, no more of this nonsense; down the stairs with you – first throwing down your firearm, however, for who knows what mistakes

150

that shaking hand of yours may not make?' She crouched there not daring to move and he repeated: 'Throw the gun down over the balcony's edge; and follow it – but by way of the steps.' He added: 'Or shall I come up and get you?'

She popped up her head, triumphant. 'You couldn't! The stairs would not take your weight,' and popped down again.

His hand fell to his side. He stood staring up at her. 'By all the saints!' he said. 'A woman!'

She came to him: slowly creeping down the stair with her gun held steadily pointing at him, though his own hung forgotten while with his left hand he slowly pulled away the mask and stood gazing, the steely blue eyes alight with incredulous, amused delight. 'A woman! And a beauty at that for all the man's breeches! For God's sake – what in the wide world, Madam, are you doing here?'

Since he disdained to trouble with his firearm, she lowered her own. She said, coolly: 'Why – I came to meet *you*.'

'To meet me? Do you know who I am?'

'You're the Englishman who calls himself the Black Toby. I am the wife of the Welshman, Gareth y Cadno. And I want to know why an Englishman rides in Wales.'

'The wife of Y Cadno? *You're* no highwayman's wife! And yet I remember now that Y Cadno is reputed a son of the old Earl, Tregaron, of these parts, who brought him up something different from the usual run of a nobleman's bastards, begot in a village hamlet. Well, well!' He stood gazing down at her, admiring, indulgent, totally indifferent to any thought of danger from her. 'But is not Y Cadno on the run now? – after the killing of the son, the old man's heir. In what circumstances does he send his wife upon such errands? – and, if it come to it, such a wife.'

'He hasn't sent me,' she said. 'I come myself. I lead the gang now, in his absence; and as leader, I must tell you, sir, that I tolerate no invaders of our territory. I'll have no Englishmen.'

'You don't tolerate—!' He went off into roars of laughter

151

again. 'I'm not to ride here because forsooth, it is your terrain
– and you come out here to tell me so, yourself, alone . . . ?'
But at that his muscles suddenly grew taut, he glanced about
him, his face grew wary and keen. 'Alone? Are you in fact
alone? Is this some ambush? Why should you come alone?
– you have a large gang, they wouldn't send you out without
escort.'

'Of course not,' she said. 'I have but to fire two pistol
shots . . .' Her voice faltered. Fool! she said to herself, you
have given it all away.

And indeed he missed nothing. 'Ah-ha! Two shots: so
they are not near, my dear, or why not just cry out? Hidden
somewhere back along the road, I daresay, and sent you on
to parley with the Black Toby – is that it? Or to rob him,
perhaps?' He laughed again, looking down at the bag of
gold.

'Not to rob,' she said. 'Though by that token, I took the
money first; it's you that robs me.'

'The farmer was *my* prey; I had tracked him down, he was
mine.'

'I know nothing of the farmer. He came in here where I
was hidden awaiting the chance to speak to you if you should
ride this way. I challenged him, held him up at pistol point,
though he made a great struggle and outcry, nearly had me
worsted: a fat man and strong. But gave up his treasure at
last and rode on his way. So, hearing your horse approach—'

'You lie,' he said. 'I listened for the sound of his horse;
heard it check once and then once again for just so long as
would take the man to rush in here, fling the gold beneath the
hay and be on his way again. Finding him empty-handed, as
I after that expected, I estimated the distance and so came to
this place. You watched from your eyrie while he hid it, my
dear, and nothing more. Come out with it – is it not so?'

He had the better of her and she knew it. Her lip began
to tremble. 'Must I go back then and – tell my men that you
won't heed my request, you won't stay away from my pre-

152

serves? Must I creep back without even gold to show them?'

'It's very sad,' he said, 'but I fear you must.'

'But . . . It's true, after all, that this is no domain of yours?' pleaded Gilda. 'There's not enough for those of us who are already here. If you would but go back to England – which surely is richer by far—'

'But which for the moment I like not so well. I find Wales very agreeable; the scenery is beautiful, and seeing so much of it as one is obliged to do, riding the roads . . .' He shrugged. 'The country suits me. Why should I go elsewhere, just for you?'

'If you knew what it meant to me, I think you would,' she said. She stood before him, very small, very slight and frail in comparison with his tall frame, the marvellous hair, escaped a little from its neat black bow at the nape of her neck, shining in the light from the tumbled window : the flower-face innocent of coquetry, absorbed in its own private troubles, looking up into his. 'Unless they take me as their leader in my husband's absence, great misfortunes will result to innocent people, who have nothing to do with – with you or with the gang. But they won't take me as their leader; not until I prove myself. And – I boasted to them that I would – remove you; and they've taken me at my word. And this is my test . . .'

He stood looking down at her, laughing. 'In which test, Jack-the-Giant-Killer, I fear you must fail. For to be frank with you, there are reasons even better than the scenery which for the moment prompt me to remain out of England.'

'There are other parts of Wales,' she said. 'I don't insist upon England.'

He laughed even more, looking down at her from his great height. 'Oh, you don't insist? That, I confess, is very good of you. But you see, I don't care for your other parts of Wales. I find it very pleasant here, there are good communications with London, where in fact I belong, I have a neat hideaway, a couple of complaisant ladies in the neighbouring farmhouses . . . ' He stooped and picked up the bag of gold and swung it in his hand. 'Come, there's more here than I'd hoped. I'll divide it with you so that at least you go back not empty-handed.' He unwrapped the string round the mouth of the bag and tipped into each pocket of her coat a small handful of coins. 'And so,' he said, tying up the bag again, hefting it away into his own pocket, 'we may go our ways. And my ways, I fear, my pretty one, must continue for a little while at least, to lie upon these chosen paths.'

So there was nothing for it after all – was there? – but to put her two hands behind her back and go up very close to him and stand there, saying nothing, looking up into the brilliance of the steely blue eyes.

He stood unmoving, looking back at her, just faintly surprised.

It was but a moment, of course, but it seemed like an hour, that interval of his un-response; and through every minute of the hour the courage was draining away through the toes of her gay, dashing riding boots. But she could not now accept defeat. She raised herself on tip-toe, caught at his shoulders to pull him down a little from his great height and, not kissing him, murmured with her lips just brushing his: 'Please!'

He drew back his head, eyebrows hugely raised. 'Please – what?'

'Please – well, please, if you would just do as I ask you: go away from here ...'

'Go away?' he said. 'What – now?'

She dropped her hands from his arms, looked up at him doubtfully. 'Now or later. As long as you won't come back?'

He was teasing her: amused, indulgent but totally unmoved by this magical proximity which in her innocence she had supposed irresistible to all men, a simple attribute of any woman sufficiently attractive. 'You make it very difficult,' he said. 'Before this butterfly caress of yours – perhaps. But now ... For if I go before its promise is realised – won't the

154

temptation to return prove too much for me? And if I go later, it will surely be increased a hundredfold?' He held back his head, looking down, his eyes full of mocking laughter, pretending deprecation. 'Never since the Garden of Eden, my dear, has a first kiss been more mistimed.'

'It wasn't a kiss at all,' she said, crossly.

'Wasn't it? You surprise me. It had all the effects of one.'

'This is not *my* experience of the effects of kisses,' said Gilda.

'No?' He went on laughing. 'What is your experience then, if I may ask?' And he invited: 'Come, show me!'

'I'm talking about the effect upon a man.'

'As a man, then, don't I measure up to expectation?'

She took a deep breath. She said, sweetly now: 'That we have yet to discover – haven't we?'

But it was very difficult to seduce a man who would keep on laughing. No blanching face here, no nostrils growing pinched and white, no avidly searching fingers, ripped clothes and buttons flying... His kiss was sensuous, yes, when at last it came, and she felt that within him that little flame had leapt, the first kindling of the blaze of passion. But still he laughed; the breeches and boots amused him vastly, he vowed he had never made love with a boy and must first have undeniable proofs that she was the woman she claimed to be. She produced the proofs but, she could not help feeling, in a somewhat business-like fashion. Used enough to laughter herself, she still could somehow find none here – the whole affair puzzled and a little bewildered her, accustomed as she was to the swiftly ignited conflagration of Y Cadno's love-making, that blazed and glowed and sputtered and flared like a box of fireworks lit by a single match, till at last both parties burned up and were consumed by it to ashes. The great bed of hay was heaped in its corner, sweet-scented, dry and inviting; by now she should be writhing and panting there, fighting against her own inevitable, delicious surrender. Instead the gentleman remained upon his feet and if he held

155

her, did so almost more as though he submitted to her cajol-
ments than courted them; and laughed and kissed and teased
and titillated but by no means seemed himself overwhelmed
by any great longing for the comforts of the bed of hay.
Good heavens! she thought – am I so far reduced that I must
ask a man outright to accept my favours? And yet it was so
deeply necessary that she should extract his promise. She
decided at last upon provocation, a pretence at retirement from
the fray. 'It grows late; my men must be wondering what's
happening to me . . .'

'I hope not too anxiously,' he said at once, all concern.
'For after all – nothing is.'

'Very true. And so therefore may you not just as well
release me—?'

'But it's you that holds *me*,' he said, standing back a little,
lifting up his hands, leaving himself, sure enough, still in her
embrace.

She dropped her own hands immediately. 'All I mean is,'
she said, hanging on tightly to her rising exasperation, 'that
I think the time has come when I must ask you to let me
go home.'

'I do so with infinite regret,' he said courteously, stepping back and motioning her gracefully to precede him to the
door.

She was startled into exclamation. 'You'd let me go? You're
not going to – take me?'

'At least I am not going to force you.'

'At this rate,' she said tartly, 'it seems almost more a case of
my forcing *you*.'

'And never a more willing victim,' he assured her, still
laughing, and held out his arms to her, wrists crossed as
though bound for the sacrifice.

And now she did at last burst into laughter. 'Oh, *you*!' And
she ran at him and gave him a great push that sent him
flying backwards, landing in a laughing heap on the bed of
hay; and flung herself down after him and caught his head in

her hands and held it fast under the rain of her kisses. 'Wretch and fiend, you know very well that I must seduce you into giving me your promise – to poach no more upon Y Cadno's territory.'

'But isn't that just what I'm doing at this moment?' he protested; not, however, noticeably desisting.

'You're a wicked, wicked tease,' she said; and after a little while: 'And a wicked, wicked lover.'

'Lover is a beautiful word,' he said; and all of a sudden, laughed no longer. 'It implies in one's passion – at least a little love.'

'Yes,' she said; and, again after a while: 'I think that up to now I can have known only the passion. It's a very sweet addition – the little love.'

She rode back with him to where her two men lay hidden by the wayside and there reined in her pony and called good-night to him in accents loudly and clearly to be overheard by them. 'And I have your solemn undertaking—?'

'I go my ways tomorrow,' he swore, 'and will ride these roads no more.'

'No repudiations of this promise as having been extracted under duress?'

'No, no,' he vowed, and she heard once again in his voice the undertones of that wicked laughter. 'Though under such duress as I have never before experienced.'

'Very well; then see to it!' she said severely; and when he was gone led the men back and showed them the scene of his undoing – the little gallery from which she had challenged him at pistol point, had conducted the long, long, cat-and-mouse struggle until, finding himself finally trapped, he had held up his arms in surrender; the crooked stair down which she had crept, keeping him all the time covered, till she could come close up to him and snatch away his gun and so force him into his solemn undertaking, to – to poach no longer upon Y Cadno's preserves. And here was the bag of gold which she

157

had taken from him as he stood there helpless, poor wretch, and divided with him equally so that he ride away not too hopelessly discomforted and empty-handed to boot . . .

From that hour forward there was no more question as to who should reign as leader at the Court of Foxes.

CHAPTER TWELVE

So the weeks passed by and in the rocky fortress in the narrow Welsh valley ringed in by the great mountain plateau of Carmarthenshire, the ex-Countess, ex-Marchesa, walked and talked and cursed and swore and all the time had her way with a gang of ruffianly highwaymen and their women as violent as themselves. And alternately sat in a soft dress and tended and soothed and whispered sweet nothings and handed out tiny doses of the dulling laudanum . . . The wound was at last clean and healing, but she dared not let him risk the long ride in an unsprung vehicle jolting over the rough, pitted path that led to the rough pitted lane that led to the high toby, hardly less smooth beneath iron-rimmed wooden wheels; dared not, either, let him up and out of his room – for, wandering about the Cwrt, how could he fail to perceive that other self of hers? But almost daily she called the gang together and adjured them: 'At your peril, let his lordship know how I fight and plan for you . . . !'

And she fought and planned. Under her leadership they were prospering now but with less work (and therefore less danger) than ever before. The old days of wild brave forays under the leadership of the Fox were gone; now every move was thought out beforehand, her wit quick to assess the news brought in by Dai Thomas and to make deductions from it. And she rode with them always, in the dark brocade suit which she had at random picked out from the heap at the fort but which now had become like a suit of armour to her; in the tricorne hat with her hair tied back into its neat black bow. Her presence at first amused, then inspired and at last almost awed them. I am like Joan of Arc, she would think to herself, triumphantly putting up a firearm that had sent a man howling into the night; and never paused to consider how unsaintly a Joan was this who through the lengthening nights robbed rich and needy alike, wounded without mercy, terrified without compassion, rode off without pity for what ruin she might leave behind. It is all for him, she would say to herself, if for a moment her too easy conscience rose up and reproached her; but within her deepest heart she knew that the adventure, the excitement and the power were a yeast in her that had nothing to do with her love.

She had been right about the stream of visitors to Castell Cothi; all of them the more ruthlessly set upon in that, with Lord Tregaron in the hands of the gang, his family dared make no outcry to the law. Then the season was good; many of the great folks were changing their quarters while the weather yet held, going up to London or coming down to their country estates, to settle for the winter. And if there were no work on the roads, she would call for volunteers from among the older men – who came joyfully, starved of the spice of danger they had grown accustomed to – and ride through the evening to some remote farm, steal silently to the grazing-fields and drive off a dozen or so of the black Welsh cattle peacefully grazing there; chivvying them home along the muddy lanes with the help of the small brown bob-tailed Corgis, bred low and bandy-legged so that a flying hoof kicked out, passed harmlessly over their heads. Even the young boys had their share of adventure, riding off up the mountains with her to where the sheep grazed, unguarded, each flock keeping to its boundaries from a knowledge passed down through the generations; she loved to wait on the lower slopes and watch the small figures toiling up through the bracken, to hear through the evening stillness the thin, shrill

160

whistling of their messages to the clever, crouching, creeping dogs – to see the gathered sheep come suddenly pouring down the mountain side, like milk tipped out of a bucket . . . The farmers slept uneasily indeed in those days of the reign of Y Lluinoges, the Vixen of Cwrt y Cadno.

There were reverses. John Jones Tomorrow was shot and fell and had to be left to his fate, two were injured, one severely; she herself sustained a flesh wound that made her sit very uncomfortably in the saddle for some days to come, to the tune of their not un-affectionate jeering; once or twice things went wrong and they came away empty-handed. The men took these reverses badly, blamed it all on to her. Each time she would say a few brief, rough words at the council rock, formally proposing that Dio should resume the leadership in her place. 'No, no, Madam Vixen,' he would reply, half scared, half laughing, 'you've picked up the load; do you carry it!' For all their grumbling, none ever contradicted him.

A day came when Dai Thomas rode back from Caio with glad tidings. 'The Lady Blanche of Trove Hall beyond Lampeter, leaves for London two nights hence.'

'From Castell Cothi?' said Gilda.

'No, no, she was but driving to her own home that night with the two gentlemen as escort as far as Castell Cothi which is on the way to Trove Hall in Cardiganshire.'

They sat in the great cavern-hall discussing it, the weather being nowadays too cold for outdoor meetings. 'She leaves with her father day after tomorrow,' said Dai Thomas. 'An early morning start – they should pass the turning to Porthyridd a little after dawn.'

'She'll not come through the forest then?'

'No, no, squawks night and day for her father to bring her by the high road. Tegwyn Caio had it from one of their footmen who came into the inn at Caio and drank a little deeper than was wise. On Wednesday, early, by the high road from Lampeter to Llandovery, and so on to Monmouth.'

'Will you dare take her by daylight, Madam Vixen? And on the high toby? Once warned, they'll carry as little as possible.'

'She brought a lot with her when she rode this way before,' said Gilda. 'Didn't you see her jewels, as I tumbled them in the mud? She must take them back with her to London, I suppose: wherefore all this anxiety? We must think it over.'

She went away and thought it over long and carefully herself; commanded an early morning excursion to the Lampeter-Llandovery road on the Wednesday, and herself rode out alone before dawn on the Tuesday, leaving only a message to say that she would be back before afternoon.

Up and up, over the mountain, plunging downwards again, mile after mile through the hanging forests till at last she saw to her left the high peak of Twm Shon Catti's hide-out, a dark cone against the morning sky in the sickle sweep of the river Towy. No finer hiding place could exist for a man on the run, its tip commanding the three valleys converging upon it and its rocky summit providing a score of caves where a fox, on a bed of dry leaves, might lie snug enough . . . And if that's where he hides, she thought, he'll be here – not a doubt of it.

He came to her, looming up out of the chilly morning grey; and as her pony halted, brought his own close up against it, leaned across from his saddle and caught her by the shoulders, kissing, first lightly, then with the old once-thrilling violence, her unkissing mouth. She made no response; strong now in her love for David, only coolly suffered it. 'Well, well, sir – are you so lonely in your eagle's nest that you dash out to the embraces of any old rider who comes trit-trotting this way, breeched or unbreeched?'

'Why?' he said, as coolly. 'Do you think of unbreeching?'

'You know very well what I mean. In breeches or in petticoats.'

'In breeches *or* in petticoats I'd recognise you, my shining one. Besides I knew you'd come. I knew you'd not resist her.'

'My Lady Blanche, daughter of the Earl of Trove?'

'Who sends her footman all the way to Caio for his potations.'

She laughed. 'So much trouble to inform the whole world that she'd go by the high road and on such and such a day. It followed that she'd come through the forest and one day earlier; for, having found ourselves tricked, we'd be ready for her if she came later.' She gave the reins a flap and started the pony off again. 'There's a small drovers' inn by the bridge across the Towy. On man standing alone on the roof there, might command the whole cortège.'

He ambled along easily beside her. 'One man has just done so.'

'You mean—? You mean the coach has passed? I've ridden all this way for nothing?'

'You are not very civil. Have you not met *me*?'

'I had rather have met the Lady Blanche. But . . .' She could not conceal her admiration; she herself had counted on his being here to assist her. 'You managed it all single-handed?'

He laughed. 'You flatter me. Not quite single-handed, no. True, I played your very trick of conducting all from the roof of the drovers' inn; but the landlord has a pretty daughter who was not above a little scheme to help me relieve the lady – her coach once halted – of her gewgaws.'

That old, bewildering tide of jealousy welled up in her once more; and, because she was tired and hungry, perhaps, because of the shock of discovery that she came too late – somehow, absurdly, infuriatingly, the pearly morning was growing oddly grey, grey and swirly, and there was a beading of sweat along her brow and a longing only to let go, to give herself up to nothingness. But he had slipped out of the saddle – one hand gripped her shoulder, holding her upright in her own, one hard hand slapped sharply at her cheek. 'Come, pull yourself together, my pocket highwayman, what nonsense is this? The great Madam Vixen – the fearless, the bold, the prettiest cut-throat, so they say, and the savage-est, riding the

163

roads of Wales – having the vapours all over me like any silly lady of the *ton*! Come – up I say!'

And she came to herself at once, shook the cobwebs from her mind. 'I've ridden a long way, hurrying; and not break-fasted, that's all it is.'

He looked at her doubtfully. 'There's food a-plenty up in my lair. Could you ride so far?'

She was alert in a moment. 'Yes, yes, it was but a moment's malaise. And I should dearly love to see it – Twm Shon Catti's mountain.'

'Gareth y Cadno's mountain now,' he said.

The morning was growing bright and they rode very amicably, side by side on the rough little ponies; crossed the bridge over the river and saw ahead again the stark, solitary peak at so much odds with the rounded mountains about it. Below it lay the age-old farmhouse of Ystradfin. 'I find them most obliging. Milk, butter, cheese and bread appear upon a stone slab at the foot of the mountain each day, as though to propitiate a god.'

'Won't they give you away?'

'Hardly, for the gods can take very frightening revenges. But do you tell Dio, by the way, for the moment to leave their flocks and cattle alone. I need friends just now, not foes.'

'Is Dio to know you lie here?'

'He knows it well enough. But I've told you our code. 'It's for me to make the first move and not until I can no longer be a danger to them.' They had come to the bottom of the hill and he reined in his pony. 'From here we must climb and on foot.'

Up and up: up through the small stunted oaks clothing the lower slopes of the peak; scrambling over the outcrop of rocks above. Now below them lay the three valleys converging on their peak, the silver river half encircling it, slowly dream-ing by after its wild dash down the rocky waterfalls of the valley of its origins; flowing softly to meet the Towy they

164

had left behind. She said: 'It's beautiful here. No Castle of Otranto with its pine-clad heights could be more beautiful, more romantic or more – awesome . . .'

He had chosen a cave on the western side, sheltered from the east winds; here dead leaves made a bed and he had tumbled-in a couple of rocks to serve as a stool and an uneven sort of table. A niche near the entrance provided a cool larder for his food and he spread before her a meal, delicious in the fresh morning air. When this is over, she thought, eyeing the leafy couch within the cave, I shall pay for it all, no doubt, and in the usual coin. Oh, well! – armoured in her love, it all meant nothing to her now.

But in fact he made no offer to touch her – there was about him, she began to sense (somewhat uneasily, for such hold as she had over him might be important) – something a little different altogether. Could it possibly be that the girl at the drovers' inn had a hand in this? To cover over her surprise – not to say some small chagrin – she launched upon an account of her adventure with the gang. 'I've heard of it,' he said. 'And this rumour that they've appointed you leader – what nonsense is this?'

'They would have it so,' she said, off-handedly. 'In your absence only, of course.'

'I think you may safely count upon that,' he said grimly.

'And the Black Toby – did you hear of that also? How I drove him forth? – robbed him, single-handed, and forced from him a promise to remain out of our territory. You heard of it?'

'I heard something of it, yes; *and* of the weapons you employed to achieve it.'

'I achieved it by holding him up at pistol point from the chapel gallery.'

'He has another version, it seems; and one that appears to entertain him greatly.'

'He must say something, no doubt,' she said, shrugging, 'to account for his discomfiture at the hands of a woman.'

165

'No doubt. Have any other gentlemen, may I ask, been similarly discomforted?'

'Many others have been worsted: the mail coach, it's true, got clear—'

'Wounding you, one understands,' he suggested, mockingly, 'in your tenderest parts?'

'If you know so much,' she said, resentfully, 'why do you ask?' And she jumped to her feet and stood looking angrily down at him and actually a tear stood in her eye. 'You're not very grateful. I've worked, ridden, suffered—'

'And all for me and my gang?' He lay back, his slender legs outstretched before him on the sunny rock slab, feet negligently crossed. 'All for love of us?'

'Neither for you nor for them. I make no secret – to you at any rate – of why I do it; or for whom. What should I care for you and the rest of them? – riff-raff as you all are, cut-throat robbers and plunderers—'

'Report says you rob and plunder with the best; and would cut a throat too, from all I hear – shoot to kill, at any rate.'

She shrugged. 'I do what I must. And as you taught me, if you remember? I didn't, before I knew *you*, go round holding men for ransom, selling my very life for gold—'

'No,' he said. 'You were content to sell your body.'

She glared at him, speechless with rage; and only after a long moment spat out: 'Ay – and to what a buyer!'

To her surprise he turned away his head before the glare of her eyes and said, almost sadly: 'Why yes – you fared badly there.' But he jerked himself to the present. 'And how, if one may enquire, is our dear invalid?'

She moved sharply away from him, stood looking out over the lovely landscape spread below. 'The wound was severe; I don't know how much damage it's done, I know nothing of these things. But he's still very weak.'

'Long may he continue so. For I warn you, Madam—'

She interrupted. She said almost piteously: 'You mistake

the situation. If he – if he loves me, I don't even know it. He gives no sign.'

'No doubt he stifles it; ever the little gentleman of honour. For he sees you as a married woman, no doubt, and there is still the Lady Blanche. He has his encumbrances also.'

She did not rise to his mockery; only stood with her golden head bent in the morning sunlight, the lovely face grown weary and sad. 'You have never loved anyone,' she said. 'You don't know what it's like – to be so filled with it, possessed by it . . .'

'God forbid!' he said, roughly, and sprang to his feet, abruptly changing the subject. 'Come, to business! You had better be on your way.' He led the way back into the cave where, on the rock table, he had thrown down the rough bundle of his morning's spoils. 'You may have your share – keep it, hand it over to the gang, buy white roses with it for all I care; but it's yours.' And he tumbled the treasure out on to the rough surface of the rock and stood there appraising it: the small, round yellow-gold coins, the worked metal, the jewels glowing in the shaft of light from the cave mouth – ruby, sapphire, emerald, pearl . . . She stood staring down at it also, and said, because at the back of her mind something puzzled her: 'Is this all?'

'Is it all? It's all they had, that's certain. Is it not enough for you?' He sorted out the money, put it aside, sorted out a third of the jewellery, twisted the rest back into its cloth, thrust the bundle into her hands. 'I'll keep the gold, it's too hard for me, in my present position, to dispose of jewellery. This is yours.'

She pushed aside his hand. 'I want none of it.'

'Don't want it? You'd have robbed her of it; I got in before you, that's all.' And as she persisted, he almost begged, growing kind: 'Come, take it! I grudge you not a penny of it. I want you to have it.'

'I'll have none of it,' she said.

He looked at her uncertainly; a little uncertainly laughed.

167

'It's because of Mifanwy? – my blue-eyed Mifanwy, who helped me relieve the lady of it. You think she should have it?'

'I care nothing about her. No doubt she works for – love.'

'Well, the—' But now his brow grew black. 'It's that other one! It's because it belonged to her, to the lady Blanche. Once before you refused these jewels, did you not? – flinging them into the mud for her to grovel for. And now . . .' His eyes blazed. 'Jealousy! Because it belongs to her, because *he* belongs to her – as by God you'll find that he does, doting fool that you are!' And with a swift, violent movement, he caught at her wrist, picked up the bundle and slapped it into her hand. 'Come take it and spare me your maunderings, you sicken me! Take it – and then get you gone, vixen that you are and with your bright tail trailing in the slush of such sentimental vapourings as these . . .' He gestured down the hill. 'Go, get you gone! Whistle up your pony and be on your way! And within this week – for I'll play the complaisant husband no longer to that whey-faced weakling of yours – have him on his feet and packed back to his mother; and go with him for all I care, for I'm sick of you.' And he gave her a shove that sent her running and stumbling down the sharp hill, half out of control; and turned and went back into the cave, not waiting to see her go.

Running and stumbling, clutching the bundle to her breast – the bundle of Blanche's jewels, emerald, sapphire, ruby, pearl . . .

Emerald, sapphire, ruby, pearl – no diamonds. Among her possessions, Lady Blanche Handley no longer numbered, it seemed, her diamond betrothal ring.

By mid-morning she was back at the Cwrt. 'Let the men know that they needn't ride tomorrow,' she said to Dio, dumping the bag of jewels into his hand. A little lesson, she added piously, to be more wary in the future, of the so-called drunken indiscretions of gentlemen in plush breeches . . .

168

'And Y Cadno deduced this also?'

'Y Cadno? Do you know that I've been with Y Cadno?'

He laughed, shaking his great head. 'You are yet very innocent, Madam Vixen fach; do you think we don't keep an eye upon our treasure? Of course when we saw you safe into his company, we watched you no more.'

Oh, well . . . All the more reason . . . She went off to change and go in woman's dress to David's room. 'No more laudanum,' she said, taking the bottle from the nurse's hand.

The girl was surprised. 'The pain—'

'Stimots,' she said, using one of her new Welsh words. 'Never mind.' The pain in fact was no longer over severe, she had been in the habit of administering tiny doses now and again to dull down his interest in her goings-on outside the sick room. 'You must be weaned of it,' she said to David. 'We must get you strong and fit to be moved from here.'

He looked at her with troubled eyes, more incapacitated nowadays, in fact, by the drug combined with too long confinement in bed than by the actual wound. 'Has my ransom then been paid?'

She would not trouble him with details. One day it would all have to be told, somehow explained away – the Marchesa and her marriage, her present rôle at the Court of Foxes, all of it. But for now . . . 'Rely upon me, I've spied out the land, I know it all. And the only hope is to escape.'

'But if my family pays the ransom—'

'They think that once you are safely home, you'll start reprisals for your brother's death.'

The clouded eyes looked back into hers; you could almost see the effort with which he willed his brain to function. 'He's gone. What use now is – revenge?' He dragged it out slowly; he was very weak. 'If my family – gave them a promise – no reprisals . . .'

No reprisals! Fools, stupid dolts and fools that they'd been, never to have thought of it! In return for David's safe return home – no reprisals, now or ever on the part of the Tregaron family. The Fox could come back to his den, the gang would be freed of the threat that hung over them. But . . . She thought quickly. They would let him go; but what about herself? They would never take her word that in fact she was worth no ransom money, never let her get away until Y Cadno gave the word. And as for him . . . She remembered that night upon the moonlit road when she had told him all the truth about herself; the thrusting back upon her finger of the gold and ruby ring 'where it belongs', his words as she had fought off his kisses. 'No use for you to struggle against it; or for me.' She knew that love her, hate her – he would never let her go; above all never let her go to David of Llandovery, Lord Tregaron.

Once David was safely away she could ride out, of course . . . But no: had not Dio that very morning warned her, half teasing: she had been followed all the way upon her dawn expedition, spied upon, until they had seen that she met The Fox. And besides – to ride off alone, to try all alone to make her way back to London, a woman, unprotected . . . And meanwhile her lover would be once more united with his family; she was by no means certain that the absence of Blanche's betrothal ring had any real significance – might he not, weak as he was, succumb to the weight of his responsibilities? She insisted therefore : 'It'll be best to somehow get away together—'

'You and I?' He seemed astonished.

'Well, naturally. How could you ride alone even the few miles between here and Castell Cothi? And you wouldn't know the secret paths—'

'To Castell Cothi?' he said stupidly.

'Well, but naturally,' she said again and with a touch of impatience. But she had caught the faint shadow of doubt that passed across his face. She amended stiffly : 'If you will receive me there.'

'But of course,' he said quickly. 'Of course. You who have shown me so much kindness while I've lain here—'

170

'I who've saved your life,' she said, bursting out with it almost fiercely. And she thought with despair: But what do you know of all that? – dulled, unconscious as, most of the time, you've been. Of how I held you, wounded, in my arms with your dead brother lying by my side, staunching the bleeding until my arm ached with the pressure; how I brought you down through the dark forests, forcing these rough, angry men to my will; sacrificing my own chances of escape. How since then I've conquered them, offering my very body up to a stranger to gain my ascendancy over them; surrendered all my girl's ways, grown rough and crude, hunted and robbed and for all I know to the contrary killed ... A little lady-like nursing, a few kindly cheering-up visits – if upon these she must rest her hopes of a welcome in his family, the outlook was not hopeful. 'I wouldn't trouble you,' she said coldly, 'but where else have I to go? How am I to get back, unaided, to my house in London which is all I can now call home?' It's his mother, she thought. A fine welcome this great lady is likely to hand out to me, after the tales Miss Blanche will have told her of our meeting at the plundered coach! On the other hand ... 'If it's the presence of your betrothed that troubles you,' she said, more coldly still, 'I may as well inform you that Lady Blanche has gone back to London. She's left Carmarthenshire.'

He seemed astonished; perhaps that she should leave Wales while he lay wounded here in the hands of a gang of desperadoes. 'Blanche gone back home? Are you sure?'

'Well – yes,' she said ironically. 'I have reason to believe it's true.'

'And leaving me no message?'

'No billets doux have arrived, certainly, nor any powdered footmen with enquiries after your health. But . . .' She dropped to her knees at his bedside. How much would he care? If he were to find his betrothal ended – how much would he care? She had sat with his hand in hers, had crooned over him, rocking him in her arms when the pain was sore –

171

but had she been to him just the tender nurse? What in fact – but for that long ago exchange of glances, that long ago touch of the hand – what had he ever said or done that should suggest that it was not Blanche whom in truth he loved? After all, she thought, they were betrothed, he was to have married her . . . He lay back against the pillow, soft scented hay wrapped round with soft scented linen, his aching arm bandaged across his aching chest, fair hair rumpled, brown eyes still clouded, and she crouched beside him, pitying, piteous, weak with mingled hope and dread. 'If you were to find – if you were to find that she *had* after all left you a message . . . ? If you were to find that she'd left behind her in Wales, your diamond betrothal ring . . . ?'

She thought he had fainted. He lay so long silent that she grew frightened, began to stammer out that she couldn't be certain, it was only that the ring hadn't been among the jewels that she . . . She stammered and blundered, remembered the dimly glowing heap in the darkness of the cave on Twm Shon Catti's mountain peak, lit only by its ray of sunlight . . . 'If you were to hear that – that while she was in Wales Blanche hadn't – been wearing your ring . . .'

And he opened his eyes at last and put up his good arm and pulled her down close to him; and she lay across the low bed and held his thin hand against her kisses, all the wild gold floss of her hair spread over it; and burst into a storm of too long dammed-up tears.

She opened up the great subject that very day at the evening meal; sitting in the Fox's place at the head of the long, rough dining-table with the men of the gang, and, stuffing down a great plateful of roast (stolen) mutton, threw her thunderbolt. An agreed price for the ransom to be demanded from the Tregaron family; and an undertaking of – no reprisals.

No reprisals! Dio dropped his knife with a clatter and clutched with his great hands at his thatch of hair. As always his first thought went to his leader. 'Y Cadno could return—'

Sam the Saddle, ever inimical to Dafydd's cause, protested. 'No such promise would be kept. The moment they had him safe—'

'No, no, Sam bach, you don't know these great folk. They have their codes,' said Dio, 'as strict as our own. They pride themselves on their "honour", they'd never break their word.'

' "Extorted under duress".'

'No, Sam, Dio's right,' said Gilda. 'These are people who would – would stake half a fortune, none knows it better than I, upon whether a woman carried this bunch of flowers or that: and pay up without a murmur, though there'd been no bond, no witnesses, nothing but a lightly spoken word. Let them give this promise and you're safe; and the Fox is safe.' She played her ace card. 'Do you want him on the run for ever? What else but this can ever bring him back?'

Dio waited for no more. 'A show of hands on it!'

She watched, exultant, as the arms were raised. 'We'll compose a message today,' she said, wasting no more time. 'Teg the Corn will deal with it from Caio. The money will be sent by return, never fear for that . . .'

And two days later, it came: and the promise with it. They were grouped in the great hall, lounging there, singing; the women on benches, leaning back against the tapestry-hung rock walls, the men sprawled on the floor against their knees, whittling at wooden bowls or spoons or thumb-sticks, as they sang. Outside, the rain fell steadily, the soft grey mist of Welsh valley rain; within, the lovely voices rose, untrained, untaught, but strong and true, the almost universal national heritage. She leapt to her feet, waving the letter. 'What did I tell you? She pays – and promises.'

Half the gold was there; the rest would be paid directly upon the return of Lord Tregaron, safe and sound. 'And that can be tomorrow. I've thought it all out. He's been up out of bed, exercising, getting back his strength. Not fit to ride, but there's the coach that brought me here and the horses – he'll

173

do well enough, being driven. I'd best go with him, lest his wound break down—' voices rose in protest, but she finished hurriedly – 'and will return as soon as he's safely home, bringing the rest of the money, and the coach and horses with me.'

'And your own ransom also, doubtless, in your hand,' suggested Catti. Catti, ever devoted to her leader, still viewed with suspicion, Madam Vixen's feeling for Dafydd of Tregaron.

The men laughed but upheld her. 'No, no, Madam fach, you go not forth upon so silken a tether as that,' said Huw the Harp, grinning.

'Is it my fault if my ransom delays?' An idea came to her. 'If I were to go with Lord Tregaron to his home, might they not advance my share, relying upon me to pay it back to them later?'

'What, the Vixen leave her den?' said Huw Peg Leg, '—and the Fox not here to permit it?'

'Huw's right, Madam Vixen,' said Dio. 'We can't let you go.'

'I've said I'll come back.' She put on an injured look. 'You repay with little trust one who has led you so faithfully and well. Haven't I fought with you, dared with you—?'

'—bled with us,' cried a voice, and the laughter redoubled.

'Well, and risked a worse wounding, I, a woman – do you think I haven't suffered, been in dread, terrified—'

'Come, come, Madam Vixen fach, you've loved every minute of it,' said Dio. 'Don't try to cozen us. You stay here till Y Cadno comes back and says otherwise; which may be soon enough even for you, if he trusts to this promise. Then if he will, he may release you.'

But she knew he would not. Three days ago up in Twm Shon Catti's cave, he had told her to begone, to get out of his life for ever – but she knew that he'd never really let her go. And she had come not unprepared for protests. 'Then let any woman travel with him as attendant, it needn't be me.

Willie-bach will drive the coach and in case of a trap—' she used the word deliberately and with care '– simply leave the coach and horses at the gates, we've no need of them here, these town-bred beasts are no use to us – and make good your escape . . .'

'If the old mother's promised—' began Dio, but they paid no heed to him. She had chosen the right word to use to such wild untamed creatures as these. 'If it's traps,' said Willie-bach, 'someone else may drive him: not I. I put my head into no trap.' There was a rumble of assent among the men. 'There may not be a price on my head as there is on Y Cadno's, but it lies uneasy unless it lies here at the Cwrt. I drive into no traps.'

'Who else then?' They were silent. 'In that case, you'd better let me go as I first suggested.'

'Ay, and never return,' said Dio, laughing. 'As *we* first suggested.'

Blodwen with her scarred cheek came forward from the shadows, moving in her own indolent yet oddly violent way. 'For my part she never need. One vixen is enough for The Fox and I am that one.'

'Then do you drive the coach,' said Gilda, quickly.

'*I* drive?' cried Blodwen, taken aback. 'How could *I* drive four horses?'

'You have but to hold a bunch of reins, fool. Town-bred creatures as they are, they won't stray from the path, when the rest's so stony and rough. And when you come to the castle gates, pull them up there.'

'The lodge keepers—' began Huw Peg-leg.

'They won't molest a woman. Even if the family don't keep to their promise, it's men they want for crimes like these, they won't trouble a woman. Leave coach and horses at the gates and just jump down and walk away,' she said to Blodwen contemptuously. 'It's simple enough.'

'Ay, well simple enough for you. But for me . . .' All her bold brassiness was gone, she moved to Dio's side and standing there, quietly, appealed to something all of them would understand. 'My mother lives in a cottage close by the castle gates. She believes me a decently married woman, living a respectable life far away from here. If she should see me! If she should find how I'm living now—!'

There were sentimental murmurings. 'Poof, you can cover your face, can't you?' said Gilda, exultant, for with every word they played into her hands. 'Wrap yourself in a cloak, wear a hood, have a scarf across your mouth as we do when we ride out...' But she turned away with a scornful shrug of her shoulders. 'What's the use? The truth is, she dare not.'

'*I* dare not?' The women held Blodwen back. Gilda glanced at her once, at the terrible scar, at the ring on her own finger. She repeated: 'You dare not.'

'Others know me if you don't,' said Blodwen sullenly. 'There's nothing I don't dare.'

'That's what I've been told. We shall see how you prove it,' said Gilda sweetly, 'when the time comes...'

And when the time came – sure enough, Blodwen was there. Willie brought out the coach and four on to the forecourt, Madam Vixen appeared, his lordship walking shakily, leaning on her arm, Blod the Bruises on his other side. He took a courteous if somewhat ironical farewell of the gang, lined up to see him go, and was helped up into the coach. Gilda stood in its doorway; he bent over her hand and kissed it gratefully. 'He drives away very cheerfully, however,' she remarked to Dio stepping back among the men, 'leaving me to your tender mercies! I seem to have found more chivalry among villains like you, than with my own fine gentlemen.' And she called to Willie, still up on the box, to take the coach down on to the pathway, get the horses settled, so that Blodwen would have not too much trouble with them. 'If she makes an appearance,' she added scornfully, 'which I begin to doubt. Where is she?'

'Catti, Eirwen – go find her!'

'No,' said Gilda, grimly. 'I'll go! She'll not come for

Catti and Eirwen; but she'll come for me!' While Willie eased the coach horses off the rough ground and on to the hardly less rough going of the stony and pitted path that led to the forest road, she strode off back into the fortress and soon a shrill screaming was heard and Blodwen came running out, wrapped in a hooded cloak, a scarf about her mouth and nose, with the red scar bright against the brown cheek showing above it: looking back fearfully over her shoulder, running out and across the foreground, cursing and muttering in Welsh and all the time looking backwards as she ran. Willie jumped down from the box and gave her a heave and a shove that landed her into the driving seat and she gathered up the reins into a bundle and caught up the tall whip in an evidently trembling hand. The horses, fresh from their too long inactivity, went off at a frisking pace, dragging the coach, rather dangerously rocking, after them. In the entrance to the fortress, a slim figure appeared as they all ran, cheering, after the vehicle, and waved and stood there watching and turned back, into the hall. The mob ran a little way, were out-distanced by the almost stampeding horses, stood and waved and laughed and cheered, and strolled back as a corner was turned and the coach out of sight.

And the dark hood fell back; and the golden hair tumbled all about her face as she turned, hands light on the reins, and called back triumphantly: 'We're free!'

CHAPTER THIRTEEN

It was a cold, grey day. A veil of rain had begun to fall, the fine, thin drizzle that lies like a silver veil over the valleys of south Wales – laying its soft hand on her upturned face, washing away the red paint of poor Blodwen's 'scar', drenching the soft, golden floss of her hair, fallen free from the disguising hood. She tugged the four horses this way and that, reciting the rhythm as taught by Willie-bach to Blodwen, and religiously dinned by herself into ears unaccustomed to lessons. By now Blodwen would have been found. By now they would be asking, 'Where's Madam Vixen?', would have been answered by Jenny that she must be in her own room, the door was barred and (which was true enough) she made no answer to any appeal; with a hint that perhaps her ladyship had been a little more upset by his lordship's departure than she had pretended ... (Had not even gone to watch him drive off; she, Jenny, had stood for a moment in the doorway, watching, and when she turned back – Madam Vixen had disappeared.) So they would have 'left her to herself' – until they came upon Blodwen, tied and gagged – not very painfully, however – and locked away into a larder – full of the horrors she had suffered, suddenly set upon and bundled into that terrible place ... Blodwen had been very ready to enter into a scheme without danger to herself, which would rid her for ever of her rival.

And it would be for ever. She may have him and with all

my heart, thought Gilda, slapping the wet reins on the steaming haunches, lifting her face, ecstatic, to the silver rain – I am free for ever of Gareth y Cadno and the Court of Foxes.

They came to a main road and so to a village; to the great gates of wrought iron with a gilded coat of arms. A man came out of the lodge and stared without much welcome at the un-crested coach and its four post horses – those same horses which the pretended Lord Tregaron, unable to produce the family equippage, had hired to pull the shabby coach on the pretext that so unimposing an outfit would deceive observers in London, and further give them greater safety from the wicked footpads that haunted the roads between Hanover Square and Wales.

She jumped down from the box, one foot to the rim of the wheel, one to a spoke – made a quick pretence to be in difficulties – (I must, I *must* learn again how to behave like a lady!) The man came uncertainly forward. She cried out: 'It's my lord! It's the Earl! I have brought him back!' and fell into a graceful swoon, just not too soon but that the lodge-keeper had time to catch and support her.

'My lord! It's his lordship!' Other men came running out, flung open the doors of the coach. 'He's here – it's true! Oh, my lord, are you sick? – come quick, he's a-fainting!' She came to herself pretty smartly at that and rushed back to him; but it was only a faint, if a genuine one this time, reaction probably from the excitement and unaccustomed exertion. She climbed in with him. 'Send someone running up to the house with the news, and then let the coach follow – put a man up to drive it very slowly, very carefully...' And she sat there cradling him in her arms while they rumbled up the long driveway. 'You're home and safe, my dearest. Just one effort more and the long trial will be ended.'

An old woman stood at the entrance doorway, awaiting them: an old woman, not fat but enormously broad in the hips, with a small head, like a cherry perched on top of a cottage loaf: dressed in some dark stuff, a sober country magnificence that paid no tribute whatsoever to comfort. Behind her shoulder, leaning eagerly forward like a dog on the leash, yet held in by habitual control, stood a tall young woman, heavy as a lad, with a plain face above her quiet but splendid dress, a big nose and a sad, straight mouth. They said nothing, made no outcry; only stood tense and anxious as he was lifted out and carried up the wide flight of shallow steps past them as they stood there and into the great, pillared marbled hall. Gilda, following, stood unattended while they went to him, saw him laid on a couch, sent footmen and maidservants scurrying for rugs, cushions, restoratives. He must have opened his eyes and said something for after a few moments the Countess, seated erect on a chair at his side, said sharply: 'Where?' and both women turned round and looked at her, stared and looked away. For a moment she thought that the younger made an attempt to rise and come to her, but the mother restrained her. 'Leave her, she shall have attention later.' And then, evidently in reply to a further word from her son: 'Yes, yes, every attention. But first we must get you to your room, you must have doctors . . .'

Gilda stood quietly watching them; watching him carried away out of her sight. After a while a footman appeared with a tray of wine and biscuits, placed a chair for her. The old woman came to her there, marching across the marble floor, pudgy yet oddly stately. 'Well, now young woman . . .' She stopped and stared anew. 'Have I seen you somewhere before?'

Only as I hung upside-down peering in at the window of your coach, thought Gilda. Aloud she said: 'Hardly possible, I think?'

'And your voice . . . Well, never mind all that. I understand from my son that you have been in some sort instrumental in effecting his escape?'

'In so far as I stole a coach and four horses from these desperadoes, Madam, got him into it – sick and helpless as you see him – and single-handed drove it here, all at the risk of my own life – why, yes, I think you may say that I was in some sort "instrumental".' I must be modest and lady-like, she thought, and not make an enemy of her; but how can I while she stands here so safe and smug and talks to me of 'instrumental'? She took a small revenge. 'Your ladyship has received a message – and given an undertaking?'

'I have been the victim of insolent threats through the danger to my son.' It did not apparently occur to her that since her son had been 'rescued' and not delivered over to her by the gang, the undertaking no longer held. She was doubtless too much concerned in getting rid of her unwelcome guest. 'Come – I need no longer detain you. You had better be dried and have your wet clothes attended to; and then you shall be given food and drink, sufficiently rewarded for your trouble – my steward shall see to it – and you may then be conducted to any place you care to name, by what means you choose.'

She stood there in the huge, dim hall; in her bedraggled cloak over Blodwen's bright, tawdry dress, the hood pushed back and the golden floss of her hair hanging about her neck in dark streaks, her face half obscured by the red smears of the rubbed-away 'scar'. She said: 'I thank you, Madam. The other favours I will with your permission refuse, including the sufficient reward. As to safe conduct – why then, you may send me home if you will to my house and establishment of servants in South Audley Street, not far from your ladyship's own mansion in Hanover Square.' As the old woman goggled, for one moment at least at a loss, she added: 'It behoves a lady to recognise another, even under such guise as this.'

The Countess started again: stared at her anew. 'I know now who you are! You're the woman Blanche told us about: who was there when—'

'When your eldest son died, Madam, who died in my arms – not hers, for she sat shrieking in her carriage afraid to put out her coward head.'

'It was you who – who stripped her half naked, tore her

jewels from her and flung them into the road for her to stoop and pick up—'

'She and her woman must tell tales to account for their behaviour on that night. The fact is that she offered me her gew-gaws if I would not ask her to remove her petticoats – which same undergarments I needed only to staunch your son's wounds; who, but for such help, must certainly have bled to death. True I flung her jewels in the dirt; if she picked them up I know not, I was too busy in attendance upon your sons, Madam, the dying and the dead. And while she crept back to safety and drove off, leaving them there,' cried Gilda triumphantly, 'I who had stumbled upon this affair in my attempt to get away from my captors, turned back and went with them into their stronghold again – only so that I might attend upon his lordship. Whom now I have for the second time rescued and so bring back to you.' And, flown to heights of oratory by this picture of herself, so splendid and now, in her explanations to David so oft-repeated that she almost believed it herself, she concluded: 'I have lost much in these past weeks, my lady, including something of missishness, perhaps, and some of my dignity, no doubt; and a great deal, I fear, of my pretty little, lady-like ways – but I have lost them in his service. But one thing I retain, one title I retain – and that title I share, that title I have in common with you, my lady Countess. For to you, but also to me, Madam – the present Earl of Tregaron owes his life.'

The daughter came down the stairway; David's sister – came running down when she saw the great doors opening and the small figure, head up, marching in deeply offended dignity, out of the house. 'Mother! My lady! – for God's sake, stop her!' And she ran after Gilda and turned her – by no means unwilling though she put up so pretty a pretence of dignified refusal – and brought her back into the hall. 'David has told me – he owes so much to you, we all owe so much to you! Mother, this poor lady – nothing should be too much for us to offer her, no thanks too deep, no honour too great for

182

her . . .' And she added in tones in which awe now was added to tenderness and gratitude, a plea which she doubtless felt her mother could hardly resist. 'In another country, she is a marchioness.'

The Countess of Tregaron, it transpired however, thought on the whole but lowly of foreign titles. 'Who *was* this Marchese d'Astonia, I know nothing of any such family?' His relict now sat at her table nevertheless: slightly comic but totally exquisite in a gown of the huge Lady Anne's, tied and tucked up and in some sort made wearable; and was altogether made much of in obedience to very imperative commands from the sickroom. 'D'Astonia Subeggio? *I* never heard of the name.'

'The owner existed, however, without your ladyship's permission,' said Gilda. Let them but get through the next week or two and she would be back in her Bijou and David her lover – and never more than that, thank God! – so really after all there was no need to accept these gratuitous insults. 'I should know, I suppose, for he married me.'

'Evidently surviving his marriage but a short time,' said the Countess, looking her insolently up and down.

'Your ladyship's husband was less fortunate,' said Gilda; but this time had the cowardice to drop her voice a little and when challenged refused to repeat herself. She embarked upon one of her little impromptus, to forestall further questioning as to her antecedents. 'My husband had been my guardian. My father, the younger son of a great house had been killed with my mother in a driving accident, while visiting their friend in Italy – I, a small child, alone surviving. He took me into his home and thereafter made me his daughter. And if your ladyship asks me what was my father's family or my mother's, I regret I can supply you with but very little information – even if it were your right to demand it. I knew myself only as Marigelda – it was his wish to make me all his own, first as his foster-child, then as his bride; and then, all too soon, his widow.'

'A love child, evidently,' said the old woman, rich in insolence; as though to herself.

'Like Gareth the highwayman,' said Gilda; as though to *her*self.

The Countess shot up out of her chair as though she had been stung and without ceremony led the way up to where David, ever protesting his return to almost normal strength, sat cosseted in a chair in the drawing-room. He had been kept very much to his room and therefore knew nothing, presumably, of the situation obtaining downstairs. Now, confronted by his mother in a towering rage, he looked up in astonishment. 'David! You insist that you are now quite well again. Nothing keeps this – lady – here but your demand that she remain in the house until you are recovered.' He struggled up to his feet, casting aside the swaddling rugs, but she beat down his protestations. 'She may have what assistance she requires in her return to London where she claims to have an establishment – and "establishment" may well be the word,' raged Madam Countess, speaking a little more truly than she knew. 'For the rest, my hospitality is exhausted. I must ask her to go.'

He was paralysed with horror. His sister threw herself upon her knees at her mother's feet. 'Mother, dear Madam, reflect – she saved David's life!'

'So she never tires of reminding us,' said the Countess, giving her daughter a yank to bring her up to her feet, which however had only the effect of toppling her ludicrously to her hands and knees. 'If what she wants is a reward, she shall have it. But she must go.'

David made a gesture for silence, almost frightening in its chill command. He spoke quietly and calmly, but Gilda saw that his hand was shaking, and she looked up into his face and saw there, suddenly, a dark and terrible rage. Gone was the gentle look, the sweetness, the tender smilingness;

184

his jaw was set, his mouth rigid, his whole fair face now dark with anger. So had she seen Gareth y Cadno look, who had the same blood in him. But where the Fox would have sworn, laid about him with flashing eyes and words of black fury, David said with a cold control: 'Have a care, Madam! You are speaking of the woman I love.'

'Love?' cried the Countess; and 'Love?' cried poor Anne, struggling up off her knees. 'You can't love her, David! What about Blanche?'

'What about her?' he said, turning swiftly, fear in his eyes. 'Our betrothal is ended.' And he swung round upon Gilda. 'You told me—'

She faltered: 'The ring. She hadn't taken with her to London her betrothal ring. She'd left it—'

'She had left it with me, lest it fall into the hands of such creatures as you have consorted with,' said the Countess. And suddenly she stiffened, her face grew grey with something almost like terror. 'How do you know? How do you know that Blanche didn't take her ring?' And she swung round upon David. 'She was robbed of all the rest by that murdering villain, riding alone. And by a woman...' Again the look of fear came into her eyes. 'David – for God's sake – you say you love this woman—'

For once she could speak the truth. 'Do you suggest it was I?' cried Gilda, high in indignation. 'I have explained it all to you a hundred times, how I was held to ransom, how in trying to escape I came to the scene of the hold-up of the coach; how for your son's sake I went back with him to the Court. How could I be working with these people? David knows—'

But David was not listening. He said heavily: 'Then it was a mistake? My engagement with Blanche still stands?'

'And you are bound to her in honour,' said the old woman. 'In honour.' She gathered up her skirts in her two fat hands and motioned with her head for her daughter to follow her and so waddled, with her own odd and oddly touching dignity,

185

to the door. There she turned. 'You are Earl of Tregaron now, David, head of a great family with all the imperative duties that position must bring. And betrothed to a virtuous woman of noble birth. What you will do about this – embarrassment—' she waved a pudgy hand towards Gilda – 'is a man's problem which I leave to you to resolve. My advice is to take your farewells of her immediately and let her go.' And she came forward a little into the room and said, for a moment almost appealingly: 'You are your brother's heir, David. Ask yourself what he would have done.'

'And your father's heir,' said Gilda. 'Ask yourself what *he* would have done.' And she laughed out loud and curtseyed deeply to the two backs, one squat, one tall and ungainly, that hurried off, scandalised, resentful, down the corridor away from them. 'You are not free, David,' she said, 'and neither am I. But don't you see that it's just that, that gives us our liberty?' And her mind swam and her eyes grew dim and she fell in a dead faint into his outstretched arms.

CHAPTER FOURTEEN

And so Marigelda came back to the Bijou, turfed the house-keeper out of the frilly white bedroom – which, in her absence, Mrs Brown had thought it only reasonable to appropriate to herself – and settled down at last to a life of un-wedded bliss. The dreaded explanations had after all proved easy. The Earl of Trove, delicately approached, had proved adamant in keeping Lord Tregaron to his bargain – and he was so enraptured at finding that after all he might eat his cake and keep it, that he was only too happy to accept any account his poor innocent angel might give him, of her unfortunate espousals: (she told him all about the struggle she had had, finding herself deceived and betrayed, to keep the marriage one in name only.) The ravening wolves also were a little, though only a little, explained; he was delighted – seeing in their intransigence, an opportunity to provide for her entirely, as though she were indeed his wife. All that money could buy – since his name, alas! might be neither offered nor accepted – could at least be lavished upon her. She clung to her house; but some more furniture and redecoration upstairs would be charming; a whole trousseau replaced the white dress and widow's weeds; now rifled coachloads of jewels could not have outshone her own. Her housekeeper and the page most fortunately were still available. A little gilded phaeton for afternoon drives round the park, wrapped in luxurious furs, completed the fulfilment of her dreams; a box at the playhouse was not among them, her enthusiasm for the drama having unaccountably waned.

November, December. Upstairs in the once shabby 'housekeeper's room' they gathered as so often they had before; so long ago as it seemed, though it was but half a year since first they had come there. She perched on George's knee, as of old, in the close, happy, family way, Mrs Brown making chocolate, little Jake handing round the cups; he had been sent running to summon her brothers, now established, with the secret help of her inexhaustible pin-money, in various positions of their own choosing. 'How delicious it is to be here! I used to think of it so often, down at the Cwrt, and long for it – to see you all and talk and laugh and just be together again.'

'To have been through so much,' said Mrs Brown, fondly, 'and come out of it all unmarked!'

'Unmarked! Don't believe it! – you should see the great scar on my backside—'

'—and with her language so refined,' said Rufus.

'If you'd heard the language *I* have!' And for a moment she was back with them, riding the road, cursing with the best of them, half in English, half in incomprehensible Welsh. 'It was fun! Sometimes it was frightening, much of the time I was worried, anxious about David; but – even when I was scared out of my wits there was something exciting about it, something thrilling. And when you'd succeeded and were riding back with your pockets full of treasure . . . !'

'Tell again about the Black Toby, Gilda, how you took the farmer's money from him at pistol point—!'

'Now, Jakey, you think too much of all this adventure. It was necessary; but only for a little while. I wouldn't have you mixed up in it for all the gold in England.' She obliged all the same with a suitably edited version. 'There he stood: I could see his blue eyes glittering through his mask . . .' But not a word, never a word of all this to David! she adjured them for the hundredth time.

'He really believes you sat there mum all that time and came away unscathed?'

'Unscathed – so I did. Not mum, perhaps; but none dared lay a finger on me. I was the Vixen.'

The Vixen: a creature of the wilds, slinking along the moonlit roads after its prey, predatory, ruthless; fighting and scratching among its own sex, tumbled in its lair and out, by such males as sought it and not always of its own will ... And yet – she had struggled, had conquered: a woman, alone, she had used her wit and her courage to subdue at last a gang of men, lawless and dangerous, ugly and violent; and to trick them in the end. 'You seem almost proud of it,' said Bess, watching the great eyes kindle in the lovely young, soft, sweet face; and, 'I am proud of it in a way,' she had to admit. And after all, it had all been for David.

'You and your David! Do you remember, Gilda, how you said you should spend more time in the family arms than in the family carriage? You've made that one good, at least. Three Earls of Tregaron: one false, and you married him, one true and you buried him, one new and you—'

'Love him,' said Gilda.

'Yet you're complacent as to this marriage of his ...' Lord Tregaron had been called down to Wales for discussions on his forthcoming wedding.

'I've told you a thousand times, Mother – he is head of the family, he must marry. And better after all this Blanche whom he hates already – or at any rate resents, upon my account – than someone else whom he might like a little.'

'I still think you should make some effort to divorce this husband of yours; deception, coercion, whatever grounds you choose to bring forward ...'

'I expect he'll soon die,' said Jake, 'and then you'll be free anyhow. He told me himself that a highwayman's life is a short one. Isaac Darkin died when he was twenty, did you know that? And McClaine at twenty-six and he's most famous of all. He said he'd already overstayed his time – the Fox said so, I mean. I hope he doesn't die,' he added, 'because I liked him very much; and I hope you don't divorce him, Gilda, because fancy me being brother-in-law to such a great highwayman as he is! But I daresay he will and then if you've put off his lordship from marrying this Blanche, you can marry him yourself.'

'I don't *want* to marry him,' said Gilda. 'You haven't seen that old woman!'

'You'd be mistress then,' said Mrs Brown, 'and might bring her to heel.'

'I'd rather be mistress in the other sense and have no truck with her at all. You don't know these great establishments – I couldn't live in them. Conducted from room to room as though you didn't know your way about, every mouthful watched lest, I suppose, you grow weary of chewing and need someone to do it for you. And the beds! – four great posts as high as two floors of this house, with feathers at the top as though you lay in a catafalque...'

'If Tregaron should leave you, Gilda, and without provision...'

'There are other men in the sea,' said her mother.

'Not for me. But he'll never leave me,' said Gilda. 'And besides...' She did not say what 'besides' and only when David came back, with her white arms about his neck and her silky gold head against his heart, told him that she thought – she was almost sure now – that she was going to have a baby.

He was beside himself with joy; would have sent for half the physicians in town to certify to the fact and stand guard over his burgeoning darling... 'Dearest, nonsense! My M – my housekeeper sent for a doctor and he simply laughed at me for being so eager and told me to send for him again when I had more reason. And so I shall – for him. I want none of your great family physicians running back with tales to your mother. But tell me you're happy!'

He was happy; but it redoubled his wretchedness about his

190

approaching marriage. 'This child will be my heir; my real heir.'

'Perhaps it'll be a girl,' said Gilda comfortably.

'But if it's a boy—'

'Then it'll be no worse off than Gareth y Cadno; who, no one denies, was in fact your father's eldest son.'

'My father could do nothing to acknowledge it; and neither shall I be able to. If only Blanche's father—'

'Whatever the Earl of Trove does, I'm still married to the Fox.' She put her arms about his neck again. 'I'm happy as I am, dearest, I wish nothing different. Our child shall be just our child; I don't ask a great name and position for any babe of mine. Let Blanche's children grab all that, and for my part welcome.'

'It's not her fault,' he said, rather miserably. 'Her father insists; my mother has told him the whole story and they two agree that, for everyone's sake, the marriage must go forward. And having given my word – as a man of honour, what can I do?'

'No one wants you to do anything, David. While you still love me, I ask for nothing more. I know you will always look after me and our child – our children, perhaps . . .'

'I'll have a settlement drawn up, Gilda, straight away . . .' She murmured a word about the ravening wolves, but he ignored it. 'With the child coming—'

'We don't even know for certain that it is coming,' said Gilda, laughing.

'I shall tell my mother,' he said. 'Perhaps if the Earl of Trove knows of this . . .'

But the Earl of Trove thought an illegitimate brat, begot upon the run-away wife of a common highwayman, need interfere not at all in the plans of his august daughter; and the Countess only requested, frigidly, that her son keep his present disgraceful situation as free as possible from public gossip. 'And this I must do,' he said to Gilda. 'She is after all an innocent girl, her father made up the marriage and

191

persists in the arrangements – she plays only a passive part. And if she's to be my – if she's to be Countess of Tregaron—'

'If she's to be your wife,' said Gilda, firmly, 'you want no scandal to touch her. Of course, my love; of course it mustn't. I care not two pins what happens to Mistress Blanche herself, silly, stuck-up, whey-faced prude that she is – or rather I wish her nothing but ill: a woman who despises *me*, yet will take a man unwilling to have her, a man in love with another, fresh from that other one's bed; will accept a husband forcing himself to some sort of passion to get her with an heir – and so go off back to that other ... But what happens to your wife happens to you, and as such of course she must be protected; and she shall be ...'

And she kept herself, indeed, very circumspectly as the weeks and months passed, while the marriage plans went forward: the Marchesa d'Astonia Subeggio – forgotten now even by the gay gallants of her theatre-going days (who for a little while besieged her house but soon were discouraged out of existence). She went out very little; now and again she drove in the park but with only her mother at her side – she knew no women and must entertain no men. It was all a trifle dull. 'We were more free to amuse ourselves, Jake and I,' said her mother fretfully, as they drove in the carriage one day, 'before you came back from Wales.'

'Perhaps you'd rather I went back there and left you in sole enjoyment of my house and possessions?'

'I only remark that life is not much fun, my dear. There's no need to be unkind.'

'Well – it isn't perhaps. I seem fated,' said Gilda, 'to dull respectability.'

'*You* have your lover; I daresay it's not dull when he's here. But when he's married and you have even less of his company—'

'We shall have to make do with that of the baby,' said Gilda. She added crossly: 'And the sooner the better.'

The sooner the better. Her frame was too slight and small

for comfortable child-bearing, already the infant seemed disagreeably obtrusive. July was the month decreed by the doctor for its birth. David had pushed forward his marriage to June so as to have his wife sufficiently established in her new position and various great houses, to be left to her own resources. 'After that – well, she takes me with her eyes open, I haven't deceived her. She'll have to be content with only half a marriage. I must be free to be with you, my dearest, all the time of your confinement...'

February passed and they were into March. The Earl had brought his daughter to London, preparations were going forward for an elaborate ceremony: royalty itself would be present – (Gilda remembered Y Cadno's reluctance to proceed with *their* marriage without the presence of his intimate friend the Prince of Wales, and burst into one of her nowadays rare fits of giggling.) The Countess and Lady Anne were now installed in Hanover Square, and were much received at court – for which their ugliness and dullness, said Gilda in the bosom of her family, exactly suited them. Not but what poor Anne had been a kindly creature enough and only in such abject fear of her mother as to make her of no account. 'They're taking the opportunity to try and get her settled in life, while all this business of her brother's wedding goes forward. David says his mother is angling for Lord Crum – you remember him, Mother? Last summer he was sending me bouquets by the cartload.'

'He never paid for them; but Bess palmed off the most faded on him and he never observed it – he's as blind as a bat.'

'No doubt that's why the Countess has lit upon him,' said Gilda more cheerfully. 'He won't see what a bargain he's got with poor great gawky Anne.'

'Surely Lord Tregaron won't permit it? She's but sixteen.'

'No, indeed. Anne, it seems, laughs at his poor little lordship, privately when she and David are together; which shows more fun in her than I ever imagined. He's told her to

193

resist, but the old Countess persists. Till she has both her children settled in misery, I suppose she'll never rest happy. She's making up a party this very night, David told me, for Ranelagh: dear Blanche and her father and some others and Anne and little Crum. David, of course, won't be there.' He had gone off on a brief visit to the continent to conclude the business interrupted by his mother's hasty return at the time of his capture and his brother's death.

'To Ranelagh! How long is it, Gilda, since I was at Ranelagh! In the old days, indeed, before I married your poor father ... Well, well!' Mrs Brown broke off, sighing. 'And you've never been there at all?'

'No, never, and I do long to see it. But first I was the unattainable great lady and mustn't be seen anywhere, and now I'm exactly the other thing and once again mustn't be seen anywhere. The truth is, Mother dear,' said Gilda laughing, 'that between us we've muffed the whole business. Other doxies flaunt their triumphs, go everywhere, their lives are the gayest of the gay; but here am I, neither fish nor flesh nor fowl nor good red herring.' Well, flesh, perhaps, she amended, laughing again, ruefully; but even that must be subdued, kept hidden away in this little house from the eyes of all but her belovéd. And anyway, nowadays there was a great deal too much of it. 'It will have to be a wonderful child, that's all, to be worth this great belly.'

'You'll be a deal greater than that before the end,' said Mrs Brown complacently. But her mind was still on Ranelagh. 'Could we not go down there, Marigold, and quiz them? Just for the fun of it: life will get ever more dull as the baby comes nearer – this may be our last chance.'

'Go where and quiz whom? And for heaven's sake, Mother,' said Gilda automatically, 'don't call me Marigold!'

'Why to Ranelagh, child, and quiz little Crum and the old Countess.'

'Quiz—! Mother, you must be mad!' But her eyes had begun to shine, she bit on her knuckle to stifle the naughty

194

laughter. 'If we went up to the gallery... If we wrapped ourselves in cloaks and veils...' And she struggled to her feet. 'Let's do it! I'm sick of sitting twiddling my thumbs and if I get any bigger, even that will soon be denied me. Call Jake, send him for my brothers, as many as will come with us.' And she was rushing off downstairs, big belly and all, rootling through her clothes-press for suitable apparel. By the time James and George arrived, indeed, she had reached a little more discretion and proposed instead of Ranelagh a visit to Marylebone, but her brothers refused it. 'To Ranelagh or nowhere. The Jew's Harp is no place for women of quality these days.'

'Well, Vauxhall then?'

'Vauxhall will be too chilly, especially for you in your condition. At Ranelagh they have great fires in the Rotunda, it's as warm as summer. We'll go there or not go at all.'

'But if the old woman is there and Blanche and Anne—'

'Why, that's the very reason we go,' protested Mrs Brown and, the coach having come to the door, they hustled her in. 'You will promise,' she implored them, 'to be utterly discreet? You won't betray me? I gave my word to David.'

'How could they ever see us? We'll stay up in the gallery, where such great ones as they never come; they'll have bespoken a table down below, by the fire.' And there would be huge crowds, promised Mrs Brown, it would be a marvel if in fact they ever glimpsed the Tregaron party, though they looked out for them. 'You'll never believe till you see them, Gilda, how many people! All the height of the mode in their gayest clothes, walking about laughing and chattering or sitting at the tables having supper... And the lights, a myriad lights like fireflies, even outside in the gardens – but of course that would be in the summer...'

And in fact the gardens were deserted, only a few flames flickering bravely in their glass chimneys, a few braziers glowing in the alcoves where none but those most earnestly in search of seclusion would venture. But within the huge circular hall of the Rotunda, it was indeed as George had promised 'warm as summer'. The place was like an inverted bowl, supported by four central pillars and these enclosed a great chimney, with furnaces facing in four directions so that all areas of the hall were heated. All round the room, tucked under the balcony which encircled it, were alcoves where supper parties were already in progress; in the gallery above, more tables were laid, with waiters running urgently to and fro. They peered over the parapet. 'You may recognise the Countess by a great head of flowers and feathers – David was telling me about it, she's worn it a week now without disturbing it, sleeps with her neck on a block. A year out of fashion, heads are much smaller now; but her ladyship's above la mode, of course; makes poor Anne sport one too, who's six foot high already ... And there,' cried Gilda, excitedly pointing, 'there they are, the supper table close by the fire! Trust her ladyship to place them where the girls' faces will turn red as turkey-cocks from the heat! – and their feathers in danger of being set alight every time they turn their silly heads ...'

They found a table with an excellent view of the party and ordered supper, Gilda throwing back her cloak but careful to keep the black veil safely about that too recognisable flame of hair. 'It must be admitted,' said James, 'that she's very lovely.'

'Who, the Countess?'

'Oh, yes, of course, the Countess; and the Lady Anne too. But I meant the Lady Blanche, my dear sister; who is a beauty after all and you must admit it.'

'Of course I admit it. Why not? – as long as David thinks me prettier.'

'And so you are prettier, a thousand times prettier.' James put out a hand and took his sister's chin, turning the lovely face towards him. 'Your skin is so white and fine, it's like the finest lawn, so that one may see the colour come and go beneath it. Hers is magnificent, but it's like linen, a dead, matt white. And her face is almost perfect but with a cool

196

perfection; in this little mug of yours, the feeling comes and goes, like the colour, without concealment. As for your hair...' He pushed back the heavy veil to catch a glimpse of it for comparison. 'She's clever to wear no powder and it takes some courage I dare say when most of the rest of the world is like a flour-bag; but that chilly moonlight gilt is no match for our sunshine and marigolds . . .'

She laughed, freeing herself from his hand. 'Thank you, brother, you wax lyrical in my defence; but meanwhile you disorder my sunshine and marigolds which are already pulled awry by this wretched shawl.' And by the same token, she added, moving back for the waiter to place the first plates before them, what thought they of the Countess's coiffure? *There's* powder enough to bake a cake with! A whole ostrich farm must have gone to the feathers alone. And as for poor Anne—'

'I agree with you, one backward toss of her head and she'll be ablaze. What a piece of nonsense to crown the poor girl with!'

'And you were right about her face,' said Jake. 'Already it's scarlet.'

'That's because of little Crum. Do see, Mother, how he must lean over half backwards to look up at her!'

Below them, the Tregaron party sat at a long table, her ladyship in black with a hoop far too large for the present fashion and a great deal of jet spangling. The wretched Anne sat with her back to the fire, her white silk dress and sac also not quite up to date, hoop too large and too oval, hair dressed too high; and from her height looked down upon Lord Crum who was evidently trying hard to please. Lady Anne no doubt would have a fortune and his lordship needed money; and could offer a good name and future prospects in return. Gilda saw to her great amusement that the Countess had placed these two on one side of the table, a little apart from the rest of the company; Blanche and her stout father sat with herself and two or three others, opposite. Blanche looked as James had said, very cold – cold and proud. 'She was a deal less haughty as she hopped in her pantaloons about a muddy road in the moonlight,' said Gilda, laughing at the memory of it. 'And scrambled for her trinkets in the dirt – which after all Y Cadno took off her later at the drovers' inn.'

'Gilda, for shame! – there's nothing to be proud of in these disgraceful adventures with that vile highwayman. You needn't repeat them for all the world to hear.'

'I repeat them for only my family to hear. And as for being proud of them – it was all for David.'

'That's an oft-heard story. For my part,' said James, 'I believe you enjoyed every minute of it.'

'Some parts of it I did, at any rate,' said Gilda, looking mockingly down upon the Lady Blanche.

'And yet nowadays you loyally protect her.'

'That also is for David. How could he go through this wedding, begin a new life with her, if all the world knew of his liaison with me? In a year or two, yes – a man having married a wife and established a nursery, grows tired of monogamy and takes to himself a mistress: this is common practice. But to do it while this marriage was actually going forward, would be a little too cynical and therefore we must protect him and, incidentally, her also.' She leaned further over to watch the supper party at the fireside. 'Lord Crum grows desperate, he is turning to the bottle to support him.'

Below them the hall was now filled to overflowing. The cold March night had driven all amusement seekers to Ranelagh, which was known to be the best heated of the pleasure gardens – and indeed at this moment a footman was making the rounds of the four furnaces, throwing more wood upon the heaped embers, built up high in the central pillar. In the alcoves beneath the balcony, all the tables were crowded; it was probably only the uninviting dignity of the Countess of Tregaron and her party that had prevented others from requesting a share of their table. As it was, the mob jostled against them, pressing them nearer the fire and Gilda's hand gripped the edge of the balcony in a suddenly more serious anxiety, as Anne moved her head back away from Lord Crum's increasing importunity, and her tower of feathers came within really perilous distance of the newly leaping flames. She said uneasily, 'Someone ought to warn her. Doesn't that silly old woman see that there's a real danger? But no, she's intent upon keeping Blanche and her precious father occupied, so that his lordship may press his suit.'

'Mightn't James or George go down?' suggested her mother, 'and as though in passing, casually give a word of warning. No one knows them. Or send little Jake to do it.'

'Yes, yes, I'll go,' said Jake, all ready for any activity.

'Very well then, Jakey; for certainly none of them can recognise you. Pretend to be passing by and in doing so lean forward and say only, "The lady should beware of her head-dress; it's too near the fire," or some such words as that; and then immediately return here.' He scuttled off gaily and they watched him worm his way through the mob and with a somewhat overdone nonchalance, approach the table. Others in the gallery had observed, from this better vantage point, the danger to the feathers and there were small gasps of thankfulness as, too indifferent to do anything about it themselves, they saw that the matter was in hand. 'The young lady appears to be in some small peril,' said Sam to those nearest, disclaiming acquaintance with the party,' and her friends too much occupied to observe it. I've sent the boy to warn them.'

Lord Crum had by now sidled close to Lady Anne and was trying to take her hand; she was moving away from him along the bench, her head held back as though his presence was actually physically offensive. Gilda's fingers clutched at the wooden edge of the balcony as she bent over anxiously, watching her little brother; in a moment he might be too late. She saw him approach the Countess who was leaning forward in earnest converse with Lord Trove, and put out a timid hand to attract their attention. The old woman, afraid perhaps of being accosted by one of the vulgar mob, moved back sharply. At her movement, Anne, head still flung back away from Lord Crum's importunings, swung sharply in her mother's direction and Gilda leapt to her feet, leaning far out over the balcony and cried out, above the noise of the chattering throng: 'Anne! Lady Anne! Your feathers . . . !'

Jake took one startled look up at his sister, a second at the Lady Anne – and leapt forward and seized the singeing feathers in his small bare hands. Throughout the crowd a sudden silence fell and they all craned to see what was happening, staring up at the balcony.

She took no notice of it. 'Madam! Countess! Look to your daughter, quick, she's in danger!' The Countess turned to glance round and her brothers seized Gilda by the arms. 'It's over now, she's safe; quick, come away before they recognise you!' But the old woman had turned back and was staring up again. Behind her Lady Anne had collapsed upon the bench beneath the crumpled mass of real hair, horse hair, powder, flowers and feathers to which Jake had succeeded in reducing it. Lord Crum was staring owlishly, but the beginnings of a snigger were building up in him; Jake standing back abashed at so great a ruin for so small a cause – for there was a light smell of scorching and no more. He stammered: 'She sent me – Gilda sent me . . . She thought . . . I thought the lady was on fire . . .'

'Gilda?' cried the Countess. 'So that's it! I thought I had known her!' She stared up at the balcony, black with rage. '*You* sent him!' And the boy called up anxiously, holding out his stinging hands: 'I thought she was on fire, Gilda.'

'So she would have been,' said Gilda, leaning over to call down to him, lovingly. 'You did quite right, you were very brave. One more second and she'd have been ablaze.'

'Fiddlesticks!' cried the old woman. 'There was no danger, none at all.' She carried an ebony stick, silver-handled, and now whacked it down upon the table, making the glass and china jump and ring. 'The whole thing has been a plot, a plot to come here and insult us, to mortify me, to mortify my daughter, to mortify Lady Blanche . . .' The Earl of Trove muttered at her shoulder, beseeching discretion perhaps, but she had seen the crushed headdress, the poor plain face streaked with powder and tears, the incipient grin on the face of little Crum – not only a coiffure had been lost that night – and she was beyond control. 'Why is she here, why should she come where her very presence is an insult? – and with Lord Tregaron not here to defend us as she too well knows, strumpet as she is!'

Gilda's white fingers gripped the wooden ledge, she freed her arms from the grip of her brothers' hands. 'Well for you that he's not, Madam, to hear you speak to me so! How dare you accuse me?' She raised her voice to shout down the old woman's furious rumblings. 'I came here incognito, intending no intrusion whatsoever; but for this accident, who would have known I was present? All these months have I not observed discretion? – to my own great discomfort, let me tell you. It's you, not I who have brought your son's name into this – both his and the lady's.' She folded the dark shawl about her head, and stood upright. 'I'll say no more. I'll go now and let that be the end of it. I intended no harm and there need have been none.' She turned away.

Turned away; and her cloak swung away from her body and into the petrified silence the old woman screamed, beyond all control: 'Pregnant! Look at her! You slut, you shameless strumpet: you're pregnant!'

'Come away, Gilda, come away!' urged the brothers; but once again she shook off their hands and now the blue-grey eyes were beginning to glow with that glow that Blanche had known by a midnight wayside, that Blodwen had known as she fought like a wild-cat on a muddy bank and felt across her cheek the searing edge of the Vixen's ring. 'Do you call me a strumpet? Don't use that word again, Madam! I am no strumpet and I will not be called so. I make no claim to what such as you call virtue; but while I love your son and

201

while I love him only, no one shall call me a strumpet.' And she stood there, white as snow, crowned with flame, the black veil falling away from her head; and cried down with a voice of ice and flame also: 'Take back the word! Take it back!'

Now the silence was absolute, all faces turned, first to the balcony and then back to peer towards the small, stout, black-clad figure with its glitter of jet, impregnable in rage and resentment and to the wretched group around her. On chairs and supper tables, people stood, craning their necks to see, all along the edges of the balcony the women hooked themselves over, their skirts held by their gallants, to get a better view. At the table, the wretched Lady Anne still sat holding her wrecked head in her hands, ludicrous and pitiful, Lord Crum at her side, only longing to be anywhere else. Between them, the Earl of Trove hovered, horrified and protesting. And the Lady Blanche — the Lady Blanche rose and went and stood by the old woman's side, waiting for her to answer. And after a little while, the Countess not speaking, spoke out herself — and now was haughty and cold no longer but trembling with long pent-up, white hot rage, with outrage, with something that perhaps might be pain. 'Very well — if no one else will name you, and publicly, then I will. I've seen you before, Madam, have I not? — and more than all the rest, know you for what you are. Dirt from God knows what gutter — cut-throat mate of a cut-throat footpad — thief of other women's men, bearing their bastard children, it now seems, like the slut you've just been called . . .' And she cried out, shrill and violent, angrily pushing aside her father's restraining hands, 'You won't be called strumpet, you say: but I say you shall and by me, who know you, more than any other can, for a slut and a strumpet indeed.' She repeated it deliberately, turning her head so that all might hear. 'For, God help me — and him — a slut and a strumpet you are!'

For one more moment she stood there, white fingers taut on the balcony edge, grey eyes blazing down. Then she lifted her shoulders and with their movement seemed to throw off all the troubles of the world, all the months-long ennui and weariness and dullness, all anxiety and care. 'God help you!' she cried. 'God help you indeed! You do well, Mistress Blanche, to pray that prayer!'

Upon the afternoon following the disaster at Ranelagh, Lady Blanche with some friends attended Mrs Salmon's wax-works in Fleet Street – and who should be there but the Marchesa d'Astonia Subeggio, sporting a huge muff of sable – so held, however, as to materially increase the appearance of her pregnancy: who bowed most killingly and for the rest of the time stood beside the effigy of the late McLaine, famous highwayman, and laughed and chattered with her escort of two personable young men – quite evidently at the expense of the Lady Blanche. And in Artillery Lane the next morning, where the future Countess went to choose silks for the refurbishing of her new home in Hanover Square – there was Madame Strumpet again and had bought up all the very silk her ladyship had some days before almost certainly decided upon . . . And at Lady Stone's rout, of all places! – how could Blanche guess at the billet delivered by hand to Sir Harry, 'In the past you sent me flowers and twice I carried them and so earned you a fortune in wagers. Oblige me now in a little scheme of wickedness – persuade her lady-ship to allow me to walk up the stairs of her house tonight and curtsey to her; after which I will immediately be gone and she may explain away my intrusion as she will . . .' Lady Stone who had been jockeyed by Lord Trove out of hopes of a Tregaron match for her daughter, entered into the con-spiracy with zest, only insisting that she be allowed to deny all knowledge of it. And so that evening, the Marchesa, in a white satin gown and pink sac, with a little wreath of roses perched on her white-powdered hair, walked up the great curving flight of stairs and made her curtsey – acknow-ledged with a curtsey likewise and a look of pretended astonishment and dawning outrage – and stood aside just long enough for all to watch the Lady Blanche upon her father's arm, follow the Countess of Tregaron up the stairs – in an exact duplication of white dress, pink sac and wreath of roses in white-powdered hair; and if it was true that that stupid girl, Anne, actually burst into hysterical giggles, why it had to be admitted that she was in good company, for throughout the gallery every fan was raised and over each peeped eyes sparkling with the scandal and daring of it.. And when, sick with mortification, Blanche demanded her carriage, it was nowhere to be found; but returned half an hour later, the coachman, crestfallen, explaining that a lady had hurried down between the links at the doorway into the darkness and had told him to drive at once to an address in South Audley Street; and not till he arrived there had he realised that the lady was not her ladyship. For after all, she had worn the same 'head' and the very self-same dress – if milady would pardon him . . .

Two days later, a white-powdered footman brought a letter to the door of the house in South Audley Street. Jake came up with it in his hand. 'The man waits in the hall. Gilda! – the letter's from the Earl of Trove.'

Gilda was curled up in a chair of the 'housekeeper's room' happily contemplating more mischief. 'What – capitulation already? Call Mother, quick! Mother – a note from Mistress Blanche's papa!' And she read it aloud. 'Oh, Mother, listen to this!'

'The Earl of Trove begs to inform the Marchesa d'Astonia Subeggio—' ('Come, come, my full title! – not a word of bawd and strumpet!') '—that on the day before yesterday, the wagon carrying his daughter's chattels to Castell Cothi, was set upon by the highwaymen of the Court of Foxes and robbed of everything. The escort was given a message to be repeated verbatim, to your ladyship. That "the goods will be returned to Lady Blanche Handley if, one week from receipt of this missive, she will from a box at the playhouse, bow to *the Earl of Tregaron's strumpet*, who will take care to be in the

204

box opposite; and so make public apology for an insult no less publicly delivered." The Earl of Trove deeply regrets that the terms of the message oblige him to refer to your ladyship by the above appellation.' 'Well!' said Gilda, dropping the letter into her lap, 'who could have believed it?'

'Is this the doing of that Devil as he calls himself?'

She thought it over, 'I think it's the doing of another devil: I think it's the doing of the Fox himself.' And for a moment her heart rose to him. '*He* won't see me insulted. *He* won't hear me called strumpet.'

'Well, but so you are a strumpet,' said Mrs Brown, reasonably, 'when one comes to think about it.'

'Not while I love only one man: not while I love him only and give myself to him only and never will to any other, even though he leave me. I was married – more's the pity – and lived with my husband; a little only and unwillingly. Then I went to him I love. Two men in my life,' cried Gilda, conveniently obliterating the memory of a ruined chapel by a moonlit roadside. 'Does that make a whore? No one shall call me so!' And she scribbled on the back of the Earl's note the one word 'Done!' and thrust it back into Jake's hand. 'Let the footman take that back to his lordship. Leave the letter open, so that the news may spread. Meanwhile...' Unwieldy with pregnancy, but all alert now, with dancing eyes, she held out a hand to be hauled up from her chair. 'Meanwhile, Mother – it must be the old dress, the old white dress and no jewels of course: I must be as I was in those other days.' In the days of my purity, she thought, perhaps; but behind the thought lay ever that other, which to her was truth. 'I love only him. I came to him pure because I never gave myself to any other man in love.' 'If we let out the gathers at the back, Mother, cover over all with the sac...'

And so she sat once again in her box at the play, and once again was the cynosure of all eyes – the Unattainable Lady who of late had been somewhat too easily attainable perhaps; but dressed all in white, just the same, wearing no jewels, no touch of colour save for the soft, lambent marigold light of her hair. Once again the house rumbled and stirred as, lovely as a white flower with its pollen of gold, she came forward into the front of the box, her duenna at her elbow – for all London knew by now of the words spoken at Ranelagh Gardens ten days ago; everyone knew that the walls of the bijou fortress had been stormed, all were avid to learn more of the mysteries half disclosed, that lay within; and the brothers had used old tactics to spread abroad the news of the gage that had been thrown down for tonight. The Earl had replied with a promise, had later acknowledged the return of his property: now the debt was to be paid.

A white flower, slowly settling into its place; a white flower, crowned with an aureole that shone, pale yet brilliant, a glimmer of gold against the dark crimson hangings of the box. Below and around her in the great ring of the auditorium, crimson-hung, bright with the glitter of candlelight winking in glass holders, heads turned to look at her, eyes stared, voices buzzed in gleeful anticipation of some sort of scene to come. It was whispered that Her Majesty herself was present, veiled and incognito; everyone knew for certain that Carlton House was represented; certainly half fashionable London had sent underlings ahead to fight for places and keep them warm until it should be convenient to claim them. The mob would be not so much hydra-headed, a wit was saying, as a Janus-mob, facing two ways: for all the men had been rivals for the favours of the Marchesa and all the women rivals with the Lady Blanche for those of the late Earl of Tregaron or his brother of Llandovery.

She seemed oblivious of it: sitting there, still as a flower, with her crown of pale gold, looking down, modest, cool and quiet, at her white, folded hands.

Opposite, the box remained empty.

If they don't come! she thought; and panic rose in her suddenly, panic and a hint of her own ever-ready self-mockery. A fine fool I shall look, sitting here all dressed up, waiting to crush her with my condescension – if she doesn't even turn up!

But the door of the box opposite opened at last, a curtain lifted and the old woman, the Countess, came through, black-faced, grim, in her feathers and jet; and at her side a vision in pale blue, ice blue, dazzling against the red and gold; brilliant with diamonds, powdered hair swept up into a snowy cone with small blue feathers and flowers – who came forward, not hesitating, to the front and centre of the box, leaving the rest of the party clustered behind her, and stood there, looking over the sea of powder and feathers, the velvets and silks, the up-turned, goggling faces, into her rival's eyes.

She did not move from her seat; merely sat there, calmly gazing back – Miss Marigold Brown of Aston-sub-Edge – Madam Vixen of the Court of Foxes – Marigelda, Marchesa d'Astonia Subeggio: pale as a lily in her white dress, cool as a lily in her indifferent disdain, quietly sitting there, staring her rival down. White unadorned, versus shimmering pale blue silk at the height of the mode: sheen of gold hair versus shimmer of diamonds: radiance of a warm loveliness beyond perfection, matched against a flawless beauty as cold as snow. Between them the house stood staring and held its breath.

(If she doesn't bow after all! If she doesn't bow!)

But she bowed. Coolly, condescendingly, the tiniest sketch of a bow; and the Lady Blanche unhurriedly averted her eyes, looked round with chill indifference at the gaping crowd beneath and, in one studied, graceful movement, quietly sat down.

She had not reckoned with this: Miss Marigold Brown. Humbly born herself, she had not reckoned with the in-born, unassailable hauteur of a long tradition of lineage, wealth and culture. Before it her own eyes fell; for a moment she saw herself through the eyes of this other girl – small, cheap, shoddy, an adventuress, without truth or purity, mistaking boldness for courage, insolence for pride. Up over the white skin flooded a tide of scarlet. She knew that all about her the silent house was coming alive with rustlings and murmurings: with the dangerous beginnings of an amused contempt . . .

She was barely conscious that her mother came to her side, made a bob curtsey, placed something between her white hands, tightened now into fists in the lap of the white gown. Only – suddenly there was a fragrance that acted upon her half-swooning senses like a glass of champagne: half-forgotten, heavily sweet, at this moment exquisitely evocative – the scent of red roses.

And she lifted her head; and saw, standing in the open doorway of the box opposite, a small, slender figure – bright eyes laughing at her across the wide space of the auditorium, the old, teasing, half-sweet, half malicious smile. And a word was spoken and the Earl of Trove jerked to his feet and stood, mouth a-gape; and spoke in turn into his daughter's ear. She also rose; turned her head in one brief, startled glance towards the back of the box, turned back and faced the box opposite. The house was silent again, holding its breath; and the Lady Blanche looked across once more into the eyes of her rival, and this time bent her proud, beautiful head and sank into a deep, slow curtsey that had nothing in it but abject humility; and stood erect again – waiting.

Cool, condescending, ironical – scornfully triumphant now, the golden head bowed back.

But next morning all London rang with the news: the notorious highwayman, Gareth the Fox – apprehended right here in the heart of the Metropolis and safely caged up for good and all in Newgate Gaol.

CHAPTER FIFTEEN

Little Jake came to her, heartbroken. 'It was my fault. It was my fault for detaining him outside the playhouse...'

Gilda sat huddled in the huge armchair, up in the attic room, her feet on the fender. 'No, no, not your fault, dearest; they must have been watching for him.' She held the small hard brown hand tight in her own. 'But tell me, tell me again – everything he did, everything he said...'

'Why, I told you, Gilda, last night. I heard they were saying in the Bag o' Nails what she planned – that Blanche! – to humiliate you, to keep only to the letter of the bargain. So I ran to the playhouse to warn you. But they wouldn't let me in; and just as I was arguing with them – there he was! So elegant, Gilda, dressed like a fop as he always was in those old days, you remember? – in his green brocade coat...'

'He had it off a rich gentleman travelling by coach towards Fishguard: took it off the man's back – to come courting the Marchesa Marigelda.' Even now, she couldn't help smiling. 'Well, but go on—'

'Well, and so he caught me up in his arms and laughed and ruffled my hair and seemed so happy to see me. And said I was the very fellow he needed, for I should carry the roses to you.'

'He wouldn't bring them himself?'

'No, for I asked him and he said – Gilda, he said it was

as much as his life was worth to be recognised in that place; for whatever the family might promise, there was still a price on his head, for the shooting of the Earl of Tregaron.'

'But he did come in,' she said, a cold hand on her heart.

'Because of what I told him was being said – that she'd make a sport of you. Then he laughed no more, his face grew quiet, his eyes – his eyes flashed, Gilda, like a – like a sort of fire . . .'

'So I have seen them,' said Gilda, 'often enough.'

'And he said: "We shall see about that. I have made a bargain with them—"'

'Then it *was* he who held up their wagon. He must indeed be back at the Cwrt.'

'Why yes, and said he brought you a thousand messages, and they couldn't but laugh at your tricking them all and wished you good fortune out of it – especially since they learned no ransom would have come to them even had you stayed. And then he – he caught me by the arm and asked me how you did, and were you happy—?'

'You told him I was so? – deliriously.'

'I told him you were happy and – and with child.'

'And he—?'

'I *told* you, Gilda, yesterday. Made a bow and a scrape and said I should give you his felicitations.'

'And after that smiled no more?'

'Well – he smiled, Gilda; only not with his eyes. And then – and then we saw the Earl of Trove's carriage drive up, and waited in a dark corner till they were gone through the entrance and towards the boxes. And then he said: "You go that way, little brother—" little brother, he called me, Gilda, "and I this," and started off into the house after them. I caught at his coat and begged him not to place himself in danger; but he brushed away my hand and said . . .'

She held the small hand tight. 'Yes, well, continue . . . Tell me again what he said. Last night I hardly listened, but now that he's apprehended, and all through me, that I be not made a mock of ... Come, tell me again. He said he would not hear me called slut and strumpet—'

'Although – although a slut and a strumpet indeed you were – but should not be called so in a public place and by a woman who would sell herself for wealth and position, and to the very man whose slut and strumpet you were. Not—'

'Not—?' said Gilda.

'Not while you bore his name,' said little Jake; and fished suddenly in his pocket. 'Why, but that reminds me that all this time I've forgotten the note that was to go with the roses.'

The old message: the same message. '... till I die.'

She sent for her brothers. 'You must help me, you must find out what's going forward, you must arrange for me to see him.' Against their protestations she was adamant. 'For me, entirely for me, because he wouldn't have me publicly insulted – he's got himself into this terrible situation. There's nothing I must leave undone, that I can do to save him.'

'Gilda, for heaven's sake! – what is this fellow to you?'

'Among other things he is my husband.'

'A forced marriage – a trickery.'

'Legal and binding,' she insisted, shrugging. 'If not, do you think David wouldn't long ago have married me, Blanche or no Blanche?'

'If they should hang him ... Gilda, once he was dead ...' But James brushed the thought away. 'Well, no: we couldn't wish that.' And he confessed: 'There is after all a – something – about him ...'

'There's nothing about him,' said Gilda, crossly. 'It's nothing to do with that. You're dazzled by the memory of a man in a green brocade coat who flourished and made pretty speeches while you handed round cakes—'

'It was I who ate the cakes,' said Jake. 'But I'm not dazzled by a man in a grand coat. I remember that he's a highwayman, brave and daring and clever and gay—'

211

'There's nothing brave and gay about a highwayman,' said Gilda. 'If you were a frightened woman in a coach on a lonely road, you'd soon discover that!' But there came back to her the memory of herself, hanging down from the branch of a great tree, to look into just such a coach: and of how his bright eyes had looked across into hers from the opposite window; and she burst forth for a moment into laughter. 'Well, well! – perhaps there is some romance in it, after all. And in him some – charm; though he's nothing but a rogue . . .'

'A rogue and a robber,' said George, steadily.

'And murderer to boot,' said Sam.

'Who offers his life that a slut and a strumpet – as he civilly calls me – shall not be insulted in public. Which life I shall save if I may, and you cannot refuse me your assistance.'

And that very day she went, with no escort but little Jake, her elder brothers being constrained by their occupations from accompanying her – and joined the throng of other women clamouring at Newgate Gaol for a sight of the highwayman. To visit such unromantic romantics was the fashion, and, curious, excited, shameless in sensation-seeking, they crowded the foetid, narrow corridors leading to his cell – bright in their silks and velvets, the great ladies of high society, struggling like alley-women for a glance from him, a word from him – from him who had robbed just such women of their property, rough-handled their menfolk, not seldom 'insulted' themselves with his violent attentions. Thief, plunderer, murderer – now safely caged, he was to be the hero of the few brief days remaining to him; and they his slaves.

Little Jake struggled along behind her, the tears streaming down his face. 'Gilda, this is a terrible place . . .'

Yes; it was terrible. Due to be pulled down soon and re-erected on lines at least a little more humane, it consisted now of a higgledy-piggledy of dark, dank passages of sweating stone into which no gleam of daylight entered; lined with abominable cells – mere niches in the walls, ten feet long, perhaps and not half that width across, windowless except for the barred upper half of the wall fronting on to the corridor – itself windowless; furnished with a stone bench built against the inner wall – and with nothing more. Through the bars, hands reached out as they passed: filthy, unshaven, poor wretches due for death craved a last charity of the great ladies pressing by. But the ladies held their muffs to their noses and hurried on; and at last came a mob so dense that Gilda, following, knew that they must be near him. 'Oh, Gilda,' said the little boy, raising his pale child's face to hers, 'if we should find him in such a kennel as these—!'

'What gold can buy him, dearest, he shall have.'

What gold could buy had been bought already. She should have known him better! He had bribed his way to a cell twice the size of any other, with good blankets, a warm carpet of deep, clean straw on the stone floor, a table and two chairs. His face was cleanly shaven, his dark hair, caught back by its black velvet ribbon, was smooth brushed as ever; he wore his green coat and if the ruffles at his throat and wrists were a little soiled, no matter for she saw that fresh shirts had been brought to him and lay in readiness, spread out on the bed – the fine ladies, it seemed were well versed in the needs of such heroes and only too eager to forestall them. And the table was laden with wine bottles and good things to· eat; and he, with a pretty girl on each knee was feeding himself and them alternately with hothouse grapes and exchanging badinage with the mob outside the bars.

A turnkey, filthy and villainous, barred Gilda's way with outstretched palm. 'No nearer, Madam. Orders is orders.'

'Others are right inside the cell.'

'Lord knows by what means; unless it may be said,' he mumbled, slyly insinuating, 'that they have greased the key.'

She looked at him, revolted. 'I see grease enough already.'

He refused to be offended. 'Doubtless, Madam, for this is a

greasy old place. But the ointment I speak of is golden.'

She gave way: sovereigns chinked and he forced a way through for them, roughly jostling the fine ladies as he went, and so left them at last, close up against the cage. But now that she was here, she grew frightened, the women behind her, indignant at having being ousted from their places, pressed forward, she was afraid of being crushed against the bars, afraid of danger to her unborn child. Within the cell, he sat laughing, pouring brandy for the girls, bandying mockery with those outside. She called out sharply: 'Gareth!' but he did not hear her. 'Oh, Gilda,' whispered Jake, 'it's no good, it's all horrible – let us go!'

'He is but play-acting,' she said, looking down at him, compassionately, 'to put on a brave show,' and she called out again, shrilly, forcing her voice above the din: 'Gareth! Gareth y Cadno!' and added in Welsh all the vile words she knew.

He lifted his head; shouted out suddenly to the chattering women: 'Be silent!', turfed the two sluts roughly off his knees and stood up. 'Who called to me then, in Welsh?'

'I,' said Gilda, into the comparative silence. 'And in terms you could not but recognise.'

'What, is it you, my Vixen?' And he came across to the bars of his cage, but slowly, almost it seemed reluctantly, kicking the straw as he came; and put his hand through the bars and caught at hers. 'Gilda,' he said, half whispering, 'you shouldn't be here.'

'No, I shouldn't; and I see that in fact there was no need for me to come. But since I *am* here – is there anything I can arrange for you? Whatever you name, I'll do if I can.'

He laughed. 'Oh, as to naming – I could name quite a lot. But not here, my love, alas! – not here.'

'Very well, very well,' she said irritably, 'spare me the speeches; for that sort of thing you have candidates a plenty.

But you're in deep danger – and through me, I know; so that I feel obliged to help you if I can.'

He lost his laughter. 'But I think you can't, my dear; nor God, nor any man – not this time.' His strong hands grasped at the bars. 'This place wasn't built for escaping from.' He saw Jake's scared face peering up at him. 'I told you, my would-be highwayman, didn't I? – long ago: that all of us must end one day upon the Three-legged Tree. And so, you see, must Gareth y Cadno of the Court of Foxes.'

'You shall not, you shall not!' cried the little boy, weeping.

'Ah, but I shall and you mustn't shed tears, my boy, and make me grow weak with you. Dry your eyes; and one day not too far ahead I'll undertake to make you the proudest boy in Christendom – to you alone will I wave, I swear it, as the cart goes by. Which reminds me, Madam Vixen, this at least you could undertake – pay I know not who, but you can doubtless discover – for a coffin and shroud to be loaded on the cart and go with me—'

'I've thought of that,' she said.

He bowed. 'You are all consideration.'

'It was in case – in case—'

He shrugged. 'Accept it; this time there's no "in case".'

'Oh, Gareth!' She lifted her lovely eyes to his and met his own, dark and unfathomable. She whispered: 'Under all this – unreality: are you not afraid?'

'Afraid?' He turned his head aside, looking away from her, for a moment closed his eyes, almost as though he were about to faint. But he turned back almost immediately, looking down, brilliantly smiling, into the little boy's tear-stained face. 'Afraid? she asks me. What, I – afraid? Shall I not have my friends about me – they'll come up from the Crwt, you'll see; I'm not the first of the gang to end up my days on the Nubbing Chit and they know all the tricks, how to pull on my legs so that of the manner of death itself I need have no terrors. And for the rest – a triumphal progress: how better can a man go to meet his end? Do you be there, Jake, little brother, to see me pass, with the flowers at my feet and the girls in white dancing by the cart, and bouquets from half the fine ladies of London . . .' He broke off. 'Will you send me a bouquet, Madam Vixen? Red roses: will you send me red roses? – and those I'll carry, if you will, and let all the rest rot. Jake, see that she sends me red roses. I've sent them often enough to *her*.'

'And with a message,' said the little boy, sobbing still, trying to rub away the tears with his sleeve.

'Ah, well, as to the message – she could send me no such message: though since the time would be short enough, my Vixen, perhaps you might essay it – just for that brief progress to say that you will love me till I die? I wouldn't keep you waiting.' And he put out his hand through the bars and caught at her own and pulled it through to him, the small, white, scented hand and kissed the palm and folded her fingers over the kiss; and ruffled the boy's hair and turned away from them without another word.

Half fainting, she forced her way out again, from the noise and the crowd, and the dank, foetid stench; and within her muff, her fingers were unwrapping the paper he had slipped into her hand with the kiss. Secretly, sending the child forward to find out where the carriage was waiting at the prison gate, she read what he had written there, prepared in advance apparently, for any true friend that should come.

For God's sake – get me laudanum!

The days passed. She obtained laudanum, wheedled her brother Sam into taking it for her to the gaol; the experience had sickened her, mentally and physically too and her mother was insistent that, if only for the sake of the baby, she should not go again. But on the third day as she lay fretful and anxious on her bed upstairs, little Jake came pounding at the door. 'Come, Gilda, quick! Here's such a rabble below that my mother is having the hysterics. A woman and three villainous-looking fellows, but they'll only say that they're friends of her ladyship . . .'

216

She struggled out of bed, flung on a white wrapper, all ribbons and lace, flew down to the hall. 'Catti! Dio! Huw! My little Willie-bach!' And she flung her arms round their necks and drew them with her into her elegant drawing-room, too excited to observe how gingerly they perched themselves on the silly little gilded chairs. Dio y Diawl, in fact, struggled up immediately to his feet again. He cut across her suddenly faltering flutterings of welcome. He said: 'Have you seen him?'

'Have I seen Gareth? Yes, I've seen him. And my brother has been to him. I was ill but my brother took him – took him laudanum.'

'Laudanum?' said Catti, her hands to her mouth.

'He asked me for it. He must keep up his courage . .' Into the heavy silence she said, as though excusing him: 'It's a terrible way to die.'

'We've seen a few go the same way,' said Dio, 'and without the aid of laudanum.' He stared at her blindly opened his mouth to say something; cleared his throat. Huw the Harp said awkwardly: 'We don't know you, Madam Vixen, in this guise.'

She sat there on the little scrolled sofa with its upholstery in heavy white silk, embossed with gold roses, the blue ribbons and lacy ruffles of the white wrapper gathered about her pregnancy. 'Huw bach,' she said, almost sadly, 'I am Madam Vixen no longer.'

'No, indeed,' said Catti. 'Madam Countess now, again; or Madam Doxy, which you will. But sitting very pretty, either way; while he lies in Newgate – and as ever through your fault.'

'Whisht you, woman!' said Dio, in Welsh. 'Shut your mouth!'

'How could I have known he'd come to the theatre? God knows, if I could help him—'

'If you can't, Madam Vixen fach,' said Dio, in his own old, fond way, but sadly and heavily, 'none can.'

'*I* help him?'

'You *must* help him,' said Catti. 'You must help *us*.' She stood up suddenly, small, slender, lithely strong, in the red woollen petticoat, tight jacket and little black shawl, her keen, dark face alight with a fierce resolution. 'You must help us to rescue him,' she said.

To rescue him! She stared back at them, astounded. And yet . . . And yet the old tingling began to set fire to her blood; sudden and fresh as a spring bursting up out of the green mountain side, a new and undreamed-of hope came bubbling through her dull acceptance of what was to be. To rescue him! To get him out of that fearful place, to save him from that fearful death! And to her, to their leader, to the Fox's own Vixen – they turned with the old trust and faith to ask, quite simply, how it was to be done.

She lumbered to her feet. 'Come upstairs, come where we shall be more comfortable than amongst these foolish gim-cracks.' And she took them to the old attic room, sent Jake running to the tavern for ale, went down to the kitchens to cajole from Mrs Brown, great plates of ham, salad and bread. 'Now, Mother, we do but talk over the plight he is in . . .'

'You'll lay no plans, Marigold, for getting this man released?'

'For getting him released – no indeed! What would be the use of that?'

'It would be very wrong. He's what he is, a highway robber.'

'As I have been myself,' said Gilda.

'Necessity drove you.'

'Few take to the road from choice,' said Gilda, dryly. 'It's hardly a life of luxury and ease.'

'It's a life of adventure and wicked daring,' said Mrs Brown, shrewdly, 'and may well take precedence with some over luxury and ease.'

'Well, the life he leads at the moment is neither, and not

218

much left of it. Give me food for my friends and leave us in peace to talk it over.'

And she went back to them, curling up in the big, old chair; and her sickness had vanished and her eyes were shining as they had not shone for many a long day. 'I've been thinking. There's a great crush of ladies goes each day to see him. And the turnkey is old and very vile and has a villainous lust for gold . . .'

They would not sleep in the house; they had friends, they said, and would find quarters elsewhere – and besides, wouldn't Dafydd at any moment return and what would be his feelings to find them all consorted there? But they all met each day to compare the progress of their preparations. They had sent to the Cwrt for reinforcements who arrived and, cagey, grudging, curious oddly tamed and made diffident by the different surroundings in which they found themselves, also herded into the attic room and listened and learned and promised, and slouched back again into the strange world of a metropolis, to await the day when the attempt should be made.

And the day dawned; and at ten o'clock in the morning of that day – the Earl of Tregaron came home.

She was ready in the hall: standing, dressed in her utmost finery with Jake at her side, the carriage at the door. He saw her face blanch, the hesitation in her greeting, rapturous though it might outwardly be. 'What's the matter, Gilda? Where were you going?'

Her mother had warned her how it would be. 'This rogue, this horrible villain – what will your lover say when he finds that you scheme with your parcel of ruffians to rescue such vile trash as that? And when, by his death—'

'Don't say it, Mother!' she had cried. 'Don't say it!'

'All I say is that David will put a sharp end to all this. His wife, the mother of his child—'

'I'm not his wife.'

'In his heart you are, Gilda: and that you should go running at the bidding of this other man ... Because David is quiet and kind, you think him easy-going, you think he'll be afraid to oppose you. But he's no milk-sop, for all he's so sweet tempered ... '

No: he was no milk-sop. She stood in the little hall before him and literally trembled. She stammered out: 'The Fox is taken. He lies in Newgate Gaol.'

He said sharply: 'Upon what charge? Highway robbery?'

'Not that, no. For murder: for the shooting of your brother.'

'An undertaking was given—'

'This is nothing to do with your family. The law works, I suppose, without waiting for private charges to be made. I have to admit,' she said reluctantly, 'that there has been no sign of any interference from them.'

He opened his mouth to speak, but closed it again. All the happiness had gone from his eyes, all the joy of their reunion after their longest separation since they had come to the Bijou. He stood, the three-caped travelling coat thrown back from his shoulders and looked down at her. 'And you, Gilda – you were going to see him?'

'We've been before,' said Jake, joining innocently in. 'It's terrible there. He's locked in a cage, and the women pester him all day as though he were some side-show—'

'Go now, Jakey,' she said, interrupting him. 'Run out to the carriage, tell them to wait, I shall soon be there—'

'Must you go?' said David. 'When I'm but just home. Go this afternoon; I'll come with you and see you safe.'

'I've promised,' she said, feebly. The gang would be gathering at the gate of the prison, already the scheme had been set in action. 'I've made – appointments ... '

'With whom?'

'Some of them are up to – to see him; from Cwrt y Cadno.'

He was silent for a long moment, looking down at her. He said at last: 'Gilda – I know you better than you think I do.

Some mischief is planned.' And he took her by the hand and went into the little drawing-room and closed the door. 'You'd better tell me,' he said.

She made no denial; but she insisted: 'It would be better for you not to know.'

'Do you think I shall prevent you?'

'Will you not?' she said, looking up doubtfully into the steady brown eyes. She reminded him: 'Have you forgotten – that he killed your brother?'

'Have you forgotten,' he said, 'that he *is* my brother?'

So she told him; trusted him. 'The turnkey is old and may be bribed and there's a press of women, in and out of the cell. They'll all be there, Dio y Diawl and Huw and Willie-bach and the rest; and Catti and Red Jenny and others of the women. All dressed as women, David – save for Dio, whose bulk and great head couldn't be disguised, and one or two of the others who will seem but to conduct their women-folk. The plan is to cluster about the cell, having bought or over-borne the turnkey according to necessity; and then, having freed Gareth from the cell itself, to fling on to him a woman's disguise and, making a great jostling and outcry, get him out of the prison before the cell is discovered empty.'

He sat quietly, apart from her, on one of the small gilt chairs, his hands between his knees. 'It sounds very simple,' he said at last.

'There's so great a mob there; we shall be lost among the real visitors.' She described to him the narrow corridor outside the cell.

'But between that and the main gate – there must be many locks?'

'They're opened before the fashionables and everyone let through without question.'

'That's when no prisoner is known to have escaped. Once the hue and cry is raised—'

'Why should it be raised?'

'Some form of check *must* be operated, Gilda; a counting

of heads if no more. And at the very first check – all remaining gates will be guarded.'

'If it's but a counting – someone may remain innocently enough, behind; and as many sheep as go in will be allowed out.'

He shook his head, sitting staring down at his locked hands. 'This is all foolishly hopeful. Y Cadno's a famous criminal; he'll be better kept than your plan assumes.'

For the first time her high heart wavered. 'You think we shall fail?'

'The moment the cell is seen to be empty—'

'We shall have seen to it that the turnkey holds his tongue.'

'But the rest won't hold theirs, Gilda. These women who flock to stare at him – what do they care for the man himself? – the sensation is all. Do you think that, having seen him escape, they'll come quietly away? And if they do – won't the mass departure warn the outer guard that something's amiss?' He said slowly: 'What you want is someone who'll remain in the cell and be taken for the Fox.'

She was restless, excited, the moments were ticking away. 'Any of the men would do it for him, but then they in their turn would be apprehended and he wouldn't allow that. Besides ...' She threw out helpless hands. 'Who is there that bears the smallest resemblance to him?'

He got up quickly to his feet. 'You have forgotten again,' he said, 'that he is my brother.'

Dazed, half in tears, she went with him upstairs, selected a coat of green brocade. What to do with his fair hair was a problem but she ran to the kitchen, smeared her hands with soot, rubbed his blond head with it, crammed down a tricorne hat. 'And your eyes aren't dark enough and your height far too great; you must remain sitting as though in a fit of depression, keep your hand to your brow. But the lower part of your face – yes, that would deceive any but those who knew you well.' And she came to him and put her arms about his neck. 'David,' she said, 'whether we succeed or fail – with all my heart I thank you. I know that you are doing this for me.'

He returned her kiss gently and calmly. 'Yes,' he said, 'for you.'

'Not because you think I care for him, David?'

'No,' he said, not protesting, simply accepting it.

'I have loved you from the moment I saw you,' she said. 'I have never loved anyone else.' And she borrowed a phrase, not giving a thought as to why it should be familiar to her. 'I will love you till I die.'

A man came to her as she awaited their return from the gaol, sitting huddled in the darkest corner of the tavern close by: for they had been adamant in refusing that she should go with them on the rescue attempt. A very tall man, dressed all in black but with eyes so fiercely glittering that they gave to his whole aspect a blue steeliness – who bowed and took her hand and, with a quiet air far removed from the old, gay malicious mockery, kissed it. 'Well, Madam Vixen – so we meet again.'

The Black Toby.

She rose, caught at his sleeve. 'What are you doing here?'

'Since I was banished from Carmarthenshire – by what means you know – I have returned to my old haunts.'

'But here, in this ale house?'

He suggested: 'Upon the same errand as yourself, perhaps?'

She stammered: 'Y Cadno?'

He shrugged lightly. 'I was at the moment unemployed and – let's say that I owed him – some return of favour.'

'And so—'

'Come, sit down,' he said. He glanced down at her condition. 'You are with child?'

'Yes, I'm ... My title nowadays is Strumpet to the Earl of Tregaron.'

'He has all my felicitations,' he said, bowing.

'But – Y Cadno. Sit here by me and tell me. You've seen him?'

'Several times and sent emissaries. A lady of my acquaintance has gained favour with the janitor and so made her way into the very cell with him, and there unfolded such plans as I had developed. But . . .' He spoke very low, almost whispering into her ear. 'I had half a mind to stop your friends from going – it's all hopeless.'

'Hopeless? You don't know our plan.'

'It wasn't hard to guess: all these huge feathered hats pulled down over painted faces, wide skirts with great boots peeping out from beneath. And one who looks not unlike the Fox in features. A brave man.'

'But—?'

'But your other is a brave man too, Madam Vixen. And a proud one. He won't reveal to those who flock in admiration of him – perhaps especially to those that go out of love for him – that beneath the straw of his cell floor, he drags a chain that all the steel files in Christendom won't sever.'

She remembered now the slow, shuffling step with which he had crossed the two paces of the cell floor towards her. 'Dear God! He's chained there like a dog!'

'To a staple dug deep in the wall. We smuggled in tools, but first the chain and then the staple have been renewed as soon as the mischief was seen. They've held notorious criminals before, Madam Vixen: held them and lost them. This one they don't mean to lose.'

She began to weep bitterly. 'Then if we must fail – what next?'

'Why, alas, then he comes up for trial and will be very heavily guarded – being who he is. And after that . . .' He put out his strong hand and took hers. 'You must face facts, Madam Vixen. After that he will be with the rest in the Condemned Hole, guarded day and night, and not by some doddering old turnkey but by a young man, strong, settling down to a long life of less hazardous briberies. They're bring-

224

ing in a brute from the hulks, they say, specially chosen.' And he glanced up and saw a face in the doorway and said: 'They're back – and having failed.'

They came in gloomily, wretchedly: oppressed, she thought, by something more, even, than the failure of the plot. She told them what the Black Toby had said. 'And if he's found guilty—'

'Upon what evidence?' said David. 'They can have none. The charge is one of murder; not of being a highwayman, but of the murder of my brother. And my family has given its word, and that stands for our servants also – no reprisals. No one will speak.'

'There is one who will speak,' said Gilda, 'being not of your family – yet.' And next morning she left the house, secretly, and presented herself at the door of the Trove mansion in Grosvenor Street – almost as huge and quite as dull, she thought, as its neighbour in Hanover Square – and sent up her name. The servant returned. 'I regret, milady. Milord, the Earl of Trove has nothing to say to the Marchesa d'Astonia Subeggio.'

She stood, grey-blue eyes huge in a face now shadowed with her anxieties. She repeated stupidly: 'Nothing to say?'

'I regret, milady. That was the message.'

Nothing to say. But suddenly the Marchesa d'Astonia had something to say, after all: and was Marchesa no longer but Madam Vixen in a snarl of bitter rage. 'Then take a message back. What has my lord to say to Marigelda, Slut and Strumpet – the future Countess Tregaron?'

That brought him. Trembling, ashen-faced. 'What does this mean, Madam? My daughter is the future Countess Tregaron. Lord Tregaron is betrothed, he has given his word.'

'He gave his word before he knew me. He has kept to it while I have been unavailable - unavailable as a wife, I mean!' She said sweetly, viciously: 'It's for you to judge, my lord, having seen him in his part as happy son-in-law to be, whether his enthusiasm for the marriage will keep him to it,

225

once I am set free. And only the testimony of your daughter and your daughter's servant can set me free: for if they give it, I am a widow — my husband dies.' And she spent no more time on him, but went to the door and called peremptorily to the footman to show her out. The Earl caught the whisk of her skirts and a backward, taunting glance as, old, dazed, stupid with the shock of it, he blundered through the great hall to his daughter's room.

No evidence would be given by the Trove faction, at Gareth y Cadno's trial.

CHAPTER SIXTEEN

The day of the trial. Trembling, she went with them, with his friends, arraigning herself unashamedly with his gang of ruffians, the women rigged out in stolen finery from a dozen plunderings, that accorded ill with their strong, wiry bodies and weather-worn faces, their rough brown hands; the men unmannered, raucous, ill-controlled. She had seen nothing of Y Cadno since the day of the escape plot; the crush and stench of the corridor outside his cell made her ill, queasy as her stomach was from her pregnancy; she sent messages but she could not go. The gang from their visits reported him to her as still high of courage – and yet always with an odd exchange of glances that puzzled her. On the day of the trial, however, he would receive no one at all; she contented herself with sending in a new coat and fresh linen. The coat was of russet silk, the colour of a fox's pelt: Y Cadno he is, she thought, and Y Cadno he shall be seen to be – bright-eyed and brave and clever and strong, fit to out-wit them all yet, base packs of dogs as they are that try to hunt him down . . .

A voice cried out and another voice from the cavernous cells beneath the court; and into the dock came two dirty tip-staffs, shambling, ill-shaven, armed with their heavy sticks. And between them . . .

A flash of russet brown, of white lace foaming: a dark head bent, hair caught back into its black velvet bow. A roar

227

rose up in the court and she cried out with the rest, her voice high above theirs, and uncovered her head so that he might pick her out in the crowd and know that she was there with him. 'Gareth! Gareth y Cadno!' And waited for the flash of the bold, dark eyes, the old wicked, half savage, half tender smile. But – he did not lift his head, lolling there between the two men, hands blindly seeking the support of the wooden rail of the dock. She thought, He's dissembling...! It was a new plot, he was acting a part, would break out suddenly, throw the men aside, leap the high box, be off through the stifling mob in the court and away . . . But she knew that it was not so; and she remembered the half-bewildered, half wretched looks of the gang when they had returned that first time after the escape plot had failed, all the times since, when they had been to visit him; and Catti saying, quick and sharp then and on each other occasion 'that he had been high in courage. And the note that he had folded into her palm with what might well prove to have been his last kiss 'Get me laudanum!'

When she came back to full recollection of where she was, David, Earl of Tregaron, was entering the box to give his evidence.

Useless to deny that he had been with his brother that night; useless to deny that his brother that night by a pistol shot had died. But as to who had fired – he could not say. The shot had come out of the darkness. That this man in the dock had fired it, he could not possibly swear. No, he could not swear that the man had *not* been present; he simply had no knowledge of it either way. The mob grew restless, called out noisily, began for a horrid moment to suspect that it might be balked of its prey; but he stood there, resolute, strong and adamant – he had not seen who fired.

'My lord the Earl of Tregaron, your brother, was shot that night and so died; will you say that you did not see this man kill him?'

'I have said it,' said David. 'I did not see him there.'

228

'You yourself were taken prisoner and spent some weeks in the lair of the self-styled Fox—?'

'I was held for some time. If it was his lair, I can only say that I never saw him there.'

Out of the mutterings of the crowd, voices were raised to cry Traitor! and the name of his brother; and jibing reminders that through his brother's death he succeeded to the family wealth. He paid no heed to any of it. 'I am here to speak the truth and the truth is that from start to finish, I saw nothing of this man.'

And the waiting woman – Blanche's woman . . . From her place, squeezed in between Red Jenny and Hal the Hop, Gilda stood up suddenly; and having let herself be seen, as though re-settling herself sat down again. The woman gaped across the court at her with scared, gooseberry eyes; of his lordship and Lady Blanche, no sign.

The mutterings and rumblings grew louder, a tipstaff bawled threats into the court – crumbling on his bench, the old, grey judge sat hunched in his red gown and clutched to his offended nose the bunch of aromatic herbs. The woman stood waiting, trembling. The mob stared back at her with a universal threat.

But . . . Yes, she had been there that night. Mishandled? – yes. Mistreated? – yes. And her mistress also? – yes. Robbed? – yes. Had she seen the Earl of Tregaron die? Yes . . .

Yes, she had seen my lord die and his brother lie wounded in the road. But as to who had shot them – the weapon had been fired from the shadows, stammered the woman, whimpering, and of this man here, the prisoner, she had seen no sign.

From the dock he raised his head for the first time, shifted about him with a blearily triumphant eye; turned towards Gilda and the gang a look that said, dully, can there be hope after all? Crushed, jostled on the filthy benches, out of the blur of open mouths screaming curses, of fisted hands shaking as the woman was led away, they looked back at him, willing him back to courage and faith. And as the coachman and two

229

footmen followed and the outriders in their turn, and – with whatever show of reluctance – offered the same testimony and 'thought' and 'supposed', but could not be persuaded to swear – he did indeed seem to come alive a little, shake away the cobwebs that clouded his brain; even for a moment as the last of the men sneaked away to the unrestrained execrations of the people, turned upon his friends a ghost of his own old bragadoccio smile . . .

For which smile, thought Gilda, I have sacrificed a great title, huge wealth, marriage, the future of my children . . . By working as I have to keep him from the gallows . . . David had been angry when he knew of her conversation with Blanche's father; but had she been made free to marry – could they still have kept him to his engagement, after what she had said . . . ?'

Too late: for now it was done, the trial must be over – except for the woman and those four men in charge of the coach that night with Lady Blanche Handley, there could be no more witnesses. To be a highwayman, true, was a crime punishable by death; but what evidence had been given? – none – that this was in fact Gareth y Cadno, the highwayman. The charge was a charge of murder and only that. She caught at Catti's hand and Red Jenny's, leaned across to touch other hands held out to her in exultant relief. 'There can be no more witnesses: he must be safe!'

A man was climbing up on to the witness stand: no, not a man – a youth, thin, nervous, looking about him with apprehensive shifting eyes. Thomas Wragg. Lately page in the household of the Earl of Trove; subsequently dismissed. Present in waiting upon her ladyship in the coach that night...

Gilda turned her head wildly. 'There was none such present.'

'Hush, hush, they'll hear you! No,' said Dio, heavily, 'they've tricked us. There was none such there.'

'If the Earl of Trove—'

'It's not the Earl; it's the court. Do you think they haven't prepared – lest the case go against them . . . ?'

'But can we not say—?' she whispered back urgently.

'How can we? To speak a word would be to confess that we were there. And since we're known to be his friends...' He was silent, wretchedly listening to the boy in the box.

Yes, Thomas Wragg had been present that night. Yes, he had seen the pistol fired and the Earl fall and his brother also. Yes, he had seen the man that held the pistol – by a trick of the moonlight what might have been shadowy to others, from where he stood, was clear. Yes, he had seen the trigger pulled. Yes, the man who had fired had come forth from the shadows and stood out clearly to be seen. Yes, it had been this man.

The thunder of the court rose up in her ears, the foetid stink overpowered her senses; the figure in the dock, slumped, half stupefied against the rail, blurred, grew to a pinpoint of whiteness, faded into utter darkness.

When she came-to again she was outside, in some cold corridor of dank stone, with her head in Jenny's lap and voices whispering urgently together. Catti said: 'She's coming round,' and a hand slapped none too gently at her cheeks. But reality was too terrible to be borne and she let herself slip into half-consciousness again; and, her name recurring in the whispered conversation above her head, lay still and forced herself to a secret alertness...

Something about herself. Something about Gareth. Jenny protesting, horrified, terrified; accepting at last. 'But yet you said nothing, Catti—?' 'Dio forbade me.' But now – to protect Y Cadno?' 'Y Cadno made him swear.' 'Yet Dio told *you?*' 'He told me that night, a-bed; am I not his woman?' 'But, Catti – now?' And Jenny imploring and yet unsure of herself, Catti angry, rebellious, yet still in fear of Dio the Devil, rightly so named, though he could be so easy-going and kind. 'If I dared, Jenny! But I dare not...'

Gilda lay very still; listened, and at last understood; moaned a little, moved, opened her eyes... And there came a clamour from the courtroom and they spared no more words but hauled her to her feet and forced their way back there, dragging her with them. The mob was on its feet, waving, huzza-ing, throwing up into the air dirty caps and battered hats, screaming exultation; unquestioning, unreasoning, stupid as beasts of prey scenting the smell of blood. The tipstaffs bawled for silence, in the dock the russet figure swayed and slumped in the clutch of the warders; Dio and his men were up on their bench howling defiance, the women blubbered with tears, screaming as loudly, hitting out with viciously flailing arms at those nearest to them in the crush.

Guilty!

She looked into Catti's face, terrified, indecisive, deathly white; she looked at the half senseless figure, hanging forward from the arms of his gaolers, in the dock – and she thrust herself forward, fighting her way through the mob with beating fists and scratching nails, using the gold and ruby ring on her left hand as a weapon, and so came with torn dress, bruised face, disordered hair, at last to the witness stand; and unnoticed in the noise and fury all around her, climbed up and stood there, above them all, alone. In a doorway, the hunched old figure in the red gown was disappearing from sight. If she was to speak it must be before he was gone. She lifted her voice and above all their heads, above all the din, screamed out: 'He's innocent. It was I!'

In the doorway, beneath the upheld curtains, the old figure stiffened, turned. A hush fell upon the mob beneath her, all eyes turned upwards to the slender figure with its bulge of pregnancy, to the upflung hand imploring silence, to the radiance of her hair caught in the light that slanted down from the high windows, leaving all the rest in gloom. Into the hush she repeated it: 'It was not he who shot the Earl of Tregaron. It was I.'

A tipstaff moved forward, shoving his way through the crowd, but the judge made a motion that held him back. The old, red-clad figure crept forward a little. The old rusty voice croaked out: 'Madam – who are you?'

And she was back at the Cwrt: Miss Marigold Brown, the Marchesa d'Astonia no longer, but Madam Vixen of the Court of Foxes, who had laughed with him, dared with him, fought with him: found in his violent arms a wanton joy that made her blush to remember it. She said: 'I am she whom they call the Vixen of the Court of Foxes.'

In the dock the limp figure stirred, seemed to struggle for words, mumbled out: 'Madam – Vixen . . . ?'

'I am here, Gareth y Cadno – if you are Gareth y Cadno, and in this court not one word has been spoken that could prove it. But whoever you be, it was I who shot the Earl that night, and killed him. I confess it before the court. They must set you free.'

He raised his bleary eyes, focusing on the candlelight of her hair. He muttered and mumbled. 'No . . . No . . .' The judge said: 'The youth Spragg – Sprigg – what was his name?' – says it was the prisoner shot and killed Lord Tregaron.'

'This creature, Spragg, my lord, was not present. He's brought here falsely by the court.' She stared across the up-turned, gaping faces into the rheumy old eyes. 'I know this fact; and that alone should prove to your lordship – for you know it also – that I was there that night. For I *was* there. I stood in the shadow as the women have described, and there was – was one who stood beside me. The Earl was at the horses' heads and his brother, who gave witness here today. And she lifted her hands and ran them through the marigold gold of her hair so that it stood up around her head like a halo, an aureole. 'In the moonlight, the Earl caught a glimpse of my hair – as you see it now, my lord, in the ray from the window – and spoke a word and they both levelled their weapons; and in defence of my life, sir, I fired. I fired first and then this – this other that was with me, he also fired. And the Earl dropped and soon after died; and David Llandovery was wounded, as you have heard from him today. But, my lord – it was I fired first; and Lord Tregaron was the first to fall.'

Utter silence. She stood there, her hands gripping the edge of the box, the light slanting down on the halo of her hair. The old man said at last: 'Witness has been called that the prisoner fired the shot. What witness have *you?*'

She bit upon her lip, glancing over covertly to the benches where, hemmed in by the mob, Dio y Diawl stood, torn with indecision, one hand held like a vice upon Catti's wrist, forcing her to silence. To confess himself a witness would be to condemn them all: would be to condemn the Fox himself who was known to be of their company. While he remained in fact un-named – for it was true that no proof had been brought that he was in fact Gareth y Cadno, the highwayman – there might yet be hope for him, if the charge of murder be disproved. Dio's glance edged over to the dock, beseeching a sign.

And it came. The sodden figure raised its head, the dim eyes squinted in an effort of concentrated thought. 'Not – true . . .' And he leered over woozily, with blood-shot eyes to where Dio gazed back, imploring. 'No – witnesses . . . Not – true . . .' And at last, with a visible effort he raised his voice to instil into it the old note of absolute command. 'No – witnesses!'

Now when once again she came to herself, she was in the court no longer nor in the dark corridor outside, but in her own bed at home; and it was Catti who sat by her side and tenderly bathed her aching forehead and the bruises on her face and hands, and for the first time called her Madam Vixen and smiled at her, though she smiled with lips swollen from weeping. 'Forgive me, Madam Vixen fach; all you could do for him you have done and it would have meant your life if you'd been believed.'

'I didn't know it, Catti, till I heard you speaking of it to Jenny. I never thought of it . . .'

'You saved me also; for if I'd spoken, Dio would have killed me for it.'

'But Catti, it was all in vain?'

'In vain. The old man said that you lied to save your paramour, trusting to your womanhood and your condition to save your own life.'

'So for what I did – he dies!'

She shrugged miserably. 'Ah, Madam Vixen, why do we deceive ourselves? He dies because he's a highwayman: Tregaron or no Tregaron, now that they have him they'll never let him go.'

She went to see him only once again; with Catti, now her devoted friend, David himself protecting them, she braved a new and more terrible squalor leading to the dungeons where, as the Black Toby had warned her, he was now herded, as a convicted felon due for execution, with a dozen other wretches, like cattle into a single cell. No fashionable ladies now: and no wonder... He crept to the bars, lurched there sick and heavy, muttered only one word: 'Laudanum.'

They took counsel; for a day or two starved him of it, desperately hoping to bring back the old fire, the old wish to live. But he seemed beyond hope: he who had lived with high daring from day to day, now seemed from day to day, little by little, since he was to die – to die. They gave it up at last, conscious perhaps that it was less for him than for themselves that they tried to force him back to life and recognition; to cling to the old trust in him, the pride in him, the admiration – the love. 'He is less than we thought him,' said Gilda to Dio, privately. 'Why should he suffer the terrors of death – since he himself chooses to stifle it in drugs – just so that we should think otherwise.' And she sent him red roses, daily, with enough hidden in each bunch for another day's bemusement. More they dared not give him, lest he use it to end things altogether. And even that... But she could not bring herself to it; a foolish hope still stirred in them all that the fox who had run through the moonlit valley and mountains so bold and free, must even yet summon up the old, bright courage and cheat the hounds once more.

They would not let her go near him when the day came.

235

She was now seven months gone with child and ill and hysterical with the horrors of the past weeks: lying sick and languid, a prey to nightmares, on her frilly white bed in the Bijou with no comfort but the arms of her belovéd when he could come to her. They were not easy days for him either, poor David; torn between the railings of his mother, the tears of his sister, the stony resolution of Lady Blanche and her family, clinging to their rights in him. 'But *I'll* go there, Gilda, and if there be anything that can be done for him. I'll do it.' That it had been she who in fact had fired the shot that had killed his brother, he refused to believe, or at any rate to seem to believe; her action in standing up in court to accuse herself, he regarded with deep admiration, despite the pain it brought him. With the gang, he remained on terms of a sort of friendship, all of them united in support of his half-brother, and their leader. 'Only,' he said to Gilda, 'once all this is over – then it must be the end between you and them, as it will be the end between them and me.'

'They'll go back to the Cwrt. What am I to them that they should ever wish to see me again?'

'You called yourself their leader once to me,' he said. 'They call you the Vixen.'

'And so I was their leader.' Sick, peevish, over-excited, she snatched up a mirror and looked into her own white face, pale and puffed now with child-bearing, with sleeplessness and unavailing tears. 'So I was! – the Vixen, the Fox's mate, running with them over the mountains, leading them all to success, never failing them; not a silly, spoilt vapouring woman, saying Yes, David! No, David! Yes, David, I'll stay here as you order me! No, David, I'll not go there if you bid me not...!' And she struggled up off the bed. 'I *will* go. I'll stay with him, at least, to the end. Let him at least see me as he dies!'

'Gilda, for God's sake! – he'll not see you.'

'But if he should look for me...'

'He'll not look for you, Gilda.'

'You don't know that. He may – and if I were to be not there . . .' And she stumbled across to her dressing-table and took out the small, crumpled piece of paper that he had sent to her that night with his bunch of red roses – the night he had offered his life to save her from a moment of humiliation – and stared down at it wildly and thrust it into the bosom of her dress, close to her heart.

He got up slowly to his feet. He said: 'I have known it for a long time. You love him.'

'I love no one but you,' she said. 'But he . . .' And she fumbled for the paper again and held it out to him blindly. 'But he . . .'

I will love you till I die.

He persuaded her at last; or believed himself to have done so, believed her to have taken a calming drug and to be sleeping. She waited till he had gone with Dio y Diawl and the rest of them, then got up and dressed herself. 'Come Jake, we must go and very quietly. Is my mother safe out of hearing?' They crept out of the house and into the coach he had found for them while she dressed. 'Drive to Tyburn Way – where it crosses the way with the street out from the square. We'll wait there in the coach,' she said to the boy, 'and see how he passes. And if – if it seems as though he might need me . . .'

'He promised to wave to me, Gilda, as he went by. I hope,' said the little boy miserably, 'I hope he does not.'

'I have sent him red roses,' said Gilda, forgetful of all griefs but her own. 'If he carries them . . .' If he carried them it should be a sign that he was enough aware at least to make it imperative for her to be close by the gallows when he died, lest he wish for a last sight of her.

The highway was lined with people, more thinly to their right where the Oxford Road and 'the heavy hill' of Holborn led almost without curving from the church of St Sepulchre close by to Newgate, directly to the corner of Hyde Park where the gallows stood; the corner called in criminals' slang

237

The World's End – more thickly to their left where, ringed round by open galleries for the sightseers, she could discern the tops of the three posts from whose cross-beams the hanging ropes were slung. 'Where is David, Gilda? – and Dio and the rest?'

'They'll wait at St Sepulchre's to speak to him when the cart stops there; and run by his side the rest of the way to be near him.'

'Will the bellman preach to him across the wall of St Sepulchre's?'

'I dare say,' said Gilda; (and much good that would do any of them! He at any rate was likely to benefit more by the drink at the Half Way House.)

'They say that girls go all in white and strew flowers before the carts . . .'

Nor would that be any more appropriate, she thought; half sardonic, half in bitter tears – praying only that he might at least be aware, not sunk in the unworthy slough of his laudanum dreams.

'Why does he have no coach? Couldn't we have paid for it for him? Why need he come in a cart with the ordinary malefactors?'

'He would have it so,' she said, laconically. The fact was that they hadn't been able to get the idea through to him; he had simply sat stupidly, they had reported, or thrown maudlin arms around the necks of other prisoners and declared that he would die with his friends. David, tireless in generosity, had been to the Governor himself – such arrangements were easy enough, all prison servants paid for their appointments recouping themselves with money extracted from the prisoners and their friends. The Governor had accepted the bribe but made no promises except that the prisoner might take with him, in coach or cart according to how he finally elected to travel, his own coffin and a woollen shroud: by law, for the sake of the trade, wool was obligatory for all shrouds. Asked with an attempt at casualness whether friends

238

might remove the body for private burial, he had replied, however (with evident regret for further chances of milched gold beyond his powers to grasp), that no such arrangement would be possible. The matter was in any event not in his hands but in those of the Sheriff; and in this case there would be no getting round the Sheriff. There had been too many cases of felons cut down only half hanged (by bribery of the hangman) and rushed round the corner for waiting surgeons to revive. Not that they often succeeded but it was setting the law at nought, which was apparently strangely painful to the feelings of the present Sheriff; and moreover he had himself had experience with the gentry of the road, and the Fox was a feather – or a brush, said the Governor, laughing heartily at this pleasantry in his cap. He had specially appointed an officer to satisfy himself that prisoners were dead before they were cut down; and they were to be handed over for interment in the common grave, or to the hospital—

'Dear God!' said David, '—not that!'

The Governor shrugged. What matter once a man was dead whether he came beneath the anatomizer's knife or be thrown naked into a shallow grave, scraped out under the greasy cobbles of the highway. 'There is no sum,' said David, slowly, 'that would not be paid for his body – still with breath in it.'

'The Sheriff looks to be Lord Mayor one day; and anyway is already rich,' said the Governor. 'Put away your purse, my lord. No money will buy Y Cadno's life.'

By no means all of this had David told Gilda; by no means all of what she knew did she tell the little boy. 'If he rides in a coach, the people won't see him,' she said. 'It may be that he prefers to – to be seen. But he will have his coffin and decent burial . .'

'If a fox must die, he should die in the country,' said the boy, 'and lie under the heather and become a part of the hills he used to roam . . .'

To their right, the long road by which he must come at last; to their left the open galleries ringing the Triple Tree,

239

where the old women, 'the Tyburn pew-openers' would be collecting the half-crowns of those who could pay to see the fun from a comfortable vantage point. Today there were a round dozen to be hanged: four carts, three men to each, with the 'hempen cravats' all ready, about their throats, to be thrown up over the gallows bar and there fastened taut while the carts jerked away leaving the puppet bodies dancing in the air. She stood leaning out of the coach window to see above the heads of the crowd. Far, far to their right, an echo of the bell tolling at St Sepulchre's; closer to, the first rumblings of the uproar that greeted the leading cart: a thin wave of sound rolling nearer and nearer, crashing about their ears at last as the cart came into sight. Pulled by a stout horse, the driver gaily cracking his whip and bowing left and right with mocking salutation to the mob who jogged along-side, they came – three men, faced backwards, perilously rock-ing as the wooden wheels lurched and clattered deafeningly over the cobbles, stooping to clutch for support at the low sides of the cart. One man hugged the coffin standing upright beside him, wearing already the shroud bought for him by his friends; the two others took with them to their deaths only what they stood up in – the dirty rags of old finery or humble frieze, good enough to be stolen later by Jack Ketch from their dead bodies, or so filthy and worthless as to go into the pit with them.

The little boy shrank and trembled. 'Oh, Gilda – is he there?'

It gave her strength to have to be of comfort to him. She craned to look. She could not see their faces but there was no green coat among them nor one of russet; and one of these two he must wear, for he had no other. To think, she thought, that I must know him only by a piece of silk! – I who have . . . And she turned her mind from those memories of his lithe strong body in her arms, of the violence, the passion without tenderness, the terrible joy of his love-making. 'He's not there,' she said to the child. 'Not yet.'

240

The cart passed them, passed on out of sight. And a roar went up around the gallows far to their left, that swelled into a howl of excitement, falling suddenly to a sort of moan and then silence; she sensed in the distance the shudder of the three tall posts as the cart pulled away. But the shrill uproar was coming again from her right and the second cart approached: no russet coat, no green – only a man dressed like a bridegroom all in white, who grinned and capered and waved his hat to the crowd so drunk that he hardly knew what he did; and another who declaimed as he rode that he repented his sins and hoped for mercy and begged them that saw him to take heed, from his fate, that the wages of sin was death: and one that knelt huddled, and wept or prayed – who knew? And they passed and the tall posts shuddered again; and the third cart came in sight . . .

Still he was not there; and a sick hope rose in her heart that fought, however, with a hideous longing that she should see him, that it should all be over, that the unendurable tension should come to an end. 'He's famous,' she said to Jake, huddled beside her, his arm around her waist to support himself, his head poked out of the window, craning to see. 'Of course he'll come last – we should have thought of that and spared ourselves this much wretchedness of expectation at least.'

And the outcry came again, rolling down the cobbled highway towards them like a tidal wave, louder this time, on a strange note that rose to exultation and fell away into a sort of groan . . . Because he fails them, she thought. Because he doesn't bow to right and left and bandy jokes with them as befits a famous highwayman. She had sent him the drug herself, but, torn between love and un-love as she had ever been, it was horrible to find him at the last unworthy of such admiration as at least had never failed her. For a moment she wondered whether somewhere, hidden away beneath all this, there could not be still some plot for a last-minute escape; but she knew the gang too well, she knew that they could

241

not have concealed it from her if there had been any hope; she knew that they too were heart-broken at the discovery of those feet of clay.

And the cart rumbled into sight and was passing them; and she saw . . .

She saw not the green coat nor the russet: but a blur, a blaze of red, a blaze of red roses that he carried crushed close against his body as though his heart had broken and its red blood stained all his breast. 'Dear God!' she said to the little boy. 'Yes – he's there!'

He wore the green coat – the green coat that he had worn that night when first he came to the playhouse and had sent her red roses with that message so oft repeated: Till I die . . . ! And now he was to die – with her red roses clasped to his heart. 'We must be there! Drive on, drive closer!' she cried to the coachman, reaching out of the window to call above the uproar, up to the box. 'I must be near.' And she pulled Jake in with her, falling back with a jerk as the vehicle jolted into action, the man cursing as he fought his way round the edge of the crowd, fanned out now about the execution place. 'Jake, don't look, don't witness it, you mustn't have this to remember all your life. But I must be near him, I must be there!'

He was wretched, bewildered, huddled in the seat beside her. 'Why wasn't he bowing, Gilda, and looking about him and making jokes? He – he stood there as though he were – as though he were already half dead. He never lifted his head . . .'

'He isn't a fool, dearest, who would spend his last moments in silly bravado – whatever he might say to cheer you when your heart broke for him. He – he is at his prayers.' She improvised: 'He told me in the prison that when the time came to stand before his Maker, he would repent of his sins and pray. He said he had much to answer for; and that was true, Jake.' And she leaned out to call to the man, for the coach had stopped: 'Can you get no closer?'

'No closer, she says! Have I not mown down half the populace already and the horses frightened out of their wits? Besides,' said the driver, 'while we've fought our way here, the cart has gone unimpeded. They are already beneath the Tree.'

'Oh, God!' she prayed, 'Oh, God! Let me have courage – give me this last moment of courage and I'll ask no more of you! Give me courage – to see: and to be seen!' And she forced the child back, blocking the window with her body, standing up, lifting her white face, throwing back her veil to let him know her by that flame which in the dark playhouse of those other days, had caught his eye and all eyes by its ambience. The coach had drawn up behind a group of spectators standing in an entrance to the galleries; over their heads he could see her if he would but look up: would see at least the brightness of her hair and know that she was there. 'Gareth! Gareth y Cadno! I'm here, I'm with you! Raise your head, look at me!' Across the space where the three posts stood, she could see Catti and the other women, huddled, piteously weeping; posted somewhere near the Chit, she knew, would be the men, ready to run forward and swing upon the dancing legs, as he slowly strangled in the jerking noose. A plot, she prayed, a rescue! – even at this last hour. But as she had known that the lolling figure in the dock was truly less than half-conscious from the effects of the laudanum, so she knew it also now. Well, then – even half-conscious: might there not be a sudden assault, a scattering of the few attendants at this grisly scene, might they not bear him away and out of the crowd to safety? But she saw how densely the people were packed about the small ring kept free for the carts to come and go, and knew also that there could be no escape through that roaring, screaming, gin-soaked mob, howling only for blood. He must die. Would he but die like a man she knew!

The horse had been pulled up beneath the three posts, set in a triangle, joined by stout bars a foot or two above the heads of those standing in the cart. For a moment the green coat was lost to her sight as men leapt up beside the three condemned and roughly gathered up the ropes already about their necks. She caught a glimpse of a green sleeve, of a lolling body supported while they flung up the ends of the nooses, one to each cross-bar; crumpling against the side of the cart as they jumped down and stood away. 'Oh, Gareth!' she prayed, 'look up, stand straight, for this last moment be the man that you are: leave us not with this – degradation – to remember you by . . . !' She herself had sent him the laudanum, knowing that if he used it, she and all those who cared for him must pay with unworthy memories for his pain-less passing. Only . . . It was horrible to see it: to see him the object of the scorn and derision of the mob, pelted with filth scraped up from the ground round their feet, the ordure of rotted fruit and vegetables, of trodden straw, left over from other hangings there. Disappointed of a display of bravado from so renowned a malefactor, they spat and screamed, shaking angry fists, hurling abuse. His companions fended off the flying missiles, one laughing flung back as good as he got, one trembled and vomited and even at this last hour prayed mercy and begged not to die; but he – he stood as though deaf and blind to it all, sunk already into the oblivion of death.

A signal no doubt was given; for the crowd, knowledgeable, roared a last burst of mingled horror and joy. She saw the whip of the driver descend upon the startled horse which leapt forward in fear; saw the surge forward of the people, had a glimpse of faces she knew, of Dio's face and Huw's and little Willie-bach's, as they pushed forward in readiness to the front rank of the crowd; and screamed out above the tumult for the last time: 'Gareth! It is I, it's your Vixen! Gareth I'm here with you: look up at me!'

Did he lift his head for a moment? – did he in that last instant, turn his face to hers? She saw in a blur the red roses crushed like heart's blood against the green brocade of his

244

coat, saw the lurch and sway as the horse plunged forward and the cart leapt away; saw the sickening sideways jerk of the dark head as the neck took the body's weight, saw the three dummies dangle now, six foot above the ground: saw Dio and Huw and Willie-bach fling themselves forward, launching their weight upon the dreadfully dancing legs as the body jerked at the rope's end slowly strangling to death; and screamed to the coachman, 'Drive on, for God's sake drive on! Take me away from this place!'

And she looked back for the last time, the little boy beside her clinging, bitterly weeping, to her skirts; and saw that it was over, that he hung limp and only now at last bowed this way and that as he had promised he would: gently turning to left and to right with the slow twisting of the rope. The hands that had clutched her red roses had dropped to his sides, letting the flowers fall into the filth beneath his lifeless feet.

I will love you till I die.

CHAPTER SEVENTEEN

If the gang came to give her thanks and farewell, she knew nothing of it: lying between life and death in the frilly white bed, with grave old men shaking their heads over her and saying that the child must come too soon, far too soon. She was aware hazily that David sat hour after hour at her bedside; one day awoke to find herself in heaven with a vision standing there, all white and blue and crowned with gold, and cried out for Gareth who also was dead and must come to her now, must help her now . . . But the vision withdrew and somewhere out of sight spoke in low murmurs but in the language of the living. 'You're besotted, David; she was in love with that villain highwayman, even in her dreams she calls to him.'

'Very well but he's dead; she has nobody now but me.'

'And are you to be sacrificed, your whole life, your whole family – am I to be sacrificed? for this – this adventuress, who gives you not even her whole heart in return. No! – I will *not* release you: not for this.'

'Blanche, for God's sake, in your mercy . . . Now that you've seen for yourself . . .'

And a sad voice saying in tones very different from those that Gilda had heard in other days: 'You loved me once, David.'

'And would love you still, Blanche, in – in another way:

246

if you would show me this goodness, if you'd be merciful to her. And to my child.'

'Your children would have been mine.'

'If she dies, Blanche – if she dies and my child with her – do you think I could ever love again or love another woman's children? And if I leave her now, if I may not take her in my arms and promise her through her sick dreams that she shall be safe with me for ever – she will die.'

'You can never bring back to her the man she really loves.

'You may be right in this; you may see more clearly than I do or even than she does herself. But at least let me offer her this final proof of my love. They say the will to live isn't there: what has she to live for? – her true love gone, if you're right in what you believe; living on, a kept woman with a bastard child. And Blanche – if she dies, do you think I could ever forgive you for having robbed me of this last comfort . . .? If she dies . . .'

Only half heard, half understood, the voices faded; but through her dreams came at last a promise, oft reiterated, gently forced through to the inner depths of her consciousness – come back, my love, from this long, deep sleep, come back to life and health and be my wife . . .

He brought ministers to her bed and prayers were read and a thin hand wearing a golden ring, signed with feeble fluttering a new name: and a few days later to Marigelda, Countess of Tregaron, a son was born.

Now the Bijou was abandoned altogether, Mrs Brown moved its furniture into comfortable lodgings and embarked upon a life of her own, not untinged with romance. Little Jake was sent off to an educational establishment which might fit him for another than his chosen vocation as highwayman, Bess was married, and the brothers established in their own flourishing careers; and for the second time as Countess of Tregaron, Miss Marigold Brown entered the portals of the great, dull house in Hanover Square. Upstairs in nurseries of almost regal splendour, nurses watched over the life of the new little Viscount Llandovery; frail as a bird with wings ever fluttering, it seemed, to fly away into the cerulean blue for ever. In the great four-poster bed on the floor below, his mother lay and also fought her way back to life. And the fluttering wings at last grew still and the fluttering heart grew strong, and his tiny lordship raised hazy blue eyes and lifted a rose petal hand to the bright flame of his mother's hair; and that same candle flame was seen again at the playhouse and nowadays crowned with the glittering tiaras of the family store-house of jewels. If among the rest, she wore always a ring set with a great ruby, her new wealth of treasures was so vast that none questioned but that it was from among them. None but her husband.

The old Dowager mother-in-law came: stiff, resentful, inimical, belligerent. 'You may tell your mother from me, David, that I shall not tolerate it. I'm mistress here now – let her like me or go away.'

'My dearest, be reasonable,' he said, laughing. 'How could she ever like you? It's too much to ask.'

In other days, she also would have laughed. Now she only said irritably: 'Then let her at least be civil. Or let me leave here, let me go back to South Audley Street, I was happier there than ever I can be in this great tomb, as long ago I told you I should be. I'll take my child with me, you may live with us there if you will or only visit us as in other days you did; which days, I confess, slut and strumpet and the rest of it, were far better days for me.'

And better days also, perhaps, for David, Earl of Tregaron – with the ghost of another man always between them, the ghost of another life, wild and free. But the brown eyes were steady and kind, patient and firm. He spoke to his family, presumably – made such arrangements as would satisfy all without too much wounding any; would it not be best if his mother and sister took up residence in the Dower House in

Wales, with a house for the London season. 'But before they leave London, we must arrange the christening.'

'I'll have no christening with that old besom present. She'd spoil it all for me.'

'That's nonsense,' he said, sharply now. 'Of course the child's grandmother must attend. And my sister shall stand god-mother.'

'Very well. And Dio y Diawl shall stand god-father. I've long been resolved upon that.'

'Dio y Diawl — that monster from a robber's den?'

'He's my friend. He shall be god-father to my son.'

They faced each other across the huge, marble mantel-shelf in the huge, high drawing-room with its stiff furniture, exquisitely elegant, its protraits of past countesses wearing the jewels that nowadays adorned her own pale, haggard beauty. 'You're trying me, Gilda, to see how far I will be patient. I'll be very patient, have been very patient; you've undergone great stress, you've been very ill, I know that you've been in deep grief — I think you owe me something, if only your respect, in that I don't begrudge you your grief, don't begrudge it to *him*. But though you were a leader once, my love, and absolute in command — you're not so now. That was when the true leader, a man and therefore master, was absent. I am not absent and I am master here.'

She looked at him like a petted, wilful child, still struggling, rebellious, though she knew she had been conquered. 'I won't have the child christened here. He shall be christened in Wales, where—'

'Where your heart is,' he said, quietly.

She looked at him like a petted, wilful child, still struggling, eyes. 'Is that what you believe?'

'It's what I'm afraid of,' he said.

She came to him, came close, put her lovely arms about his neck. 'No, dearest, no: there you're wrong, utterly. I love you and only you. For him I had — something; I hardly know myself what it was. But he's gone; and with him, all but

249

memories. With him I was free. Here, it's true that I feel cribbed and cabined-in; but it's because others intervene.' And she tried to explain: 'All my life I've been used to love; only to love – to laughing and petting and loving without question . . .' Of the family of devoted brothers and sister he knew nothing, of the laughing, fond old mother, as young at heart as they. If the spectre of the supposed ancient, doting husband rose for a moment between them, that he put aside – he knew that no thoughts of life in Italy ever troubled her nowadays (as well they might not, since she had never seen stick nor stone of that country.) He said: 'You've never been loved, Gilda, as you're loved now. But to love isn't just foolishly to indulge. The child will be christened in London and my mother will be present and Dio y Diawl shall not.' He confirmed: 'And we are to call him Gereth, after my brother?'

'Or Gareth – after your other brother,' she said.

He bowed his head for a moment, with closed eyes as though he prayed for patience; gave a small thump with his fisted right hand to the marble mantel-shelf. But his voice remained steady. 'That was a private quirk – a private joke, perhaps – of my father's. To name his first born, though out of wedlock, by the family name, with only the difference of one letter.'

'What was good enough for your father—'

'We shall call the child Gereth,' he said, shortly. 'You may spell it which way – in your heart – you will. When you write it for the world, you will write it as the world will: Gereth, Viscount Llandovery.' But his stern mouth relaxed, he took her into his arms and held her close against his breast. 'Gilda, try to forget him! Try to forget!'

CHAPTER EIGHTEEN

The child was christened in the church of St George in Hanover Square as David had said it should be; and with his mother and sister present as he had said they should be, with the Prince of Wales instead of Dio the Devil of the Court of Foxes, standing god-father – she remembered again the brazen impudence with which that other had claimed that this 'intimate friend' would be disappointed at not being able to stand as witness at a great society wedding, the subtlety with which she had been led forward until it was she who pleaded for the secret marriage which must somehow be contrived – and a spurt of laughter welled up in her, she felt, for the first time in many long days, her heart leap up and dance . . . Leap and dance – and remember; and die.

And now Gereth, the small Viscount Llandovery was to be taken down to be shown to his people and the tenantry in the great, all-embracing estates in Carmarthenshire . . . (But a few short months, she thought, since I rode there and cried Stand and deliver! to just such folks as nowadays I myself shall be . . .)

A promise was extracted from her. 'No traffic, Gilda, with the Cwrt. That's understood?'

'I don't want to see them anyway,' she said drearily. 'They remind me of too much.'

But she wrote to them nevertheless, at his bidding, in the care of the corn chandler of Caio, giving times and dates, to ask for safe conduct through the Cothi valley. 'I know you will grant me this for old times' sake. And you'll never guess who rides in convoy with me,' she wrote, 'sheltering behind my petticoats – the Earl of Trove no less and my precious Lady Blanche Handley, going to their estates in Cardiganshire! They have waited for us; nowadays not daring to travel alone.' And she asked wistfully: 'I wonder how you fare? Is Dio y Diawl your leader now? I asked for him as god-father to my son, but you won't be astonished to learn that this was refused me. We had the Prince of Wales instead! Times have indeed changed, you perceive, for Madam Vixen and I confide, for your ears alone, that it's all very dull and sometimes I would feign be with you again.' She received a reply in due course, ill-scrawled upon the back of a reckoning for corn supplied (but not to the gang). 'Will give yr. messge to Y Diawl. Have no feer to come.' Signed by Dai Thomas whose comings and goings as a messenger she remembered of old. 'We are promised,' she reported to David, 'and your precious Blanche may come too; providing only for my part, that she stay in her own coach and sleep at separate inns on the way.' No doubt, she added contemptuously, they would be half a week upon the journey.

'My mother can't travel two hundred miles in a day.'

'She travelled it swiftly enough that other time – when ...' When I held up her coach, she had been going to say, but halted it. His mother had been hastening then because her first-born had been shot and killed upon that very road; and by herself, by Madam Vixen who was now Countess of Tregaron and her daughter-in-law.

They spent the second night in fact at Monmouth; but the roads were bad from recent rains and it was early evening before they drove, rattling and jingling, down the steep hill towards the Aberbranddu farm, with only the long rise through the hanging forests of scrub oak, between themselves and the chapel and smithy of Cwrt y Cadno; and then one more climb up and then all the way downwards to home. They must all now spend the night at Castell Cothi but tomorrow the old woman might be despatched to her new residence in the Dower House, the Earl of Trove could take his daughter and continue to Cardiganshire. And I, thought Gilda, I can settle down to the company of sheep and cows, as long ago we dreaded that I should have to. She had given her promise faithfully, to go no more to the Fox's lair. 'In any event, now adays it is but the Devil's Den. What is it to me without *him*?'

'Gilda, he's dead. I myself saw him nailed into his coffin, I myself saw him decently buried,' he lied. Thrown with two others, and the rest uncoffined, into a common grave, he did not say; but ended always with the old despairing plea: 'Try to forget!'

It was late summer; all about them the trees were in full leaf washed to a shining green by the soft Welsh rain; along the rough roads, foxglove and ragwort were in rampant bloom and the spreading white flowers they call Queen Anne's Lace; and dandelions and king-cups to outmatch her own marigold hair in their satiny gold. And up and over the bare mountains the gorse spread everywhere its heavily scented sweetness through an evening of sunshine now that the rain had passed. Its perfume brought back to her, almost more even than the sight of the mountain which now was all that hid the lair from her vision, the memory of those old days. For the gorse was with them always. Kissing's out of season, they said in Wales, when the gorse is not in bloom. At the Court of Foxes the gorse had been always in season: and the kissing too.

The Dowager travelled in the coach with them, Anne being in the second coach with Blanche and her father. The nurse sat opposite, the child in her lap, its blue eyes looking up, wondering, at the hanging lantern, unlit, swaying with each lurch of the wheels. 'We're coming down towards Aberbranddu,' said Gilda. 'It was here I always told them . .
It was there that she had taught them they should conduct their hold-ups, with room for the ponies to manoeuvre, not as had

253

been their custom, among the scrub oak trees, further up the hill – and proved to them time after time, how right she had been.

The Dowager Countess of Tregaron had been travelling this road before Madam Vixen had been born or thought of. 'I think we're sufficiently aware of the points of interest on our way,' she could not forbear to say sharply. Including, she did not dare to add, a tree overhanging the road a little further on, where their first acquaintance had been made – the present countess having upon that occasion, however, been upside-down. 'Do you recall,' she said to David, deliberately excluding Gilda from the conversation, 'how when you were a child we still had to ford the river here? Now that the bridge is built, it's safer; but then with the coaches brought to a halt when the water was deep, it was a dangerous place for – for . . .' Her voice faltered.

'For hold-ups?' said Gilda. 'And could be now, may I remind your ladyship. When you turn your back and address your civilities exclusively to others, recollect that but for me you wouldn't be riding here so free to exchange your reminiscences unmolested.' David shook his head at her warningly, his mother glanced anxiously at the nurse – dozing, however, with the baby on her knee. 'Oh, pish!' said Gilda. 'What do I care? Not a doubt but she knows all about it, they all do. All I say is that only through my good offices do you ride here without anxiety – you and your precious friends who must all come cap in hand to me, every time you would set foot outside your own gates—'

And a man's voice shouted from the box and there was a clatter of hooves and the rattle and jingle of harness as the coach jolted to a halt; and outside the windows movement, confusion, a swarm of riders breaking cover and galloping on the small, rough, sure-footed ponies that so well she knew, across the river bank towards them, surrounding them. The nurse awoke with a shrill squeal of terror and clutched the baby to her breast, the old woman shot out a fat, mottled hand to catch at David's arm; from the coach behind came the familiar high note of a woman beginning to scream. 'Pouff, what a fuss! – it's nothing to be afraid of,' said Gilda, contemptuously. 'We're promised safety. They come but to pay their respects to me.' She stood up to lean far out of the window and cried out for Dio, for Huw, for Willie-bach and Hal the Hop and Dai. But from behind her David said in a small, cold voice: 'Gilda!' and she turned her head.

A blotting out of the light from the opposite window; and a darkness there that revealed itself as a tall figure, cloaked in black with a black mask through which two eyes glittered, steely blue. 'Well, Madam Vixen – so we meet again! And this time it's *my* turn.'

The Black Toby.

He was her friend of course – of course! Had he not been good to her, truly good, looking for no reward, in those days of Gareth's imprisonment? But now . . . She said sharply, subsiding into her place, looking up at him, trying to hold fast to her waning self-confidence: 'What are you doing here?'

'I believed myself to be holding up a coach,' he said, mockingly assuming doubt.

'This coach has been promised safe conduct,' said David angrily.

'Not by me. And if you're groping for a weapon, my lord, pray desist from it. I've taken the precaution to have mine more readily to hand.'

Did the old woman, even in her extremity, find heart for one glance of triumph at her daughter-in-law? 'You're teasing me,' said Gilda, not too certainly however. 'These men with you are of Y Cadno's gang.'

'Who however lies four feet below the Oxford Road.'

'Do you mean that *you*—? But you're one that hunts with no pack,' protested Gilda. 'You're one that rides alone.'

'As you have good reason to remember, Madam Vixen,' he assented, laughing. 'A leopard may change his spots, however.

I told you I had a fondness for this part of Wales; and so, since I was under an obligation – whose price you will recall? – not to ride in opposition to Y Cadno's pack, why, what was there to do but to join them?'

'And to lead them?'

'I am like you,' he said. 'Not one to trot behind another less able than myself.'

She was defeated. And yet – not quite defeated, never quite defeated while she held still that old power over men which had won him before and might yet win again. For such gold as they carried, for a few jewels, she cared nothing; but to have the old besom crow over her unsuccess in protecting them, to have Madame Blanche toss that corn-coloured nob of hers and smile her cool smile at the failure of her rival – that she would not endure. 'What is it you want?' she said at last: deliberately.

'What is it you offer, Madam Vixen?' he said – and laughed again.

If David caught a hint of the meaning in her voice, he stifled his awareness; there was no mistaking however the undertones of the reply. He said as though to end the matter: 'We carry little that is of value. Take what there is and let us go.'

'On the contrary you carry a great deal that is of value – to me at any rate.' The barrel of a pistol appeared in the window, a steady hand gestured with it briefly. 'Come Madam Vixen – out!'

David made an effort to launch himself forward but he was helpless, penned in between the women, struggling to get at a weapon which, since they had entered the Cothi valley he had, under promise of safe conduct, kept not easily within his reach. Gilda implored: 'Keep still, don't make matters worse!' And she swore: 'I know this man, he makes a grim joke of it but he's a friend. You saw him, David, in the inn at Newgate. Was he not then our friend?'

'Well said,' said the Black Toby. He pulled off the mask,

showing clearly in the evening light the keen, dark face and the brilliant eyes. 'I am everybody's friend. What is he afraid of?'

'That you may become a little too friendly,' said Gilda, coolly. 'In short that you may carry off his wife and ravish her, which no doubt is in fact your intention.'

He went off into roars of laughter and she thought guiltily that for months she had not heard such laughter – huge, free, untrammelled by the politenesses of society manners and mannerisms; a laughter that was against her and yet with her, affectionately indulgent and yet promising no particular indulgence if she came to resist him – a man's laughter at the expense of a woman whom he could not help but admire and – a little – love. (So had that other one laughed in days when freedom and laughter had been commonplace.) 'Why, Madam Vixen, what ideas you have! And yet, what good ones!' The steely eyes peered into the interior of the coach. 'Who have we here? Why, my lady the Dowager, no doubt? – your good mother-in-law. Come now, Madame Dowager, yours shall be the choice. Will you buy your safety and your son's and that of your friends in the coach behind – at the expense of Lady Tregaron's virtue?'

The old woman stared back at him viciously, stared back and then turned away her head. 'We could hardly trust to promises purchased at so low a price as that.'

'David!' cried Gilda, furious; but he had not heard, he was up now and out of his seat and had launched himself headfirst, weaponless, at the black-cloaked figure in the window. 'You filthy brute, lay so much as a finger upon her—!' He fought and struggled, bursting open the door, rolling out on top of the tall figure which, taken unaware by the suddenness of the onslaught, had tumbled over backwards with the violent pushing open of the door, into the road. Sam the Saddle ran up and Hal the Hop, limping, and hauled David off. 'For heaven's sake, good sir,' said the Black Toby, getting up, still laughing, brushing himself down, 'it was your lady

257

mother said it – not I!' But in the sudden small silence, while David stood, held back by two pairs of hands, he slowly swivelled round to face the coach again. 'Why, Madam Vixen – what have we here?'

She stood upon the step of the coach, behind her peering out the two anxious faces of the nurse and the Dowager; and now she held David's pistol, aimed with a deadly menace at the heart of the Black Toby himself. 'What we have here,' she said, 'is indeed Madam Vixen: and with her claws unsheathed. You perceive that I am armed.'

He still laughed. 'It was quite other arms I had intended.' His own arms, nevertheless, were held well away from his coat pockets in earnest that he would not draw and attack.

She stood there on the step: not taking her eyes from him, issued orders. 'Dio – Huw! Get the women out of the other coach.' Now that she had the upper hand, Miss Blanche should see whether she had 'failed' or not. And she waited till the golden head appeared, stooping to clear the low doorway; then she motioned, still watching him, with the butt of the weapon. 'You want arms, sir – there's a pair for you, as white as mine; and at least no more unloving.'

David, still held fast by Hal the Hop, had forced his way round to stand close to her. 'Gilda, for God's sake—'

'Hold your peace, David, and let your mother speak. Well, Madame,' she cried back over her shoulder to the shuddering old woman behind her, 'what say you now? You were ready enough to sacrifice my virtue – non-existent as you suggest – for your gew-gaws—'

'Gilda, my mother said no such—'

'Be quiet!' she said angrily again and again motioned with the gun. 'Come Mistress Blanche, come closer, let him look you over. It's you or me. My Lord the Earl of Tregaron has preferred *me*: let's see if you'll be more fortunate with the highwayman!' And she remembered: remembered the insults, remembered the broken promise, for it had amounted to no less – the cool little, chill, contemptuous nod across the gaping faces of the playhouse audience – remembered that to force the humble curtsey that had made amends for it, Gareth y Cadno had died. 'Now I'll make you pay,' she said in a voice of cold rage that astonished even herself. 'I saw him dance on the gallows, I saw all his courage brought low – now you shall dance my fine lady, and we'll see how *your* courage keeps up. As you danced that night in the moonlight, not a hundred yards from here and with your petticoats gone, so you shall dance again, when I bid you; and not once but a hundred times and for a larger audience and I promise you no more kind. For while I'm leader of this band...' She broke off. She called out sharply: 'Dio y Diawl – Catti, is that you standing there in the shadows? – Dio, Catti, Sam – this man who stands here at my pistol point – is this indeed your leader? Do you so acknowledge him? Of Y Cadno's gang?'

They were silent, shifting, not knowing how to reply. Dio spoke at last, his eyes questioning the others. He said: 'He is not our leader – no.'

'You hear that, Black Toby?' she said; and lifted her voice and cried out, as she had cried long ago, perched on the great central boulder of the ring of rocks that had formed the council place of the Court of Foxes: 'Who is your true leader?'

Again the long silence; the exchange of glances. And Dio lifted up his head and said: 'To us – after the Fox – you are still and ever our leader, Madam Lluinoges; our Madam Vixen.'

'For God's sake, Gilda, for God's sake!' pleaded David, at her side; helpless, held fast by Hal and by Huw who had moved round and joined them again. But she ignored him, lashed to a blindness of rage at the memory of that cool little nod across the playhouse, which for one terrible moment had revealed her to herself; and of the horror of its consequences to them all. 'Very well. I am Y Lluinoges and I rule here. And while I rule, this woman shall pay. Slut and strumpet you

259

called me, Mistress Blanche, you and all your kind, but you especially, crying it out for all to hear; slut and strumpet, those were the words he died to avenge.' For this he had died, had lost in shameful captivity the bright, bold courage of the days of his freedom, for this he had surrendered all his pride. 'Slut and strumpet. Well, you shall come to know what those words mean; for a slut and a strumpet you shall be indeed, Madam Blanche, and not in love to one man, but to any who'll condescend to take you on the rough ground at the Court of Foxes, where I've seen many a woman tumbled in my time, for the amusement of the lookers-on .. And pick yourself up and curtsey for the privilege, curtsey to me as you curtseyed that night and so sent him to his death ...' And she lifted up her hand and cried out: 'Curtsey! Curtsey now! These are his people, curtsey to them, show them what it was he died for!'

The lovely head bowed, the lovely corn-coloured head; like a swan folding its white wings, she sank down into the great, slow, single, undulating movement of the formal curtsey; and rose and stood, still as marble again. Beside the coach the old woman shuddered and moaned, her pale face staring, ugly with pain; within, the nurse sobbed and stared, clasping the child in her arms. At the second coach, two men held the Earl of Trove by the arms, feebly struggling, bleating out small agonised appeals; Jenny Coch had Anne by the wrist ... 'Gilda,' said David, standing swaying by her side, so pale that he seemed about to faint, 'can this be really you?'

She was silent for a long moment. Then she said: 'Perhaps it is; and I've never known it till now.' The rage had gone; she said, muted, almost apologetic: 'Because she wouldn't curtsey to me, David – he hung there and died.' And she listened for the answer – unable to believe that it did not come at once, that he did not respond to her without question in the old, kind, patient, all-embracing, enduring love. 'David,' she begged, 'understand me, be patient with me ...' And so beseeching, turned her head to him.

And the Black Toby sprang.

Her attention had been not more than half deflected; almost before he moved, she had the pistol trained back upon him and, without a moment's hesitation, fired point blank at him. But the ball flew past his arm and only tore his coat; and he laughed – but backed away from her, after all, and, moving faster and faster, came close to a gorse bush and dogged behind it. 'Quick, after him!' she cried; but they all seemed occupied, some at the horses' heads, some with their weapons trained on coachmen and outriders, some holding the passengers, still; and no one followed her as she ran, her left hand holding back her skirt, the weapon steady in her right hand, flying down towards the bush where he stood. His teasing voice mocked at her from behind it – from her right as he dodged to the shelter of another – further to her right again. She followed him, skimming over the rough grass, bent only upon one thing – that she would be Vixen here and would brook no impostors. He won't shoot me, she thought; I'm safe enough from that ... What else he might do, she did not stop to reckon – that she could deal with one way or another as suited her best. But she would be Vixen here!

And she passed a clump of alder and was in a small clearing; and from behind her a shape slipped out, shadowy, and caught her by the shoulders and turned her swiftly so that she stood close; and a hand in her hair yanked back her head and hard, fierce, painfully and yet wildly thrilling as it had ever been – a mouth came down upon hers.

Those lips, that slender body, hard and taut, those arms of steel – she knew them, all too well.

'Oh, Gareth, Gareth, Gareth y Cadno! – it can't, it *can't* be you?'

261

CHAPTER NINETEEN

Of the Black Toby – no sign. 'A lure, Madam Vixen: I knew you'd not be able to resist the challenge of an intruder in my place – my place or yours, whichever you prefer to call it.' And he laughed, looked down at her, dark, brilliant, mocking, so that her heart turned over with a longing to be caught in his arms again and held close and hard against his wicked heart. 'He returns soon whence he came; but he's been my good friend.'

'Gareth,' she said, 'how can it be you? I myself saw you die.'

'Oh, that!' He shrugged it off. 'You couldn't think I'd quite so meekly deliver myself over to Jack Ketch?'

'But I saw you – we all saw you. We saw you hanged, we saw you die!'

'You saw another man die, wearing a green coat and clutching a bunch of roses – I having promised to care for his family, as I have done ever since. I have them here with me at the Cwrt.'

She summoned up her old spirit. 'A fine way of caring for them that is!'

'He was a mere footpad; they'd have fared no better with him. And since he had to die, what matter how he did it? – if it meant help for those he left behind.'

'But a dozen men died. There were twelve to be hanged and twelve were hanged for I saw them.'

262

'Ah, yes, the turnkey stood in for me – hung in for me, if you prefer it so. Or rather – it's all sadly complicated – for my friend the footpad who, in turn, was acting *my* part. If the turnkey would but have hugged a bunch of flowers and undertaken not to lift up his head, it might have been more simple; but we had to keep him deep in laudanum – I thank you for such liberal supplies! – or he might have proved less quiescent than he did in the end. Or so they tell me; I wasn't there to see.'

'Where were you, if one may ask; comfortably a-bed, no doubt, while we all broke our hearts for you.'

'Why, and you guess right, my love; a-bed is just where I was.'

'A-*bed*?'

'Ay, but alas, alone – in Bart's Hospital where such accommodation as a doxy's not encouraged. They bundle you in with two or three, to be sure, but all, alas, of the same sex.'

'You were in St Bartholomew's Hospital?'

'Come, sit down,' he said, 'and I'll tell you.' He took her hand and pulled her down beside him on the rough grass. 'I was there in my part of the turnkey, don't you see? We overpowered him – my friends in the Condemned Hole entering very kindly into the plot with me, for if they were to die, they might as well amuse themselves meanwhile any way they could; and he was a villainous fellow, brought in especially for the work and a specialist in brutality. We forced laudanum down him and when he was senseless put him into my clothes and I got into his, inflicted upon myself some slight wound and cried out "Help! Help!" and, "I have been set upon!" and other such nonsense as would bring assistance running; and so was carried off to the hospital hard by, the poor fools quite satisfied with seeing the other lolling there wearing my green coat and in my accustomed condition – for I fed myself some handsome doses of the drug for many days, to allay suspicion. As I've said, the fellow was a stranger there, brought in especially upon my account and all I need do was bloody my face while they carried me away, lest anyone recognise me; and in the hospital complained of the light a good deal and there's little enough of it anyway. My friends kept him deep in laudanum I suppose for the last hours, and so, too far gone to pipe up a word for himself, he's carried off with the rest to the Nubbing Chit.' He went off into gales of laughter. 'Hung their own man, can you beat it? And I meanwhile, rose up quietly from my bed and thanked all concerned profusely, sent in my resignation at the prison, saying I dared serve no more after having been so vilely manhandled by its wicked inhabitants; and so went my ways ...'

'Not caring that you left me near on my death-bed with grief?'

'Well, but you had your dear Dafydd to comfort you,' he said coolly, 'who, by your present good looks, appears to have succeeded very well.'

She flared up angrily. 'You show little gratitude for the fact that I – and he too – stood by you till the end; soaked in laudanum though you might be – might appear to be,' she amended, conceding that much.

'Why, yes, and it seems you made a fine showing in the court also, near won over the old judge though in the end he must give way to expedience. But I fear I missed the show; then if ever was the time to exhibit myself as truly given over to such oblivion as the drug would procure for me.'

'But Dio and the rest—?'

'—knew nothing of it till the last. I couldn't rely upon their acting abilities. Only while they ran beside the cart from the Half Way, did my friends, kneeling, pretending to pray, mutter out the plot to them – to Dio and Huw and those that must see the body cut down and know it not mine – the women and others were still kept in ignorance lest they give the game away. Yet another kindness that I did for my friend with the roses, for he had no others to pull upon his legs for him, and could pay none.'

'And this wretched turnkey – an innocent man, sent to his death—?'

'Was I not an innocent man?' he said coolly. 'You yourself stood up in court it seems, and said so.'

She could not help laughing; was horrified, laughed again. 'You're ruthless,' she said. 'Ruthless!'

'I value my life,' he said. 'That's all. And have now another lease of it; the more so as they've hanged me and are done with me and dare not ever hang me again – or what will the world think of their justice?'

She was silent; all of a sudden there seemed no more to say. She stood up, brushing the golden fronds of the dried grass from the dark green of her skirt. 'Well – since the gang appear to have after all a leader—' she shrugged, deprecating '– at least as good as I – I may as well return where I now belong.' She put out a careless hand to him and he took it and hauled himself up from the grass; but at once dropped the hand, having no further use for it. She said: 'I take it we now have safe conduct? We may all be gone?'

'All but one,' he said.

'All but one?' And suddenly she saw that it was very strange, this contrived encounter, with the Black Toby employed to lure her forth, to bring her to this secret assignation, leaving them all in doubt. She faced him in the dying light of the day, the great mountain rising up grim, and yet dearly familiar, behind her; her hair flying like a blown torch in the rising wind. 'Gareth – why have you brought me here? It isn't gold and jewels, I know that. What is it you want?'

He was silent for a moment, as if for once even he was a little afraid to voice his thought. He said at last: 'It is the fox cub.'

'The fox cub?'

'The boy,' he said. 'Your child and mine.'

'Your child—?' Fear caught at her heart now. 'You want the baby?' She confronted him, the wild hair blowing away from a face grown absolutely white; and said with deliberation: 'This is a trick for ransom: and such a trick, even you, Gareth, couldn't play, and survive. There's no force in England or Wales would not be employed if you were to take this child. He's the son of the Earl of Tregaron, let me remind you: he is Gereth, Viscount Llandovery—'

'He is Gareth the Cub – son of Gareth the Fox,' said Y Cadno. And he smiled but it was grimly, with very little mirth in it. 'Born prematurely, my dear Gilda, I understand?'

Such a thought had never entered her mind; occupied as it had been during much of her pregnancy and ever since, with horror and – God forgive her! she thought now – with grief, at the fate of this villain who now stood before her. 'You truly believe that the child is yours?'

'Make your calculations,' he said and laughed outright. 'It was October, was it not? – that evening by the river's edge.'

Now terror entered into her, she began, perhaps for the first time in her life, to be truly afraid, truly bewildered in her fear, a rising panic numbing her understanding. 'The physicians—'

'The physicians were misled by you no doubt; deliberately or – it now seems – otherwise; had you forgotten your fainting attack that morning I robbed the Lady Blanche, when you came to my hide out? I confess that when I saw you at the playhouse you seemed to me remarkably far gone for a lady so recently admitted to the arms of her lover.'

And again that last day at Castell Cothi – had she not fainted away for no apparent reason at all? And if it were all true . . . Her child had been to her – a child: something of her own, no doubt, but born to her after long illness, taken from her immediately, reared by others – the little Lord Llandovery, whose very name, whose present, whose future belonged to that other world of great lands and grand titles, where such things were ordered by age-old tradition and not by owning, by motherhood, by the long travail and the pangs of birth. But now . . . Torn ever between two loves, she asked herself how much room there was in her heart for a third;

266

for this small son who, claimed on this side and that, at least without question was her own. I must cling to that, she thought; he is my own. Somewhere deep in her heart was the knowledge that this might not be the true maternal love but would do well enough in its place. 'I'll never give him up,' she said. 'I'll never give him up.'

'Who asks you to? You may come with him if you will – I care not one way or the other. But he's my son and no other man shall have him.'

'He is the son of the Earl of Tregaron. He's the Viscount Llandovery.'

'If he's the son of the Earl of Tregaron,' he said laughing, 'then he's not the Viscount Llandovery, or no more so than *I* ever was – who also am the bastard son of an Earl of Tregaron.' And he reminded her mockingly: 'For while I am alive, my dear – his mother is not the Earl of Tregaron's wife.'

'Dear God!' she said, confounded. 'It's true. And if so – I'm not truly married to David . . .'

'None knows that,' he said quickly, 'save you and I and a handful of friends who will never speak of it. You may continue as his wife if you will – since the loss of him, I perceive, brings a new blanch to your cheek and a new trembling – *and* as Countess of Tregaron, though I do you the justice to believe that that means less to you – to the end of your days; and your children his heirs. But not this child. This child is mine.'

'Gareth – Gareth, for God's sake . . .' But her mind seemed sick and dazed, she groped in a fog of doubts. She said at last (lying, for if the child resembled anyone it resembled only herself) 'Now I think of it – you're wrong – it *is* David's child, you have but to observe the likeness . . .'

'A Tregaron likeness,' he said, tossing it aside. 'Of which family, if only by blood, I also am a member.'

She was defeated. 'You've thought of everything,' she said, and moved away from him, blindly, hardly knowing what she did or where she went, half-way across the little clearing

267

and back again – found a great rock and leaned back against it, her head bowed, her hands clenched against her forehead. 'Have pity on me, Gareth! What could I tell David? What could I say? I – I told him I had resisted you ... Am I now to say that you claim parentage? – so that he'll force me to let the child go, believing it to be a bastard, after all—?'

'The child can't be a bastard,' he said, 'unless it be his child. But it's my child – born, for a wonder, in wedlock.'

'—very well then, believing it not his own. What does it matter? Either way, he'll force me to hand over my baby to you.'

'Who, however, am four foot underground. You forget,' he said, ever mocking, 'that your first husband is several months dead.'

She dashed her little fist into the hollow of her hand. 'That at least can soon be dealt with; for I shall tell him, even if I tell no other, that you are not dead.'

'What, and find yourself no longer Countess of Tregaron? You move round in circles, my dear! For, with all dear David's doting, I don't see him accepting you as his wife, knowing you to be otherwise; begetting upon you other children to be – illegitimately – his heirs. Do you?'

Her whole body sagged, she turned against the rock and, half lying there, pressing her forehead against its rough, cool surface, broke into despairing tears; and for the first time in her life, pleaded with him. 'Oh, Gareth – spare me: spare me! Why should you be so cruel to me?'

She could imagine the little shrug, the hard line of his lips, the gleam in his dark eye. 'I don't deal in softness,' he said shortly.

'When you were in trouble,' she said, sobbing, 'I offered everything – I offered my very life for you, when yours was in danger.'

'It was on your account that it *was* in danger,' he said indifferently, 'so that was but fair. And in any event, I repaid

268

the kindness, did I not? By my supposed death, you became a great lady, you married the one of your choice. And what do I ask now? – only my son. You may have all the rest – you may have your estates and your titles, you may have your belovéd; and a pack of other children to make up for the one I take.' And he put out his hand and caught at her shoulder, pulled her up, roughly, from where she crouched, leaning against the rock; turned her round to face him. 'Come, up, girl! – and show a little of the vixen in you – you've grown soft of late, lying in a soft white bed, folded in the soft white arms of my Lord of Tregaron.' He pulled out a cambric handkerchief, filched no doubt from some traveller of other days. 'Here mop up these tears, you're blubbered and unlovely to the sight!' As she sobbed and sniffed and pushed back her hair from her hot forehead, he spoke to her sharply in the old tones of unquestioned command. 'I've been teasing you; in fact it's all arranged. While we've talked here – (and have no anxieties, the Black Toby will long ago have returned to them and remained there; your love is not thinking of you as in his arms – Dio will have disappeared and be supposed talking over affairs of the gang with you) – while we've been here, I say, the women will have discovered themselves afire with curiosity to see the dear little lordling – his nurse bundled out of the coach and dispossessed of her charge; and there'll be a great dandling and cooing and running off to show the child to this one and that, each further away from the coach than the last. Tears and terrors, no doubt, from the ladies as to the little one's peril in those rough hands; but behold! – he will be returned to his nurse's arms at last, safe and sound, and all will be happiness again.' He paused; and again there came that faint hesitation as though he were almost afraid to voice his thought. But . . . 'These great folk,' he said, 'what do they see of a child? Poke beneath his cap and chuck his chin and hand him back to the nurse; and she a new one, I understand, having succeeded the wet nurse? And . . . Well, one baby is much like another; and this one also will have

269

the Tregaron blood and has, I promise you, something of the Tregaron look.'

'*Gareth!*'

'You didn't suppose me lying alone through the long nights up at Twm Shon Catti's cave? A pretty little creature – for a time I was quite seriously taken, especially when I found she was with child. Serving wench she was at the Towy Bridge inn – that same inn where I held up the Lady Blanche; my pretty Mifanwy it was who then gave me the assistance I needed. Returned now to her native Pembrokeshire; but she left me a legacy and a blue-eyed one, by heaven's favour, her own being as blue as the skies; for my information from London is that – unlike most fox cubs, I confess – this one has blue eyes.'

She was speechless; standing there helpless, confounded, the dark green dress a blot against the pale of the grass, her face white and luminous as a pearl in the evening light, crowned with the gold of her hair. 'So, Madam – dry your tears! Lord Tregaron has still a son and of the Tregaron blood; and may still have a wife. And you have my oath on it – the solemn oath of Gareth y Cadno – that from this day forth I will trouble you no more. Only . . .' He caught up her lax hand and drew from her finger the gold and ruby ring. 'This I will reclaim; not for the jewel, but for the words that have always gone with it. Another oath, but one from which I will ask you to absolve me after all.'

I will love you till I die.

She went from him without a further word, climbed back up the sloping bank between the clumps of gorse, the turf springy beneath her feet. The sky was darkling blue, at the roadside the two coaches made black humps, the horses restlessly stamping their hooves with a jingle of harness and creaking of leather, tossing nervy heads against the light restraining hands on the reins. The ground was fairly level here, ringed round with a few bushes and trees. Against one of the trees, separated by twenty yards or so from the group

270

by the coaches, the Black Toby negligently leaned, his pistol, however, resting upon a crook'd arm, pointed towards where David stood beside the foremost coach. The nurse was not to be seen – was within, no doubt, with the new little Lord Llandovery in her lap fast asleep in his hurriedly substituted rich embroidered clothes, all unaware of the magnificent future – bastard brat of a tavern doxy and a highwayman on the run, in whose veins however coursed the blood of the great family whom he would one day represent before the world. The old mother was still out, however, standing beside her son, almost as though she would protect him: deathly weary, deeply afraid, and yet with something always of that spirit that could make one, disliking her, still never quite despise her. And the Lady Blanche... Standing there like a statue, still, with no outward sign at least of the terrified dread that must be in her heart. I remember, thought Gilda reluctantly, how she took the ball from David's shoulder when he lay wounded on this very road: saved his life, perhaps – braver than I in that, for all she might hop without her petticoats and have less courage for being seen not absolutely decent than she had for probing a wound and seeing the blood flow... And she told herself bitterly, smiling, that it was as well she could find it in her to feel not too badly towards them: for through the long future, for David's sake, these were to be her companions and friends. She had this moment made the final choice.

The gang stood or sat around, each alert to guard his own charge, the women clustering, curious, their children about their skirts. In Catti's arms, a small bundle rolled in a shawl – a shawl, woven, no doubt, at the Cwrt itself of wool culled by the children from the thorny hedgerows after the sheep had passed. Catti would care for the baby, would protect it with her life; she loves me, thought Gilda, and she loves Gareth, and the fox cub will be safe with her. If it were otherwise... If it had been otherwise she could never have let him go. Would she ever see him again? she wondered: her little son – riding by, perhaps, a small boy, fierce and proud as his father was, sitting a sturdy pony, bright with the finery of pillaged passers-by? – would she, a great lady driving in her stately coach, lean out one day and say to her own son, 'I have safe conduct,' and hear him say: 'Pass friend.' Oh, David, she thought: for your sake – only for your sake!

She came out of the shadow of the trees and stood there, apart from them all; the pistol in her hand. The Black Toby roused himself from his leisurely watch. 'Well, Madam Vixen, I perceive that you are in command again; and will therefore ask your permission to be on my way.'

She nodded absently. 'And with my best thanks for your – assistance – upon this and other occasions. Which is not to say,' she added sharply, however, 'that you're absolved of your old undertaking not to poach upon Y Cadno's preserves.'

He choked up laughter. 'What, not upon any of his preserves?' And he came across to her and held her hand and kissed it – not as the fashion was, but as a lover. 'Farewell, Madam Vixen, then.' A man brought forward his horse and he swung himself up; turning, tall, splendid, in the long black cloak with the old glitter of steel in his eye. 'It's late: I have your permission to sleep this night at least upon your territory?'

'If it be for the last time. You'll find accommodation – of every kind, I understand – at the drovers' inn beside the Towy.'

'Even nearer than that,' he said. 'You forget I have ridden this way before.' And he bowed, bowed to them all: his horse's hooves thundered on the rough grass with the sudden energy of his departing; she heard them strike hard among the stones of the road as he came off the grass, slow down as he started the long, steep ascent of the mountain towards Cilycwm. 'Relax your guard, let the ladies get back into the coaches if they will, and you, my lord of Trove; there's no more danger.' And across the intervening space she advanced a little and said softly: 'David—!'

He came over the grass to meet her but slowly, reluctantly

272

and she saw that he was dreadfully pale, stricken, sick of some inner anxiety unconcerned with considerations of their physical safety. They faced each other, apart from the rest, out of earshot. 'Oh, David,' she said, flinging aside the pistol to lie on the grass at their feet, going to him with outstretched hands, 'it's over.'

He seemed hardly to hear her, staring at her with that stricken look that made her heart turn over with pity and love for him. 'Gilda,' he said, 'I don't know you. I thought I knew you; but now – I think all this time I've known nothing about you after all . . .'

'You don't know this other one, David – the vixen of the Cwrt; you don't know *her*. But she's gone now, and indeed had no existence but when the need was there. And it was your need – your need, David, that created her. Yes, I was one of them while you lay sick and helpless, you know that – rode with them, robbed with them, fought beside them, came at last to lead them. But all for you. Only because I loved you. Because I loved you, I've a dozen times risked my life—'

'As you've since risked your life for Gareth y Cadno; and also – and in this, Gilda, don't deceive yourself – because you loved him.'

'No. Because it was just. He was falsely accused. And anyway,' she said bravely, 'isn't he now dead?'

'Dead yes; but you, Gilda – is he dead to *you*?'

'To me?' she said, startled – and she looked down at the bare finger which for so long had worn the gold and ruby ring. 'Yes: believe that, if nothing else – he is dead to me now.'

'Very well,' he said. 'Y Cadno is dead; and the new leader is dismissed, at your command. So what now? I understand you've been in discussion with others of this – rabble.'

She stood staring back at him, trying to make out in the fast-gathering darkness, what message she might read in that sad face, those heavy eyes; those firm lips. 'What now? Well, simply that the whole party is to ride on. It's over.'

273

'And you?' he said.

'I?'

Did he, for a brief instant, shift his intent gaze from her face? – did he for a flickering moment glance over to where she still stood – that other one, so strong in her quiet courage, statuesque in beauty with her crown of gold; not wind-blown, with scuffed shoes from running across the tussocky grass, white faced, not yet recovered from tears . . . He said: 'I ask only – do you ride with us?'

She began to tremble. 'What else?'

'You wrangled with the Black Toby, you declared yourself Vixen here as you call it, and ruler of the gang. And that while you ruled—' Now he did turn his eyes to the Lady Blanche.

'Oh, as to that – I did but tease her, give her a fright to pay her for what she did to me; for what she did to— But I've forgotten him, all that's over now. For the rest . . .' She hunched her slim shoulders. 'Not very pretty, I grant you—'

'Not pretty at all,' he said.

She stood up very straight, suddenly; the half-pleading look fell away, she said almost roughly: 'Come, David – let there at least be truth between us. Do you prefer that I do *not* come with you?'

Where was the old look, the old, loving, tender look that said that whatever her whims or her tantrums, she was his love for ever? He said, however, at once: 'You are my wife.'

'You don't add "unfortunately",' she suggested sourly.

'Of course not,' he said, again at once. 'But since you have used the word – it is perhaps unfortunate that you should have exposed yourself quite so publicly – to my relatives (think of them what you may) – to Lady Blanche and her father; to a dozen servants of their household and our own. How you would rule – *again* – over this band of filthy murdering rascals; and how, in your power, you would serve another woman, and that woman a friend and neighbour of my family, which is now your own.'

274

'I lost my temper,' she confessed. 'I'll apologise if you wish it; and, David, I'll try to learn to like her – not for your sake only; one can't but admire her.' All the same, she could not forbear to add – when he complained of her language, he forgot that he had not heard their language towards herself, that night at Ranelagh. 'Your mother was not particular as to her audience, nor Blanche, when they called me strumpet and slut.'

'I complain not of your language,' he said, 'but of the thought behind it: the thought and what it revealed of the experience of the woman who expressed it.'

'I can't help my experience,' she said sullenly. 'I have witnessed such scenes: once again, in your service.'

He ignored it. He said: 'Perhaps I should have said – the character of the woman who expressed it.'

She stood looking into his eyes – those belovéd brown eyes that now looked back at her with a sickness of defeat. 'David,' she said, 'you will never know what sacrifice I have but this moment, made – for love of you. Are you telling me now that you no longer love me?'

He said again at once: 'You are my wife.'

She made up her mind. 'It must be truth between us.' And she put her white hands on his arm, restraining him, imploring a hearing. 'Let me tell you all, David, and only pray – with all my desperate heart – that knowing all, you'll understand; and understanding pity me and love me again.' And she poured it all out to him. 'If I behave not as a great lady, it's because I am not a great lady and never have been. I've never seen Venice nor ever had any elderly, doting husband; there's no wealth in Italy or anywhere else. I came to you as an adventuress; not expecting marriage, not desiring it, intended only for the life of a courtesan, which was all I ever asked of you. In all our life together, in all our dealings, one thing only has been true, David: that I've loved you . . .' He turned away his head, he seemed not able to listen, not able to hear her out: but she pursued it, steadily. 'Because, I *have* loved

275

you and only you. That other one's – death – came between us, because he loved me and would have given his life for me; but – that's over now, David, I'll think no more of him, never give one more thought to him in all my life, if only you'll still ask my love of me.' And as, to her terror, he still stood silent, she pleaded: 'You say that for him I offered a sacrifice of my life; I tell you again that, though you won't understand it and never will know of it – for you I've made a sacrifice but this moment, that is more than all my life to me – if only you'll love me still.' He was silent, stunned, staring back at her, stupefied in his agony, hardly hearing what she said; and, terrified, she yet crashed blindly on. 'This is our cross-roads, the moment of all moments in our lives – apart or together. I'll deal no more in lies; whatever it may cost me, I'll tell you no more lies. If you refuse me, I'm not lost; I can turn back, I can go with my gang of robbers and cut-throats, my rabble as you call them . . .' But her voice faltered, she remembered the taking back of the ruby ring. 'Well, or if not I can go back, I suppose, to my mother – for she's not my housekeeper – in her new home.' Her face was pearly white in the gloaming, her eyes huge and dark in hollows sharpened by the intensity of her prayer. 'David – I love you, I've always loved you . . . Speak to me!'

He only stammered hoarsely: 'There's nothing to be said about it. You're still my wife.'

She might have accepted it. Time would wear away the memory of this terrible evening, of her self-revelation, of her mouth spitting ugly venom at the quiet figure, the statue of pure white marble with its halo of gold. But she had said she would deal no more in lies. She thought she would faint, flung out a hand and caught at the bough of the birch tree beside which she stood, for support. But she said, steadily: 'Even that isn't true. He is alive. I am married to Gareth y Cadno, and he is alive.'

'Alive?' he stammered.

'It was all a fake; never mind the how and the why. But

he is alive. I didn't know it till this moment, but it is so. And so you see, David,' she said, 'if you wish it, you're free.' And she stood up straight again and took her hand from the supporting bough and held back her shoulders and lifted up her face to him, piteous but proud. 'Here I stand, David. He . . . He has repudiated me; taken back from me his pledge – you see that I wear it no longer – rescinded his vows of love to me and gone free. And so also am I free, because I'm caught up for ever in my love for you. For the rest – none need ever know. He will keep silent, he's sworn his oath on that. But this is all the truth, all that there is of the truth – and now you know me. And knowing me at last, only one question remains, David, between us: will you take me or let me go? As your pretended wife, or as your mistress, I care not – will you take me or let me go?'

So, long ago, over an armful of white roses, had they looked at one another: these two.

Now . . .

Now he stood and his face was sick-white and he was silent; and incredulous, unable to believe what her eyes saw, what her heart told her – yet she had her answer.

Nothing said. What words could be spoken? He asked at last: 'And the child?'

'Ah,' she said. 'The child.' And she looked into his face, standing there white, ill, hang-dog; and at the old woman four-square beside the coach; and at Lady Blanche, cold as ice in her marble propriety – and suddenly it was as though chains fell from about her leaving her wild, exhilarated – free . . . 'Ah, the child!' And at the thought of it, of the bastard changeling, she threw back her head and burst into peals of such laughter as she had not laughed for many and many a day. 'Keep the child, my lord, since this is all you seem to want out of what you and I have been to each other. Born in all good faith into supposed wedlock, you may soon, no doubt, legitimise it if you but pull strings enough and pay out enough gold. And so – if Lady Blanche will allow it precedence

277

over any little icicles you may beget upon that mountain of snow – it can yet succeed to all the greatness you may wish for it; or need not, if you find you prefer a child of hers to Madam Vixen's. Or if you weary of it, send the boy back to the Court of Foxes – there'll always be a welcome for it there.' And she swept him aside and strode into the centre of the circle, stooping to pick up the pistol as she went. 'Come, it's time to be gone! Into your coach, old besom, into your coach, Mistress Blanche, or I'll have the petticoats off you and set you to dancing again! Oh, but before you go – I'll collect such treasure from you all as you carry with you; and not small I know it to be, since you were to ride in safety . . . But you ride so no more; and take witness,' she cried to the gang, crowding now about them, 'that there be no more safe conduct for these two houses of Trove and Tregaron: united as they soon will be, not a doubt of it, or apart. No safe conduct!' She swung back to the coaches. 'Come, quick, out with your sovereigns, my lord of Trove, and don't try to deceive me for remember it was I taught you where best to conceal them . . . And you too, Madam Dowager, you have a fine emerald, I know, tucked down your stocking; so up with your black skirts and let us have at it!' She held out an insolent hand and only to poor, frightened, shocked, sobbing Anne, shook her head and showed a moment of kindness. 'Not you, child, keep your treasures. But pass me my lord of Trove's watch from his fob there; and my lord of Tregaron, you too, I know, carry gold...' And she whirled round upon him, pistol at the ready and caught at his hand and roughly forced off the ring she had given him at their marriage. 'This may yet fetch a sovereign or two I dare say; God knows it has no other value.' And she slammed-to the doors of the coaches and cried up to the coachmen: 'Drive on!' and turned back to the gang, men and women, clustered about her and commanded: 'Return to the Cwrt. Leave me a pony, but ride ahead. Go on!'

They gathered up their possessions, quietly, sensing something very strange; mounted and rode off away across the green fields, splashed through the river and began the steep ascent of the mountain that hid the Court of Foxes from her view. Catti rode last, Dio walking at the pony's head, carrying the child in her arms. Well, Gilda said to it in her thoughts, I might have loved you – for a moment did love you; but it seems that my loves are fated to be rejected. Not of his own volition, at least, did this one leave her; but that he was leaving her now and for ever was certain. Three loves – and they all had gone from her, leaving her alone.

She stood for a long time by the empty roadside, hearing the far-away, receding clatter of horses' hooves on the road, the fading chuff-chuff of the ponies making their way through the grass, the voices, carrying clearly as the group toiled up the mountain whose other side was their fortress home. Darkness was falling, the heather on the mountain top was a purple haze; soon the only sound was the scutter of the dry leaves as a little breeze blew them, tumbling, along the rutted road. The pony stood beside her, its gentle head nuzzling her arm. 'You at least are a friend,' she said, putting her hand to the soft pink velvet of its nose with its tickling of hairs. 'And while I have such a friend...' A sturdy pony, a bagful of sovereigns; and a handful of jewels, to be sold readily enough though for a hundredth part of their value, when the gold was spent... 'Many have started life all over again,' she said to the pony, 'with less than we have, you and I...'

And one other gift she had; one other gift. And, recollecting it, she burst out again into laughter. 'Fool that I am!' She began to gather together her tumbled hair, feverishly, to pin it up again into its orderly beauty; ran to the stream to dip in her handkerchief – with the cold clear water washed away all signs of tears; brushed down her skirts, pulled straight the severe green riding jacket, took a wisp of grass to bring back a polish to her shoes. 'Take heart, little one,' she said to the fretting pony, 'tonight you shall lie soft, even if you lie alone. And I...' If she lay not soft at the rough little drovers'

inn by the Towy bridge, at least she need not lie alone. 'All
else I'll accept,' she said to the pony, 'and use it to my
advantage. But not to be alone.'

He had had a good start of her but would have ridden
leisurely, no doubt, since five or six miles only lay between
himself and his supper. She set the pony at a good pace up
the hill towards Cilycwm, picking its way up the twisting
track, deep-rutted, the river flowing through the fields to their
left below them, released by the long, sheer fall of water
beyond. Ahead of them a tiny farm, ahead of that again a
great boulder that thrust itself out into the middle of the
road, so that it was ever difficult for the larger vehicles to
pass ... A fine place for a hold up! she thought and wondered why it hadn't occurred to her before and recollected
that it was a little far to be convenient to the Cwrt. It might,
however, come very nicely indeed into a territory covered
from— But that's it! she thought, excitement rising in her.
From Twm Shon Catti's cave! If Y Cadno could hold out
there with a price upon his head, why not another who also
rides alone – or not quite alone ... ? Very comfortable the
cave had been, dry and warm, sheltered by an overhanging
ledge from the winds and weather; high up on its single peak,
tucked into the bare rock, with its covering of birch and alder
below and its moat of tumbling water where the river divided
and met again, almost encircling it. This way the drovers went
and came, riding to London ... Ten miles further on, Y
Cadno's band would be lying in wait; but by the time they
reach the forests, she thought, laughing to herself, the drovers
won't, from now on, be worth the picking. Or the coaches
either; from this boulder, even single-handed, a coach might
be held up ... She began to sketch out, as she rode up the long
hill towards it, how one might stand up alone on top of the
rock and so command a whole cortège; not go down to them,
simply command them to throw out of the windows such
treasure as they carried. But they wouldn't throw all; one would
be denied the best part ... And if there were outriders, that

would be dangerous: one might separate from the others beyond reach of a pistol shot, come up around the rock somehow . . . Never mind, she thought, this is all idle planning; I shall not be alone . . .

To her left now the tiny farmhouse of Bwlch y Rhiw; she knew it from other days, there was an old farmer there and a pretty young wife for whose sake, she sometimes thought, Y Cadno had spared their herds and flocks in the gang's maraudings. She chk-chk'd her pony: no sound of hooves ahead of her and she wanted to catch him up before he came to the inn. The stars would soon be out and a lonely spot on a warm starlit night would do her work sooner than a frowsty room in a drovers' tavern. Besides – she must have company. I can't be alone, she thought. I can't be alone.

And the door of the farmhouse opened and a light shone out and the pretty wife stood there; and a tall figure, black cloaked, stooped to enter; and the door closed.

She had suggested that he would find accommodation 'of every kind' at the drovers' inn; but, 'even nearer than that,' he had said. 'You forget, I've ridden this way before.'

Now, for a moment, defeat did enter her soul. I can't be alone, she had prayed; but now she was alone – alone, in the dress of a high-born lady, with no nearer comfort than a filthy tavern where any casual marauder might have her gold and jewels from her in a moment and leave her with nothing between herself and a doubtful welcome at her mother's new menage in London two hundred miles away. For a moment she thought that she might yet turn back and ride to the Cwrt; but she looked at the bare hand where his ring had glowed with its promise of love, and saw herself second to scarred Blodwen or whoever her successor might be; suffered to remain, to hang about the court, mother of the Fox-Cub but with no greater title than that – deposed from her proud leadership because the real leader was there. Not that! she thought. Not that! I'll ride alone. But her hands shook, holding the worn leather of the reins, at thought of the long, dark, lonely road before her; of the long, dark lonely road that, now that her three loves were gone, was perhaps to be her life ...

And out of shadows from behind the great boulder a figure loomed up before her – and cried out: 'Stand and deliver!'

No black cloak here, no eyes glittering steely blue; but a little whipper-snapper fellow in a coat of russet brocade, who put out a hand – whose fingers were like steel, however, about her wrist – and caught her and pulled her down off the rough little pony and for a moment held her at arms' length. 'Whither away, Madam Vixen? – and with the pickings of two coaches to whom Gareth y Cadno had given safe conduct.'

'I robbed them in another name,' she said.

'In what name?' He burst into laughter: 'Don't tell me you've set up all on your own?'

'You're not the only highwayman in the world,' she said; 'nor yet the only man.'

He was startled; but in a moment had burst out into laughter again. 'By heaven, it's the Black Toby! Well, well, you lose no time! Cast off by the only one you love, clip, clop as fast as your pony will carry you, off you go hastening after the only one left that may love *you*. But are you so sure that he'll have you, my pretty doxy? You've proved something of a liability so far to the men who have loved you.'

'No woman's a liability who comes well provided with gold.'

'*If* she comes provided with gold. But what if ill befall her? – what if she meet a wicked highwayman on the road?'

'Gareth y Cadno – you wouldn't rob your own wife?'

'Why not? – when I find her riding to meet another man.'

'I am riding to London, to my mother's house.'

'Oh, are you, after all?' He glanced down towards the farmhouse. 'Ah, now I see it! He has escaped you. And so it must be back to mother? Well then, I may with the more conscience rob you, for you'll not be wanting stolen goods and jewels there.' And he shot out a hand and held her, while his left hand rifled the pockets of her jacket; felt in her pony's saddlebags. 'Now, Madam – it's customary I believe, in the romances, for the highwayman to kiss the lady's fingers – and so goodbye!'

She snatched her hand away from him. 'Give me back my property!'

'It's the property of the Lady Blanche Handley and of the Earl of Tregaron and his family – none of whom, I sadly fear, would willingly see it in your hands.'

'It's as much mine as yours at least; for *I* robbed them of it. Give it back to me—!' And she launched herself suddenly upon him, mad with mortification and rage, fighting him with fists and elbows, reaching up to grab at the chamois bag held high above his head while with his right hand, laughing, he fended her off. '*Give* it to me! *Give* it to me!' Her hands battered at his breast but he had got his fingers into her hair, holding her back and away from him. 'Oh, Madam Vixen, my Vixen, you are losing your cunning! I've seen you do better than this and with Blodwen herself who can fight any man and have the better of him.' And as her arms dropped wearily to her sides and she pulled away from him, defeated, he slid the gold and jewels into his own saddlebags; and said to her softly: 'You have, after all, other weapons than your fists, my love.'

So she went to him: put her two hands behind her back and went close to him, stood up close to him and put her mouth against his mouth and, not kissing him, pleaded: 'Gareth – give it back to me!'

He did not put out his arms to her; stood as rigid as she and only did not move away, or turn aside his head. He said: 'Give back what?'

'Give me back the ruby ring,' she said.

It was night and the stars were bright when they rode at last along the rough mountain track he had followed to cut her off at the boulder. 'So, my Vixen – I have you and hold you at last!'

She sat the pony easily, one knee crook'd at the pommel because of impeding skirts, swaying laxly as it picked its sure way among the rocks and stones in the tussocky grass. By now the coaches would long ago have reached Castell Cothi and hurrying servants would be bringing reviving drinks and good, hot, comforting food; there would be huge fires in the splendid rooms where they sat in their velvet and brocades; upstairs, the great marriage chamber would have been prepared for her – for her! – with lacy pillows and silken sheets ... And at home in the Bijou, there might still have been the frilly white bed and a fond mother fussing and clucking, and undemanding love and easy laughter with no wearisome standards of pretty behaviour any more than of courage and daring; but all this too she had thrown away. Ahead – ahead lay the fortress home, the roughness, the discomforts, the ever present danger from the law, the cold fear at the pit of the stomach as one rode out with the men, the dread if one stayed at home that disaster might befall and few of them return ...

'You have me,' she said, riding along the mountain path at Y Cadno's side. 'Whether you hold me – that's another thing.'

He brought his pony up close to hers and caught at her so that she half lay back against his shoulder, his arm about her. 'You may fight,' he said, 'as you ever have; but this time – as I hold you now, so I hold you for ever. For you forget, my love – the Fox Cub.'

'You have others I suppose,' she said indifferently.

'One, which I have this moment given away. For the rest – a litter run about the Cwrt which their mothers tell me are mine; but all those that have any certain claim on me are females. So this sole one – and born in wedlock, imagine it! – do you think I should ever let its mother go?'

'You let me go just now: took my ring from me and sent me packing.'

'I thought you wanted to be with – that other one, with Dafydd of Tregaron. But you don't belong there, and at last you know it. You belong with me.'

284

She sat up straight. 'I belong nowhere. A fox runs free – and a vixen too.'

'Not when she has cubs.' He put his arm about her and brought her back to him again. 'You are free no longer. I am master now. I am Y Cadno, I am the Fox and the cub is mine; and therefore, I warn you again – I will never let you go.'

Oh, well: if that were all! She said nothing, leaned back softly against his arm, the two ponies ambling gently side by side, flanks rubbing, along the starlit mountain track. The cub is mine ... Laughter began to bubble up in her, the old, effervescent, irrepressible, naughty family laughter of those other careless days. Brown Eyes was gone; and bright dark eyes looked down into hers. But hadn't her mother often told her – was it, after all, only an old wives' tale? – that a child could not be born with blue eyes unless its parents both had the same.

'What are you laughing at?' he asked, smiling, his arm about her shaking shoulders.

'Dream your dreams,' she said. 'The vixen runs free.'

A rough phonetic guide to Welsh pronunciations – (I think people don't realise how much Welsh is still spoken, with English only as a second language, hardly used inside the home. In many parts, the children don't understand English at all until they are taught it as part of the lessons in their 'big schools' – having so far had all their education in Welsh.)

* * *

The accent is almost invariably on the second last syllable.

The difficult double l is best pronounced by putting an h before the l (and not, as too often advised, a c or th.) Llan is pronounced H-lan, *not* Clan or Thlan.

The double d is pronounced like the hard th in 'the'. The double f is pronounced f, the single f is pronounced v. Y is pronounced uh and the confusing w is pronounced like the short double o in 'room' – as opposed to 'loom'.

So:

Llandovery is pronounced – Hlan-*duv*very.

Dafydd, the Welsh form of David – Da-vith (with the hard th.) The a short as in 'Dad'. *Dai*, the diminutive, as 'dye'.

Y Cadno, the Fox – Uh-*Cad*no.

Cwrt y Cadno – Coort (sounding the r) uh Cadno.

Lluinoges – a vixen – hluin*og*ess.

Bach, fach – the masculine and feminine of an endearment peculiar to Wales, perhaps most approximately 'little one', 'my pet' or even 'darling'. The French 'cheri' may come nearest to it? Pronounced bar-ch (not sounding the r) or like the German name Bach. Fach would be *v*ach.

Dio y Diawl – Dee-oh uh Dee-owl.

Diw, diw – as it were, 'Lord, lord!' To rhyme with 'dew'.